VOLUME 5

THE GOSPEL AS REVEALED TO ME

7 parts

The Birth and Hidden Life of Mary and Jesus
chapters 1–43

The First Year of the Public Life of Jesus
chapters 44–140

The Second Year of the Public Life of Jesus
chapters 141–312

The Third Year of the Public Life of Jesus
chapters 313–540

Preparation for the Passion of Jesus
chapters 541–600

The Passion and Death of Jesus
chapters 601–615

The Glorification of Jesus and Mary
chapters 616–651

Farewell to the Work, chapter 652

10 volumes

Volume One, chapters 1-78
Volume Two, chapters 79-159
Volume Three, chapters 160-225
Volume Four, chapters 226-295
Volume Five, chapters 296-363
Volume Six, chapters 364-432
Volume Seven, chapters 433-500
Volume Eight, chapters 501-554
Volume Nine, chapters 555-600
Volume Ten, chapters 601-652

Maria Valtorta

THE GOSPEL AS REVEALED TO ME

VOLUME FIVE
Chapters 296-363

Original title:
Maria Valtorta,
L'Evangelo come mi è stato rivelato

Translated from Italian
by Nicandro Picozzi

Maria Valtorta,
The Gospel as revealed to me.
10 volumes.
Second edition

ISBN 978-88-7987-185-3
(Volume five)

ISBN 978-88-7987-180-8
(Complete work in 10 volumes)

Graphic and printing:
Centro Editoriale Valtortiano srl.,
Isola del Liri (FR) – Italy

Reprinted in Italy, 2018.

Previous edition:
Maria Valtorta, *The Poem of the Man-God*, 5 volumes,

INDEX

The Second Year of the Public Life of Jesus.

(continuation and conclusion)

296. *Going to Aera on a Rainy Day. Arrival and Healing of the Awaiting Sick.* 13

297. *Preaching at Aera. Conclusion of the Second Long Apostolic Journey.* 21

298. *Jesus Rescues the Little Orphans Mary and Matthias.* 25

299. *Entrusting of the Orphans Mary and Matthias to Johanna of Chuza.* 34

300. *At Nain, with Scribes and Pharisees in the House of Young Daniel Raised from the Dead.* **Matt 15:1-11; Mark 7:1-16** 39

301. *At Endor in a Sheepfold, the Parable of the Uncrowned "Kings".* **Matt 15:12-20; Mark 7:17-23; Luke 6:39-40** 47

302. *In Magdala in Mary's House. Jesus Lets Everybody Go Home for the Feast of Dedication.* 51

303. *Jesus at Nazareth for the Feast of Dedication.* 56

304. *In Nazareth, The Blessed Virgin Is Mother and Teacher of John of Endor, Syntyche and Marjiam.* 61

305. *Jesus Comforts Marjiam with the Parable of the Nestling Birds.* 64

306. *Simon the Zealot Arrives at Nazareth. Jesus Works for John of Endor and Syntyche at the Carpente Bench . A Warning on Idleness.* 68

307. *An Evening at Home in Nazareth. A Discussion on the Nazarenes' Stiffness. A Lesson on Man's Spiritual Weakness from the Original Sin.* 71

308. Jesus and the Wife of His Cousin Simon of Alphaeus. Marjiam Is the First of the Children Disciples. 79

309. Marjiam's Abstinence for the Recovery of a Little Girl. Simon of Alphaeus' Repentance. 82

310. Jesus Plans the Departure of John of Endor and Syntyche. 88

311. Marjiam's Self-Denial Inspire a Lesson on Renunciation: Nothing is Lost in the Holy Economy of Universal Love. 93

312. Jesus Informs Dismayed John of Endor that He Will to Go to Antioch. The Year of Jesus' "Mercy" is Over. End of the Second Year of Public Life. 97

The Third Year of the Public Life of Jesus.

313. In Nazareth, Canny Peter Makes the Final Arrangements for a Secret Departure. In the Third Year, Jesus Will Be "Justice". 111

314. Dinner in the House of Nazareth Before the Painful Departure. 119

315. The Journey Towards Jiphthahel. John of Endor's Grief. 127

316. Jesus' Farewell to John of Endor and Syntyche. 132

317. Jesus' Sorrow, Prayer and Penance for Judas' Redemption. 136

318. From Ptolemais to Tyre by Boat. The Voyage of the Eight Apostles with John of Endor and Syntyche Begins. 142

319. Departure from Tyre on the Ship of the Cretan Nicomedes. 149

320. Storm and Miracles on the Ship. 154

321. Disembarking in Seleucia and Farewell to Nicomedes. 160

322. From Seleucia to Antioch on a Cart. 165

323. The Stay at Antigonea. Hermione, the Good Proselyte Wife from Alexandroscene. 172

324. *The Eight Apostles Begged to Preach Before Departing. Goodbye to John of Endor and Syntyche. Farewell to Antioch.* 180

325. *The Eight Apostles Join Jesus in Achzib.* 192

326. *A Stop in Achzib with Six Apostles.* 201

327. *Evangelizing at the Border of Phoenicia. A Sermon on the Common Origin of Peoples and Races.* **Matt 13:33; Luke 13:20-21** 204

328. *In Alexandroscene, Meeting with Hermione's Brothers.* 209

329. *At Alexandroscene Market, the Parable of the Vineyard Labourers. The Roman Soldier Aquila.* **Matt 20:1-16** 213

330. *James and John of Zebedee Become "the Sons of Thunder". Towards Achzib with the Shepherd Anna.* 228

331. *The Bold Faith of the Canaanite Woman. Arrival at Achzib.* **Matt 15:21-28; Mark 7:24-30** 235

332. *Bartholomew and Philip Join the Master and Learn the Reason for Their Long Separation.* 247

333. *Towards Sicaminon with Ten Apostles.* 252

334. *Thomas and Judas Iscariot Meet Up with the Apostolic Group.* 255

335. *In the House of the Vile Pharisee Ishmael Ben Fabi, Jesus Cures on the Sabbath.* **Luke 14:1-24** 264

336. *In Nazareth with Four Apostles. Thomas' Devotion to the Blessed Mother.* 278

337. *The Sabbath in Korazim. The Parable on Hearts that Reject to Be Shaped. Miracle on a Crippled Woman.* **Luke 13:10-17** 282

338. *Going to Saphet. The Apostles, Except Judas, Pleased with the Good Deeds They Performed. The Parable of the Good Farmer.* **Luke 13:6-9** 287

339. *Towards Meiron. A Sinful Night of Judas Iscariot.* 294

340. *Judas Iscariot Asks for Forgiveness. At Hillel's Sepulchre at Giscala, a Clash with a Group of Hostile Rabbis.* 300

341. *The Wounded Hand of Jesus. The Deaf-Mute Cured Near the Phoenician Border.* **Mark 7:31-37** 307

342. *At Kedesh. The Signs of the Times. The Prophecy of Habakkuk.* **Matt 16:1-4; Mark 8:11-13; Luke 12:54-57** 312

343. *The Yeast of the Pharisees. Who Really is the "Son of Man"? Peter's Primacy.* **Matt 16:5-20; Mark 8:14-21. 27-30; Luke 9:18-22** 323

344. *At Caesarea Philippi, Meeting with the Disciples. The Sign of Jonah.* **Luke 11:29-32** 329

345. *A Miracle in the Castle of Caesarea Paneas.* 337

346. *Jesus Predicts His Death for the First Time. Peter's Disavowal and Jesus' Sharp Reproach.* **Matt 16:21-28; Mark 8:31-39; Luke 9:23-27** 342

347. *Martyrdom Foreseen for Marjiam and Peter. The Blind Man at Bethsaida.* **Mark 8: 22-26** 352

348. *At Capernaum, Manaen Gives an Account of Herod's Fears. Towards Nazareth with the Women Disciples. The Transfigurations of Mary, the Immaculate.* **Luke 9:7-9** 356

349. *The Transfiguration on Mount Tabor. The Curing of a Lunatic Boy at the Foot of the Mount. Jesus Exhorts His "Voices".* **Matt 17:1-17; Mark 9:1-26; Luke 9:28-43** 369

350. *At Nazareth, a Lesson to the Apostles and Disciples on the Power to Defeat the Demons.* **Matt 17:18-20; Mark 9:27-28** 382

351. *The Tribute to the Temple and the Coin in the Mouth of the Fish.* **Matt 17:23-26** 384

352. *The Greatest in the Kingdom of Heaven. A Parable for Little Benjamin of Capernaum. The Sacredness of Children. The Use of the Name of Jesus.* **Matt 18:1-10; Mark 9:32-49; Luke 9:46-50; 17:1-2** 389

353. *The Second Multiplication of the Loaves. The Spiritual Miracle of the Multiplication of the Words of Jesus, "Word of God".* **Matt 15:29-39; Mark 8:1-10** 403

354. *In the Synagogue of Capernaum, the Sermon on the Bread from Heaven. The Desertion of Many Disciples.* **John 6: 22-72** 407

355. *The New Disciple Nicolaus of Antioch. The Second Announcement of the Passion.* **Matt 17:21-22; Mark 9:29-31; Luke 9: 44-45** 422

356. *Going Towards Gadara. Judas Iscariot's Heretical Theories and John's Loving Faith.* 429

357. *The Night at Gadara. The Darkest Side of Judas Iscariot Disclosed. A Sermon on Divorce.* **Matt 19:3-12; Mark 10:2-12** 435

358. *At Pella. The Blind Youth Jaia. The Anguish of the Mother of Mark of Josiah.* 447

359. *In Matthias' Hut Beyond Jabesh-Gilead.* 456

360. *The Proceeding Hindered by Foul Weather. The Night Spent in a Cave. Rose of Jericho.* 465

361. *Mary Magdalene Warns Jesus of a Plot Against Him. Miracle on the Jordan in Flood.* 479

362. *On the Other Bank. A Prophesy on the Mission and the Destiny of the Future "Voices of God". Jesus Meets His Mother and the Women Disciples.* 490

363. *In Rama, in the House of Thomas' Sister. The Number of the Elect and the 'Narrow Door'. Invective Against Jerusalem.* **Matt 7:13-14; Luke 13:22-35** 496

(the "Third Year" continues in the sixth volume)

The Second Year of the Public Life of Jesus.

296. Going to Aera on a Rainy Day. Arrival and Healing of the Awaiting Sick.

6th October 1945.

[1] Arbela also is now far away. Philip of Arbela and the other 296.1
disciple, whose name I hear is Mark, are also in the group.

The road is muddy because of the heavy rain. The sky is overcast. A little river, but quite worthy of this name, crosses the road to Aera. Swollen with the rain which has stormed in this area it is certainly not sky-blue; it is reddish yellow, as if the water had been flowing through ferrous ground.

«The weather is now bad. You did the right thing in sending the women away. It is no longer the season for them to be on the roads» states James sententiously.

And Simon the Zealot, who is always calm in his devotion to the Master, proclaims: «Everything He does, the Master does well. He is not dull like us. He sees and arranges everything for the best, and more for us than for Himself.»

John, who is happy to be beside Him, looks up at Him with a smiling face and exclaims: «You are the dearest and best Master the earth ever had, has or will have, besides being the most holy.»

«Those Pharisees... What a disappointment! Also the bad weather has helped to convince them that John of Endor was not there. But why are they so hostile to him?» asks Ermasteus, who is very fond of John of Endor.

Jesus replies: «Their hatred is not against him or because of him. He is an instrument which they manoeuvre against Me.»

Philip of Arbela says: «Well the rain has more than convinced them that it was useless to wait for and suspect John of Endor. Long live the rain! It helped also to keep You in my house for five days.»

«I wonder how worried those at Aera are! It is surprising that my brother has not come to meet us» says Andrew.

«Meet us? He will be following us» remarks Matthew.

«No. He was taking the road along the lake. Because he was going from Gadara to the lake and by boat to Bethsaida to see his wife and tell her that the boy is at Nazareth and that he will be soon going back. From Bethsaida through Merom he will take the road to Damascus for a little while, and then the road to Aera. He is certainly at Aera.»

296.2 [2] There is silence. Then John says smiling: «But that little old woman, Lord!»

«I thought that You were going to grant her the joy of dying on Your chest, as You did with Saul of Kerioth» remarks Simon * Zealot.

«I have loved her *even* more. Because I will wait to call her to Me when the Christ is about to open the gates of Heaven. The little mother will not have to wait long for Me. She now lives with her memory, and with the assistance of your father, Philip, her life will not be so sad. I bless you and your relatives once again.»

John's joy is darkened by a cloud thicker than the ones in the sky. Jesus notices it and asks: «Are you not glad that the old woman will soon be coming to Paradise?»

«Yes... but I am not, as it means that You will be going... Why die, Lord?»

«Those who are born of woman, die.»

«Will You have her only?»

«Oh! no! How joyfully will those proceed, whom I save as God, and whom I loved as man...»

296.3 [3] They cross two more little rivers, one close to the other. It is beginning to rain on the flat region which stretches in front of the pilgrims after they have climbed the hills at the junction with the road, which follows a valley and runs northwards. A * mighty mountain chain appears to the north, or rather to the north-west, but more north than west, with many clouds piling on the mountain tops, forming almost unreal new tops on the real ones, covered with woods on the sides and with snow on the peaks. But the chain is very far away.

---

* **as You did with Saul of kerioth**, in 78.8.

* **runs northwards**. M.V.[s] draft reproduced on the following page, does not contain any additional indication beyond the explanations in the text.

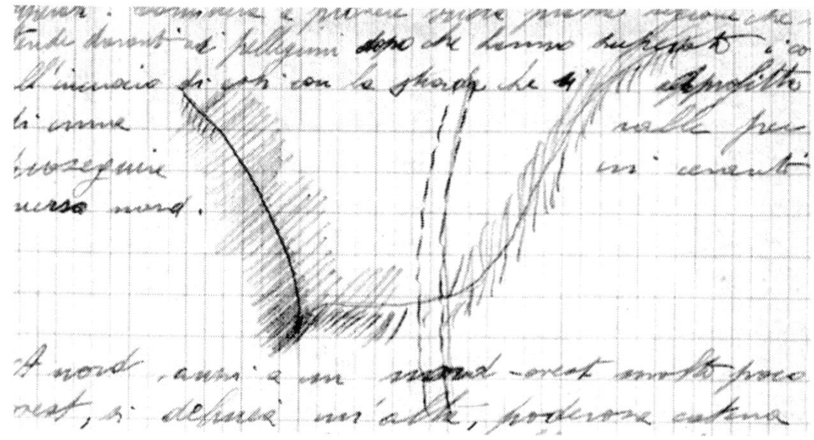

«There is water down here, and snow up there. That is the chain of the Hermon. It has covered its summit with a large white blanket. If there is sunshine at Aera, you will see how beautiful it looks when the sun tinges the high peak with pink» says Timoneus, who is urged by the love for his fatherland to praise the beauty of the country.

«But it is raining now. Is Aera still far?» asks Matthew.

«Yes, very. We shall not be there until this evening.»

«In that case, may God save us from aches and pains» concludes Matthew, who is not very keen on walking in such weather.

They are all wrapped up in their mantles, under which they hold their travelling sacks to protect them from dampness, so that they may change their clothes when they arrive, as the ones they are wearing are soaking wet and the bottom parts are heavy with mud.

Jesus is ahead of them, engrossed in thought. The others are nibbling at their pieces of bread and John says jokingly: «There is no need to look for fountains to quench our thirst. It is enough to hold sore heads back and open our mouths and the angels will give us water.»

Ermasteus, who being young, is like Philip of Arbela and John so lucky as to take everything humorously, says: «Simon of Jonah was complaining of the camels. But I would rather be on one of those towers shaken by an earthquake than in this mud. What do you think?»

And John: «I say that I am comfortable everywhere, providing Jesus is there...»

The three young men carry on talking incessantly. The four older ones quicken their steps and reach Jesus. The remaining couple, that is, Timoneus and Mark follow the rest speaking...

296.4 [4] «Master, Judas of Simon will be at Aera...» says Andrew.

«Of course. And Thomas, Nathanael and Philip will be with him.»

«Master... I will regret these peaceful days» says James with a sigh.

«You must not say that, James.»

«I know... But I cannot help it...» and he draws another deep sigh.

«There will be also Simon Peter with My brothers. Does that not make you happy?»

«It does, very much! Master, why is Judas of Simon so different from us?»

«Why do rain and sunshine, warm and cold, light and darkness alternate?»

«Because it is not possible to have the same situation all the time. Life would come to an end on the earth.»

«Quite right, James.»

«Yes, but that has got nothing to do with Judas.»

«Tell Me. Why are all the stars not like the sun, that is, huge, warm, beautiful, mighty?»

«Because... because the earth would burn with so much heat.»

«Why are the trees not all like those walnut-trees? By trees I mean all vegetables.»

«Because animals would not be able to eat from them.»

«Well, why are they not all like grass?»

«Because... we would have no wood to light fires, to build houses, to make tools, carts, boats, furniture.»

«Why are the birds not all eagles, and the animals are not all elephants or camels?»

«We would be in a mess if it were so!»

«So, do you think that such varieties are a good thing?»

«Undoubtedly.»

«So you think... Why, according to you, did God make them?»

«To give us all possible help.»

«So, for a good purpose. Are you sure?»

«As I am sure that I am now alive.»

«Well, if you consider that it is right that there should be different kinds of animals, vegetables and stars, why do you expect all men to be alike? Each man has his mission and his temperament. Do you think that the infinite variety of species is a sign of the power or powerlessness of the Creator?»

«Of His power. One species enhances another.»

«Very well. Judas also serves the same purpose, as you do with your companions, and your companions with you. You have thirty-two teeth in your mouth and if you examine them carefully, you will see that one is quite different from another. Not only in their three basic groups, but each individually in its group. And consider their task when you eat. You will see that also those which seem of little use and to be doing little work, are instead the ones which fulfil the first task of breaking the bread and conveying it to others which crunch it and then pass it to others which turn it into soft pulp. Is it not so? You think that Judas does nothing or does wrong. I remind you that he evangelized southern Judaea very well, and, as you said yourself, he is very tactful with Pharisees.»

«That is true.»

Matthew remarks: «He is also very clever in collecting money for the poor. He can ask for it better than I can... Probably because money disgusts me now.»

[5] Simon Zealot bends his head and he blushes so much that his 296.5
face turns crimson.

Andrew notices it and asks him: «Are you not feeling well?»

«No... Fatigue... I don't know.»

Jesus gazes at him and he blushes more and more. But Jesus does not say anything.

Timoneus comes forward running: «Master, over there you can see the village before Aera. We can stop there or get some donkeys.»

«The rain is now ceasing. It is better to go on.»

«As You wish, Master. But, if You allow, I will go ahead.»

«You may go.»

Timoneus runs away with Mark. And Jesus remarks smiling:

«He wants us to have a triumphal entrance.»

They are all together in a group once again. Jesus lets them get excited talking about the difference of regions and He then withdraws to the back of the group taking the Zealot with Him. As soon as they are alone He asks: «Why did you blush, Simon?»

The apostle turns crimson again but does not reply. Jesus repeats His question. Simon blushes more and more but remains silent. Jesus asks him once again.

«My Lord, You already know! Why do You want me to tell You?» shouts the Zealot sorrowfully, as if he were tortured.

«Are you certain?»

«He did not deny it. But he said: "I do so because I am provident. I have common sense. The Master never thinks of the future". Which we can say is true. But... it is always... it is always... Master, tell me the right word.»

«It is always proof that Judas is only a "man". He cannot elevate himself to be a spirit. But, you are all more or less alike. You are afraid of silly things. You worry about useless providence. You cannot believe that Providence is powerful and always present. Well: let us keep that to ourselves. All right?»

«Yes, Master.»

There is silence. Then Jesus says: «We shall soon be going back to the lake... A little meditation after so much travelling will be lovely. You and I will be going to Nazareth for some time, towards the feast of the Dedication. You are alone... The others will be with their families. You will stay with Me.»

«My Lord, Judas, Thomas and Matthew are also alone.»

«Do not worry about that. Everyone will celebrate the festivity in his own family. Matthew has a sister. You are alone. Unless you want to go to Lazarus...»

«No, Lord» exclaims Simon. «No. I love Lazarus. But to be with You is to be in Paradise. Thank You, Lord» and he kisses Jesus' hand.

296.6 [6]They have just left the little village behind when, in another heavy shower Timoneus and Mark appear on the flooded road shouting: «Stop! Simon Peter is coming with some donkeys. I met him on the way. He has been coming for three days to this place with the donkeys, always in the rain.»

They stop under a thicket of oak-trees which shelter them

somewhat from the downpour. And then Peter appears riding a donkey and leading a line of donkeys; he looks like a friar under the blanket that covers his head and shoulders.

«May God bless You, Master! I said that He would be drenched like one who had fallen into the lake! Come on, quick, all of you, mount the donkeys, because Aera has been on fire for three days, as the people have kept the fireplaces lit to dry You! Quick... Look what a state He is in! But you... could you not keep Him back? Ah! if I am not there! But I say: just look at that! His hair is hanging as if he were drowned. You must be frozen. In all this rain! How thoughtless! And what about you all? You reckless ones! And you first of all, my stupid brother, and all the rest of you. How pretty you all look! You are like sacks soaked in a pond. Come on, quick. I will never entrust Him to you again. I am almost dying with horror...»

«And with talking, Simon» says Jesus calmly while His donkey trots along beside Peter's at the head of the caravan of donkeys. Jesus repeats: «And with talking. And with talking uselessly. You have not told Me whether the others have arrived. Whether the women left. Whether your wife is well. You have told Me nothing.»

«I will tell You everything. But why did You leave in all this rain?»

«And why did you come?»

«Because I was anxious to see You, my Master.»

«Because I was anxious to join you, My Simon.»

«Oh! My dear Master! How much I love You! Wife, boy, house? They are nothing, nothing is beautiful without You. Do You believe that I love You so much?»

«I do. I know who you are, Simon.»

«Who?»

«A big boy full of little faults, under which so many lovely qualities are buried. But one is not buried. And that is your honesty in everything. [7]Well, who was there at Aera?» 296.7

«Your brothers Judas and James, Judas of Kerioth with the others. Judas seems to have done a lot of good. Everybody praises him...»

«Did he ask you any questions?»

«Oh! So many! I did not reply to any of them, I said that I did not know anything. In fact what do I know, except that I took the women as far as Gadara? You know... I did not tell him anything about John of Endor. He thinks that John is with You. You ought to tell the others.»

«No. Like you, they do not know where John is. There is no point in saying anything else. But all these donkeys!... For three days!... What an expense! And the poor?»

«The poor... Judas has loads of money and he sees to them. The donkeys cost me nothing. The people of Aera would have given me a thousand for You without any charge. I had to raise my voice against them to avoid coming here with an army of donkeys. Timoneus is right. Everybody believes in You here. They are better than we are...» and he sighs.

«Simon, Simon! In Trans-Jordan they honoured us; a galley-slave, some heathen women, prostitutes, women gave you a lesson in perfection. Remember that, Simon of Jonah. Always.»

«I will try, Lord. Here are the first people from Aera. Look how many! There is the mother of Timoneus. There are Your brothers among the crowds. There are the disciples whom You sent ahead of those who came with Judas of Kerioth. And there is the richest man in Aera with his servants. He wanted You to stay in his house. But Timoneus' mother asserted her rights and You will be staying with her. Look, look! They are irritated because
296.8 the rain is putting out their torches. [8]There are many sick people, You know. They remained in town, near the gates, to see You at once. A man who owns a timber store sheltered them under the sheds. The poor people have been there for three days, since we arrived and we were surprised that You were not here.»

The shouts of the crowds prevent Peter from doing on speaking, so he becomes quiet riding beside Jesus like an equerry. The crowds, whom they have now reached, part and Jesus passes through them on his little donkey, blessing them unceasingly.

They enter the town.

«To the sick people at once» says Jesus, Who pays no attention to the protests of those who would like to take Him into their houses to give Him food and warmth, lest He might suffer too much. «They suffer more than I do» He replies.

They turn right and there is the rustic enclosure of the timber store. The door is wide open and complaining laments can be heard through it: «Jesus, Son of David, have mercy on us!»

It is an imploring chorus as unchanging as a litany: voices of children, of women, of men, of old people. They are as sad as the bleating of suffering lambs, as melancholy as the voices of dying mothers, as dejected as the voices of those who have but one hope left, as trembling as the voices of those who can but weep...

Jesus enters the enclosure. He stands up as much as He can in the stirrups and with His right hand up, He says with His powerful voice: «To all those who believe in Me, health and blessing.»

He sits on the saddle once again and is about to go back to the road, but the crowds press Him and the cured people throng around Him. And in the light of the torches, which burn in the shelter of the sheds and illuminate the twilight, the crowds can be seen acclaiming the Lord in a frenzy of joy. And the Lord disappears in a flowery collection of cured children, that mothers have put on His arms, on His lap and even on the neck of the little donkey, holding them so that they might not fall. Jesus' arms are full of them, as if they were flowers, and He smiles happily, kissing them as He cannot bless them, since His arms are engaged in supporting them. The children are then taken away, and it is the turn of the old people who have also been cured and are now weeping out of joy; they kiss His mantle and are followed by the men and women...

It is dark when He can enter Timoneus' house and rest near the fire wearing dry clothes.

297. Preaching at Aera. Conclusion of the Second Long Apostolic Journey.

7th October 1945.

[1] Jesus is speaking in the main square at Aera: 297.1

«...And I am not going to tell you, as I did elsewhere, the first and essential things you must know and do to be saved. You know them very well through the work of Timoneus, a wise head of the synagogue of the old Law, who is now most wise, because he renews it in the light of the new Law. But I want to warn you against a danger which you cannot see in your present state of mind. The danger of being diverted by pressure and insinuations aiming at detaching you from the faith you now have in Me. I will leave Timoneus with you for some time. And with other disciples he will explain the words of the Book to you in the new light of my Truth which he has embraced. But before leaving you, and after scanning your hearts and seeing that they are willing, humble and sincere in their love, I want to comment with you on a point of the fourth book of Kings. *

297.2 [2] When Hezekiah, king of Judah, was attacked by Sennacherib, the three great men of the hostile king came to him to terrorise him, pointing out to him the alliances which had been broken off and the armies which were already surrounding him. Eliakim, Shebnah and Joah replied to the words of the powerful messengers saying: "Speak to us in such a way that the people may not understand you" so that the terrorised people might not ask for peace. But that was what the messengers of Sennacherib wanted, and at the top of their voices they said in perfect Hebrew: "Do not let Hezekiah delude you... Do with us what is useful to you and surrender and everyone of you will eat the fruit of his own vine and of his own fig-tree and drink the water of his own cistern until we come and deport you to a country like your own, a land of corn and good wine, a land abounding in bread and vineyards, a land of olive-trees, of oil and of honey, and you will live and will not die..." And it is written: "The people did not reply, because the king had ordered them not to reply".

Now, out of pity for your souls besieged by forces which are even fiercer than those of Sennacherib, who was able to harm bodies but could not damage souls, whereas war is declared to your souls by a hostile army led by the fiercest and most cruel despot there is in creation, I prayed his messengers, who, in order to damage Me through you, endeavour to terrorise both Me and you threatening dreadful punishments, I prayed saying: "Speak to Me only. But leave in peace the souls which are now being born to the Light. Vex Me, torture Me, accuse Me, kill Me, but do not rage against these children of the Light. They are still weak. One day they will be strong. But now they are weak. Do not be merciless towards them. Do not be merciless against the freedom of souls to choose their own way. Do not be pitiless to-

* **the fourth book of Kings**, corresponding in the *Neo-Vulgate* to: *2 King 18:17-36*.

wards the right of God of calling to Himself those who seek Him in their simple love".

But can one who hates yield to the prayer of he whom he hates? Can one seized by hatred know what love is? No. So with fiercer harshness and cruelty they will come and say to you: "Do not let the Christ delude you. Come with us and you will have all good things". And they will say to you: "Woo betide you if you follow Him. You will be persecuted". And they will urge you with insincere kindness: "Save your souls. He is Satan". They will say so many things against Me, to persuade you to abandon the Light.

I say to you: "Reply to the tempters with your silence". When the Strength of the Lord descends into the hearts of those who believe in Jesus Christ, the Messiah and Saviour, then you will be able to speak, because you will not speak, but the very Spirit of God will speak through your lips, and your souls will be firm in Grace, strong and invincible in Faith.

Be persevering. That is all I ask of you. Remember that God cannot agree to the witchcraft of His enemy. Let your sick people, those who have been comforted and whose souls have received peace, speak among you, only through their presence, of Him Who came among you to say to you: "Persevere in My love and in My doctrine and you will receive the Kingdom of Heaven". My works speak even more than My words, and although it is perfect blessedness to be able to believe without the need of any proof, I let you see the wonders of God, so that you may be fortified in your faith. When your intelligence is tempted by the enemies of the Light, reply to them with the words of your souls: "I believe because I have seen God in His works". Reply to the enemies by means of an active silence. And with those two replies, proceed towards the Light. May peace be always with you.»

And He dismisses them and then leaves the square.

3 «Why did You speak so little to them, Lord? Timoneus might 297.3
be disappointed» says Nathanael.

«He will not, because he is just and he understands that to warn one of a danger is to love one with greater love. That danger is really present.»

«Always the Pharisees, eh?» asks Matthew.

«Those and others.»

«Are You downhearted, Lord?» asks John worriedly.

«No. Not more than usual...»

«And yet You were happier during the last few days...»

«It may be sadness due to the absence of the disciples. But why did You send them away? Do You perhaps wish to go on travelling?» asks the Iscariot.

«No. This is the last place. We will go home from here. But it was not possible for the women to proceed in this weather. They have done a great deal. They must do no more.»

«And what about John?»

«John is ill, and is in a hospitable house, as you were.»

297.4 [4]Jesus then takes leave of Timoneus and other disciples who will be remaining in that area and to whom He has certainly given instructions for the future, because He does not give any further advice.

They are at the door of Timoneus' house, because Jesus wanted to bless the landlady once more. The crowds look at Him respectfully and follow Him when He sets out again towards the outskirts, the vegetable gardens and the open country. The more persevering people follow Him for a little while, in a group which becomes smaller and smaller, until only nine people are left, then five, three, finally one... And the last one too, turns around and goes back to Aera, while Jesus walks westwards with only the twelve apostles, because Ermasteus remained with Timoneus.

297.5 [5]Jesus says:

«And the journey, the second long apostolic journey is over. We now go back to the well-known countryside of Galilee.

Poor Mary, you are more exhausted than John of Endor. I authorise you to omit the descriptions of the places. We have given so much to curious searchers. And they will always be "curious searchers". Nothing else. That is enough now. Your strength is diminishing. Keep it for the word. I notice the uselessness of so much labour of yours, with the same spirit with which I noticed the uselessness of so much of My toil. That is why I say to you: "Spare yourself for the word". You are the "mouthpiece". Oh! One must really repeat for you the saying: "We played the pipes for you and you would not sing, we sang dirges and you *

* **saying**, in 266.12.

would not be mourners". You repeated My words only, and difficult doctors turned up their noses. You added your descriptions to My words, and they find faults with them. And they will find more to object. And you are worn out. I will tell you when you are to describe the journey. I, and no one else.

It is almost a year now that I struck you. But before the year is over, do you wish to rest once again on My Heart? Come then, little martyr...»

298. Jesus Rescues the Little Orphans Mary and Matthias.

8th October 1945.

[1] I see the lake of Merom again, on a dull wet day... Mud and 298.1
clouds. Silence and fog. The horizon disappears in the fog. The Hermon chains are buried under blankets of low clouds. But from the place where I am — a high tableland near the little lake, which is grey and yellowish because of the mud of a thousand swollen little streams and because of the November overcast sky — one has a good view of this little sheet of water fed by the High Jordan, which flows out of it to feed the larger lake of Gennesaret.

It is getting dark and the evening is becoming more and more gloomy and wet while Jesus walks along the road that crosses the Jordan after lake Merom, and He then takes a lane towards a house...

(Jesus says: «You will insert here the vision of the little orphans Matthias and Mary, which you saw on August 20th, 1944.»)

20th August 1944.

[2] Another sweet vision of Jesus and two children. 298.2

I say so because I see that Jesus, while moving along a path between fields which must have been sown recently because the soil is still soft and dark as it looks just after being sown, stops to caress two children: a little boy not more than four years old and a little girl about eight or nine. They must be very poor children because they are wearing poor faded garments, which are also torn and their faces are sad and thin.

Jesus does not ask any questions. He only gazes at them while

He caresses them. He then hastens towards a house at the end of the path. It is a country house, well built, with an outside staircase leading from the ground up to a terrace on which there is a vine pergola, now bare of grapes and leaves. Only an odd yellow leaf hangs swinging in the damp wind of a bad autumn day. Some doves are cooing on the parapet of the house waiting for the rain which the overcast sky is promising.

Jesus, followed by His apostles, pushes the little rustic gate of the low rubble wall surrounding the house and enters the yard, which we would rather call a threshing-floor, where there is a well and a stone-oven in a corner. I suppose that is what the little closet is, the walls of which are black with smoke, which is coming out even now and is blown towards the ground by the wind.

Hearing the sound of footsteps a woman looks out of the closet and when she sees Jesus she greets Him joyfully and runs to inform the people in the house.

An elderly stout man comes to the door of the house and hastens towards Jesus. «It is a great honour, Master, to see You!» he exclaims greeting Him.

Jesus greets him: «Peace be with you » and adds: «It is getting dark and it is about to rain. I beg you to give shelter and a piece of bread to Me and My disciples.»

«Come in, Master. My house is Yours. The maid-servant is about to take the bread out of the oven. I am happy to offer it to You with the cheese of my sheep and the fruit of my fields. Come in, because the wind is cold and damp...» and he kindly holds the
298.3 door open and bows when Jesus passes. [3]But he suddenly changes tone addressing somebody he sees and he says wrathfully: «Are you still here? Go away. There is nothing for you. Go away. Have you understood? There is no room here for vagabonds...» And he mumbles: «...and perhaps thieves like you.»

A thin weeping voice replies: «Have mercy, sir. At least a piece of bread for my little brother. We are hungry...»

Jesus, Who had gone into the large kitchen, which is cosy because of the big fire which serves also as a light, comes to the threshold. His countenance has already changed. With a severe and sad expression He asks, not the host, but in general, He seems to be asking the silent yard, the bare fig-tree, the dark well: «Who is it that is hungry?»

«I, sir. I and my brother. Just a piece of bread and we shall go away.»

Jesus is outside by now, where it is getting darker and darker because of the twilight and the impending rain. «Come here» He says.

«I am afraid, sir!»

«Come, I tell you. Do not be afraid of Me.»

The poor girl appears from behind the corner of the house. Her little brother is holding onto her shabby little tunic. They look timidly at Jesus and with fear in their eyes at the landlord, who casts a nasty look at them and says: «They are vagabonds, Master. And thieves. Only a little while ago I found her scrapping near the oil-mill. She certainly wanted to go and steal something. I wonder where they come from. They do not belong to this area.»

Jesus pays little or no attention to him. He gazes at the little girl's emaciated face and untidy plaits, two pigtails beside her ears, tied at the ends with strips of a rag. But Jesus' countenance is not severe while He looks at the poor wretch. He is sad, but He smiles to encourage her. «Is it true that you wanted to steal? Tell Me the truth.»

«No, sir. I asked for a little bread, because I am hungry. They did not give me any. I saw an oily crust over there, on the ground, near the oil-mill and I went there to pick it up. I am hungry, sir. I was given only one piece of bread yesterday and I kept it for Matthias... Why did they not put us into the grave with our mother?» The little girl weeps desolately and her little brother imitates her.

«Do not weep.» Jesus comforts her caressing her and drawing her close to Himself. «Tell Me: where are you from?»

«From the plain of Esdraelon.»

«And have you come so far?»

«Yes, sir.»

«Has your mother been dead long? Have you no father?»

«My father died killed by sunstroke at harvest time and my mother died last month... and the baby she was giving birth to died with her...» She weeps more and more.

«Have you no relatives?»

«We come from so far! We were not poor... Then my father had to work as a servant. But he is now dead and mother with him.»

«Who was his master?»

«Ishmael, the Pharisee.»

«Ishmael, the Pharisee! (it is not possible to describe how Jesus repeats that name). Did you come away of your own will, or did he send you away?»

«He sent me away, sir. He said: "The street is the place for starving dogs".»

298.4 [4] «And you, Jacob, why did you not give some bread to these children? Some bread, a little milk and a handful of hay on which they might rest their tired bodies?...»

«But... Master... I have just enough bread for myself... and there is only little milk in the house... They are like stray animals. If you treat them kindly, they will not go away anymore...»

«And you have no room and food for these two unhappy children? Can you truthfully say that? The rich crops, the plenty wine, the much oil and fruit which made your estate famous this year, why did they come to you? Do you remember? The previous year hail destroyed your crops and you were worried about your future life... I came and I asked for some bread. You had *
heard Me speak one day and you remained faithful to Me... and in your affliction you opened your heart and your house to Me and you gave Me bread and shelter. And what did I say to you going out the following morning? "Jacob, you have understood the Truth. Always be merciful and you will receive mercy. Because of the bread you gave the Son of man, these fields will give you rich crops and your olive-trees will be laden with olives like the grains of sand on the sea shore and the branches of your apple-trees will bend towards the ground". You received all that and this year you are the richest man in the district. And you refuse two children a piece of bread!...»

«But You were the Rabbi...»

«And because I was, I could have turned stones into bread. They cannot. I now say to you: you shall see a new miracle and you shall regret it *very sorely*... But beating your chest then say: "I deserved it".»

298.5 [5] Jesus turns to the children: «Do not weep. Go to that tree and pick the fruit.»

* **I came**, in 110.5.

«But it is bare, sir » objects the little girl.

«Go.»

The girl goes and comes back with her dress lifted up and full of beautiful red apples.

«Eat them and come with Me» and to the apostles: «Let us go and take these two little ones to Johanna of Chuza. She remembers the benefits she received and out of love she is merciful to those who were merciful to her. Let us go.»

The dumbfounded and mortified man endeavours to be forgiven: «It is night, Master. It may rain while You are on the way. Come back into my house. There is the maid-servant going to take the bread out of the oven... I will give You some also for them.»

«It is not necessary. You would give it for fear of the punishment I promised you, not out of love.»

«So is this not the miracle?» (and he points at the apples picked on the bare tree and which the two starving children are eating greedily).

«No.» Jesus is most severe.

«Oh! Lord, have mercy on me! I understand. You want to punish me in the crops! Have mercy, Lord!»

«Not all those who call Me "Lord" will have Me, because love and respect are not testified by words, but by deeds. You will receive the mercy which you had.»

«I love You, my Lord.»

«That is not true. *He who loves Me loves his neighbour.* That
is what I taught. You love but yourself. When you love Me as I
taught, the Lord will come back. [6]I am now going. My abode is to 298.6
do good, to comfort the afflicted, to wipe the tears of orphans. As a mother hen stretches its wings over the helpless chicks, so I spread My power over those who suffer and are tormented. Come, children. You will soon have a home and bread. Goodbye, Jacob.»

And not satisfied with going away, he orders the apostles to pick up the tired girl: Andrew takes her up in his arms and wraps her in his mantle, while Jesus takes the little boy and they thus proceed along the path which is now dark, with their pitiful loads which no longer weep.

Peter says: «Master! These children were very lucky that You arrived. But for Jacob!... What will You do, Master?»

«Justice. He will not starve, because his granaries are well stocked for a long time. But he will suffer shortage, because the seed he sows will yield no corn and his olive and apple-trees will be covered with leaves only. These innocent children have received bread and shelter from the Father, not from Me. Because My Father is the Father of orphans also. And He gives nests and food to the birds of forests. These children and all poor wretches with them, the poor wretches who are His "innocent and loving children" can say that God put food in their little hands and leads them with fatherly love to a hospitable home.»

The vision ends in this way and I am left with a great peace.

298.7 [7] Jesus says:

«This is just for you, O soul which weeps looking at the crosses of the past and at the clouds of the future. The Father will always have bread to put in your hand and a nest to shelter His weeping dove.

The lesson that I am the "Just Lord" applies to everybody. And I am not deceived or adulated by false homage. He who closes his heart to his brother, closes it to God and God to him.

Men, it is the first commandment: Love and love. He who does not love lies in professing to be a Christian. It is useless to frequent the Sacraments and rites, it is useless to pray if one lacks charity. They become formulae and even sacrileges. How can you come to the eternal Bread and satisfy your hunger with it, when you have denied a starving person a piece of bread? Is your bread more precious than Mine? Is it more holy? O hypocrites! I put no limit in giving Myself to your misery, and you, who are misery itself, have no pity on the miseries which, in the eyes of God, are not so hideous as yours. Because those are misfortunes, yours are sins. Too often you say to Me: "Lord, Lord", to have Me propitious to *your* interests. But you do not say so for your neighbour's sake. You do nothing for your neighbour in the name of the Lord. Look: what have your false religion and *true* lack of charity given you, both with regards to your community and to its individuals? To be abandoned by God. And the Lord will come back when you learn to love as I taught.

But I say to you, little flock of good people who suffer: "You are never orphans. You are never waifs. There would have to be no God before His children could lack Providence. Stretch out your hands: the Father will give you everything, as a 'father', that is, with love which does not humiliate. Wipe your tears. I will take you and lead you because I have pity on your languor". Man is the best loved in creation. Can you doubt that the Father may be more merciful to birds than to faithful men, since He is indulgent towards sinners and gives them time and the opportunity to come to Him? Oh! if the world understood what God is!

Go in peace, Mary. You are as dear to Me as the two little orphans you saw, and you are even dearer. Go in peace. I am with you.»

[...]

21st August 1944.

[...]

8 Mary says: 298.8

«Mary, Mother is speaking. My Jesus has spoken of the infancy of the spirit, a necessary requisite to conquer the Kingdom.* Yesterday He showed you a page of His life as a Master. You saw some children. Some poor children. Is there nothing else to be said? Yes, there is, and I am saying it to you, as I want to make you dearer and dearer to Jesus. It is a nuance in the picture which spoke to your spirit, on behalf of the spirits of many people. But it is nuances that make a picture beautiful and reveal the skill of the painter and the erudition of the observer.

I want to point out the humility of My Jesus to you.

That poor girl, in her ignorant simplicity, does not treat the hard-hearted sinner differently from My Son. She is not aware of the Rabbi or the Messiah. She has never heard Him or seen Him, because she lived almost like a little savage in the fields and in a house where the Master was despised, in fact the Pharisee did despise My Jesus.

Her father and mother, worn out by the hateful work which their cruel master exacted, had no time and possibility of raising their heads from the clods they broke up. While they were mowing hay or cutting crops or picking fruit and grapes, or crushing olives at the mill, they may have heard people singing hosannas

---

* **has spoken of the infancy of the spirit** in a "dictation" of the same day, reported in the volume "The notebooks. 1944".

and may have raised their tired heads for a moment. But fear and fatigue lowered those heads at once under their yoke. And they died thinking that the world was nothing but hatred and sorrow. Whereas the world was love and wealth since the most holy feet of My Jesus trod upon it. The poor servants of a cruel master died without seeing the look and smile of My Jesus even once, without hearing His word, which gave comfort to souls, so that the poor felt as if they were rich, the hungry as if they were full, the sick as if they were healthy, the sorrowful as if they were comforted.

Jesus does not say: "I am the Lord and I say to you: do that". He remains anonymous. And the little girl, who was so ignorant that she did not understand even when she saw the miracle of the apple-tree bare of leaves, a branch of which became laden with apples to satisfy their hunger, continues to call Him: "sir", as she called Ishmael, her master, and the cruel Jacob. She feels attracted to the good Lord, because kindness always attracts. But nothing more. She follows Him confidently. And the poor girl lost in the world and in the ignorance encouraged by the world, by the "great world of mighty pleasure-loving people", who are keen in keeping inferiors in darkness in order to torture them more easily and exploit them more greedily, the poor girl loves Him at once instinctively.

298.9 [9] She will learn later who that "sir" was, who was as poor, as homeless and motherless as she was, who had no food, because He had left everything out of His love for men, also for her, a poor little frail girl; and she will understand that the Lord had given her miraculous fruit, to remove from her lips and from her heart the bitterness of human wickedness, which makes poor people hate mighty ones, and He had done so by means of a fruit of the Father, and not by means of a crust of bread, which was offered too late and in any case would have savoured of hardship and tears. Those apples really called to mind the apple of the Earthly Paradise. They appeared on the branch for Good and for Evil, they were the sign of redemption from *all* miseries, first of all from the ignorance of God, with regards to the two little orphans, and the sign of punishment for the man, who, although he already was aware of the Word, had behaved as if he were not. And she will learn from the good woman who made her welcome in Jesus' name, who was Jesus. He was her manifold Saviour:

from starvation, from the inclemency of the weather, from the dangers of the world and from original sin.

But Jesus always had for her the light of that day, and He always appeared to her in that light: the good Lord, as good as in fairy-tales, the Lord Who had caresses and gifts, the Lord Who had made her forget that she had no father, mother, home and clothes, because He had been as kind to her as a father, as sweet as a mother, He had given a home to their tired bodies and clothes to their naked limbs, with His own chest and mantle and with the assistance of other good people who were with Him. A kind fatherly light which did not fade in a stream of tears, not even when she learned that He had died tortured on a cross, not even when, a little faithful believer of the early Church, she saw how the face of her "Lord" had been disfigured by blows and thorns and she considered how He was now, in Heaven, at the right hand of the Father. A light that smiled at her in her last hour on the earth, leading her fearlessly towards her Saviour, a light that smiled once again at her, in such an ineffably sweet manner, in the splendour of Paradise.

[10] Jesus looks also at you thus. Always think of Him as your re- 298.10
mote namesake did and be happy to be loved by Him. Be as simple, humble, and faithful as the poor little Mary you have known. See how far she arrived, notwithstanding that she was a poor little ignorant girl of Israel: at the Heart of God. Love revealed Himself to her as He did to you and she became learned in the true Wisdom.

Have faith. Be at peace. There is no misery which My Son cannot turn into riches and there is no solitude which He cannot replenish as there is no fault which He cannot cancel. *The past no longer exists, once love has cancelled it.* Not even a dreadful past. Are *you* going to be afraid when Disma, the robber, was not? Love and be afraid of nothing. *

Mother leaves you with Her blessing.»

* **Disma, the robber**, in 609.11/14.

299. Entrusting of the Orphans Mary and Matthias to Johanna of Chuza.

11th October 1945.

299.1 [1] The lake of Tiberias is a grey sheet of water. It looks like tarnished mercury, so heavy it is in the dead calm that allows just the resemblance of tired waves, which are not successful in making foam and stop and calm down after making a slight movement, mingling with the dull water under a dull sky.

Peter and Andrew, James and John are around their respective boats on the little beach of Bethsaida preparing to sail. There is a smell of grass and wet earth, and a light mist on the green stretch towards Korazim. The November gloominess lies heavy on everything.

299.2 [2] Jesus comes out of Peter's house holding by the hands Matthias and Mary who Porphirea has tidied up with motherly care replacing Mary's little dress with one of Marjiam's. But Matthias is too small to have the same treatment and he is still shivering in his little faded cotton tunic, so much so that Porphirea, who is always so full of pity, goes back into the house and brings out a blanket in which she wraps the child as if it were a mantle. Jesus thanks her while she kneels down in taking leave and then withdraws after kissing the two orphans once more.

«Just to have children she would have taken these two as well» remarks Peter, who has been watching the scene and who in turn bends to give the two children a piece of bread spread with honey, which he had aside under a seat of the boat. Andrew laughs at him and says: «You wouldn't, would you? You even stole your wife's honey to make these two happy.»

«Stole? It's my honey!»

«Yes, but my sister-in-law is jealous of it, because it is for Marjiam. And since you are aware of that, last night you stole into the kitchen, barefooted like a thief, and took enough of it to prepare that bread. I saw you, brother, and I laughed because you were looking around like a child who is afraid of his mother's slaps.»

«You horrible spy» replies Peter, laughing and embracing his brother, who kisses him saying: «My dear big brother.»

Jesus watches them and smiles frankly standing between the

two children who eat up their bread.

[3]The other eight apostles arrive from Bethsaida. Perhaps they 299.3
were the guests of Philip and Bartholomew.

«Quick!» shouts Peter and he embraces the two children together to take them to the boat without getting their bare feet wet. «You are not afraid, are you?» he asks them while he paddles in the water with his short strong legs, bare to about a span above his knees.

«No, sir» says the girl, but she clings convulsively to Peter's neck closing her eyes when he puts her into the boat, which sways under Jesus' weight, Who also gets into it. The little boy, who is braver, or perhaps more astonished, does not say one word. Jesus sits down drawing the little ones to Himself, and covers them with His large mantle, which looks like a wing stretched out to protect two chicks.

They are all on board, six men in each boat. Peter removes the landing board, he pushes the boat farther out and jumps into it, imitated by James in the other boat. Peter's action has caused the boat to sway heavily and the girl moans: «Mummy!» hiding her face in Jesus' lap and grasping His knees. But they are now moving smoothly, although it is laborious for Peter, Andrew and the servant who have to row with the help of Philip, who is the fourth oarsman. The sail hangs loose in the heavy damp calm and is of no use. They must row.

«We are having a good row!» shouts Peter to those in the other boat, in which the Iscariot is the fourth oarsman and Peter praises his perfect rowing.

«Come on, Simon!» replies James. «Row with all your might or we shall beat you. Judas is as strong as a galley-slave. Well done, Judas!»

«Yes. We will make you head of the crew» confirms Peter who is rowing as hard as two. And he laughs saying: «But you will not succeed in beating Simon of Jonah's record. When I was twenty years old I was already first oarsman in competitions among villages» and he joyfully gives the stroke to his crew: «Heave ho!... Heave ho!» Their voices spread in the silence of the lake deserted in the early morning.

[4]The children pluck up courage again. Their emaciated faces 299.4
look up from under the mantle, one on each side of Jesus, Who

embraces them, and they smile faintly. They take an interest in the work of the rowers and exchange comments.

«I seem to be going in a cart without wheels» says the boy.

«No. In a cart on the clouds. Look! We seem to be walking in the sky. Look, we are climbing on a cloud!» says Mary when she sees the prow of the boat plunge into a spot which mirrors a huge woolly cloud. And she laughs faintly.

But the sun dissipates the mist and although it is a weak autumn sun, the clouds become golden and the lake mirrors them shining. «Oh! How beautiful! We are now going to a fire. How lovely!» exclaims the boy clapping his hands.

But the little girl becomes silent and bursts into tears. They all ask her why she is weeping. She explains sobbing: «Mother used to say a poem, a psalm, I don't know, to keep us quiet, that we might be able to pray even with so much grief... and the poem mentioned a Paradise which will be like a lake of Light, of a gentle fire where there will be nothing but God and joy and where all those who are good will go... after the Saviour has come... This golden lake reminded me of it... My mummy!»

Matthias also is weeping and everyone pities them.

299.5 [5]But Jesus' sweet voice rises above the murmur of the various voices and the moans of the little orphans: «Do not weep. Your mother brought you to Me, and she is here now with us, while I am taking you to a mother who has no children. She will be happy to have two good children instead of her own baby, who is now where your mummy is. Because she wept, too, you know? Her baby died as your mother did...»

«Oh! so we are now going to her and her baby will go to our mother!» says Mary.

«That is right. And you will all be happy.»

«What is this woman like? What is she? A peasant? Has she a good master?» The little ones are anxious to know.

«She is not a peasant, but she has a garden full of roses and she is as good as an angel. She has a good husband. He will love you as well.»

«Do You think so, Master?» asks Matthew who is somewhat incredulous.

«I am certain. And you will be convinced. Some time ago Chuza wanted Marjiam to make a knight of him.»

«Most certainly not!» shouts Peter.

«Marjiam will be a knight of Christ. That is all, Simon. Be quiet.»

The lake turns grey again. The wind rises and ripples the lake. The sail is filled and the boat sails swiftly along vibrating. But the children are dreaming of their new mother and are not afraid.

[6]Magdala passes by with its white houses among the green 299.6
vegetation. And the countryside between Magdala and Tiberias passes by. The first houses of Tiberias appear.

«Where, Master? »

«To Chuza's little harbour.»

Peter veers and gives instructions to the servant. The sail drops when the boat goes near the little harbour, and then enters it, stopping near the little pier, followed by the other boat. They are one beside the other like two tired ducks. They all land and John runs ahead to inform the gardeners.

The little ones press fearfully against Jesus and Mary, pulling His tunic, asks with a big sigh: «But is she really good?»

John comes back: «Master, a servant is opening the gate. Johanna is already up.»

«Very well. Wait here. I will go ahead.»

And Jesus goes away alone. The others watch Him go commenting on His action more or less favourably. There is considerable doubt and criticism. But from the place where they are they can only see Chuza hastening towards Jesus; he bows almost to the ground at the gate and then enters the garden on Jesus' left. Then nothing else can be seen.

[7]But I can see. I can see Jesus proceeding slowly beside Chuza 299.7
who shows how happy he is to have the Master as his guest: «My Johanna will be delighted. And I am, too. She is feeling better and better. She told me about the journey. What a triumph, my Lord!»

«Did you mind?»

«Johanna is happy. And I am happy to see her like this. I might have lost her months ago, my Lord.»

«Yes, you might have... And I gave her back to you. Be grateful to God for that.»

Chuza looks at Him perplexed... he then whispers: «A reproach, Lord?»

«No, advice. Be good, Chuza.»

«Master, I am Herod's servant...»

«I know. But your soul is the servant of no one but God, if you wish so.»

«That is true, Lord. I will amend my way of living. Sometimes I am seized by the fear of public opinion...»

«Would you have minded last year when you wanted to save Johanna?»

«Oh! No. At the cost of losing all respect I would have applied to anyone who could save her.»

«Do likewise for your soul. It is even more precious than Jo-
299.8 hanna. [8]Here she is coming.»

They quicken their steps towards Johanna who is running along the avenue to meet them.

«My Master! I did not hope to see You so soon. Which kindness of Yours has brought You to Your disciple?»

«A favour, Johanna.»

«A favour? Which? Tell us and if we can, we will help You» they both reply together.

«Yesterday evening on a desert road I found two poor children, a little girl and a little boy... they were barefooted, ragged, starving, all alone... and I saw them being driven away, as if they were wolves, by a hard-hearted man. They were dying of starvation... Last year I gave so much wealth to that man. And he denied two orphans a piece of bread. Because they are orphans. Orphans wandering on the roads of a cruel world. That man will receive his punishment. Do you want to receive My blessing? I am stretching My hand out to you, a Beggar of love, for those orphans who have no home, no clothes, no food, no love. Will you help Me?»

«But, Master, why ask? Tell me what You want, how much You want; tell us everything!...» says Chuza impulsively.

Johanna does not speak, but with her hands pressed on her heart, tears on her long eyelashes, a smile of desire on her red lips, she waits and her silence is more eloquent than words.

Jesus looks at her and smiles: «I would like those to have a mother, a father, a home; and the mother's name to be Johanna...»

He has no time to finish because Johanna's cry is like that of someone freed from prison, while she prostrates herself to kiss the feet of her Lord.

«And what do you say, Chuza? Will you receive in My name My beloved ones, who are much dearer to My heart than jewels?»

«Master, where are they? Take me to them and upon my honour I swear to You that from the moment I lay my hand on their innocent heads, I will love them in Your name as if I were their real father.»

«Come, then. I knew that I was not coming for nothing. Come. They are coarse and frightened, but good. You can trust Me because I can read the hearts of men and the future. They will give peace and strength to your union, not so much now as in the future. You will find yourselves again in their love. Their innocent embraces will be the best lime for your home of a married couple. And Heaven will always be benign and merciful towards you because of your charity. They are outside the gate. We came from Bethsaida...»

Johanna does not listen any more. She runs away, seized by a great desire to caress them. And she does so, falling on her knees to clasp the two little orphans to her heart, kissing their emaciated cheeks, while they are amazed looking at the beautiful lady with garments adorned with jewels. And they look at Chuza, who caresses them and takes Matthias in his arms. And they look at the beautiful garden and at the servants who gather round them... And they admire the house which opens its halls full of riches to Jesus and His apostles. And they look at Esther who covers them with kisses. The world of dreams is open to the little waifs... Jesus watches and smiles...

300. At Nain, with Scribes and Pharisees in the House of Young Daniel Raised from the Dead.

12th October 1945.

[1] It is a feast day for the people of Nain. Jesus is their guest for 300.1
* the first time since the miracle of young Daniel, who was raised from the dead.

* **the miracle**, narrated in chapter 189.

Jesus is going through the town, blessing, preceded and followed by a large number of people. The people of Nain have been joined by incomers from other villages, who have come from Capernaum, where they had gone looking for Jesus, and from where they were sent to Cana and then to Nain. I am under the impression that now that Jesus has many disciples, He has set up a kind of information network, so that pilgrims looking for Him can find Him, although He moves around continuously, even for a few miles a day, as the season and the short days allow. And among those who have come looking for Him, there are some Pharisees and scribes, apparently respectful...

300.2 [2] Jesus is a guest in the house of the young man raised from the dead. The notables of the place have also gathered there. And Daniel's mother, when she sees the scribes and Pharisees — seven of them, like the capital sins — humbly invites them, apologising for not being able to offer them a worthier abode.

«There is the Master, woman, and that attaches great importance even to a cave. But your house is much more than a cave and we enter it saying: "Peace to you and to your house".»

The woman in fact, although she is certainly not rich, has done her utmost to honour Jesus. All the wealthy families in Nain have certainly entered the lists, joining their efforts to adorn the house and the table. And the various women who have collaborated are casting glances, from all possible spots, at the group passing through the hall towards two rooms, facing each other, in which the landlady has laid the tables. Perhaps that is all they have asked for, as compensation for the loan of kitchenware, tablecloths and seats, and for their work in the kitchen: to see the Master close at hand and breathe the same air as He does. And now they appear here and there, flushed, covered with flour or ashes, or with dripping hands, according to their tasks in the kitchen, they watch Him closely, they take their little share of divine sight, of divine voice, drinking in with their eyes and ears His kind blessing and figure and look delighted when they go back to the kitchen stove, cupboards and sink, more flushed than ever.

The happiest is the one who with the landlady offers the basins for the ablutions to the guests of consequence. She is a young dark-haired and dark-eyed girl, but her complexion is suffused with pink. And she blushes even more when the landlady informs Jesus that she is the fiancée of her son and that they will soon be getting married. «We waited for You so that the whole house might be sanctified by You. Please bless her as well, that she may be a good wife in this house.»

Jesus looks at her and, as the little bride bows, He imposes His hands on her head saying: «May the virtues of Sarah, Rebekah* and Rachel flourish again in you and may you give birth to true children of God, for His glory and the happiness of this house.»

Jesus and the notables have now completed the purification rite and they enter the dining-room, with the young landlord, while the apostles and less influential persons of Nain go into the opposite room. And the banquet begins.

[3]From their conversation I gather that before my vision be- 300.3
gan, Jesus had preached and cured in Nain. But the Pharisees and scribes pay little attention to that; they, instead, harass with questions the people of Nain for details of the disease of which Daniel died, of how many hours had elapsed between his death and resurrection, and they ask whether they had completed his embalming etc. etc. Jesus pays no attention to such investigations and converses with the revived man who is very well and is eating with a wonderful appetite.

But a Pharisee calls Jesus to ask Him whether He was aware of Daniel's disease.

«I was coming from Endor by mere chance, as I wanted to please Judas of Kerioth as I had pleased John of Zebedee. I did not even know I would be passing through Nain when I set out on our Passover pilgrimage» replies Jesus.

«Ah! Had you not gone to Endor deliberately?» asks an amazed scribe.

«No. I had not the least intention of going there, at that time.»

«Why did You go then?»

«I told you: because Judas of Simon wanted to go there.»

«And why that fancy?»

«To see the cave of the sorceress.»

«Perhaps You had spoken about it...»

«Never! There was no reason why I should.»

---

* **Rebekah**, was the wife of Isaac and the mother of Esau and Jacob, as narrated in *Genesis 24; 25:19-28.*

«I mean... perhaps with that episode You explained other witchcraft, to initiate Your apostles in...» *

«In what? To initiate anyone in holiness, there is no need of pilgrimages. A cell or a desert barren land, a mountain top or a solitary house serve the same purpose: providing there is austerity and holiness in the teacher, and the will to become holy in the disciple. That is what I teach and nothing else.»

«But the miracles that Your apostles now work, what are they if not wonders and...»

«The will of God. That is all. And the more holy they become, the more miracles they will work, through prayer, sacrifices and obedience to God. By no other means.»

«Are You sure of that?» asks a scribe holding his chin in his hand and looking Jesus up and down. His tone is rather ironical and pitiful.

«I gave them those weapons and that doctrine. If among them, and they are many, there should be anyone who becomes corrupted through basic practices, out of pride or for other reasons, he will not have received such advice from Me. I can pray to see the culprit redeemed. I can undertake hard penance in expiation, imploring God to help him particularly with the light of His wisdom so that he may see his error. I can throw Myself at his feet to entreat him with all My love of Brother, Master and Friend to abandon his sin. And I would not consider that a humiliation, because the price of a soul is such that it is worth suffering any humiliation to save that soul. But I can do no more. And if after all he perseveres in his fault, the eyes and heart of the betrayed and misunderstood Master and Friend will shed tears and blood.» How much kindness and sadness there is in Jesus' voice and expression!

The scribes and Pharisees look at one another. They exchange meaningful glances, but say no more on the subject.

300.4 [4] They instead ask young Daniel questions. Does he remember what death is? What did he feel when he came back to life? And what did he see in the gap between death and life?

«I know that I was suffering from a mortal disease and I suffered agony. Oh! what a dreadful thing! Don't make me remem-

* **episode**, as seen in 188.1.

ber it!... And yet the day will come when I will have to suffer it once again! Oh! Master...» He looks at Him and is so terrified that he turns pale at the idea of having to die once again.

Jesus kindly comforts him saying: «Death is in itself expiation. By dying twice you will be completely cleansed of faults and you will rejoice at once in Heaven. Let this thought make you live a holy life, so that you may have only involuntary and venial faults.»

But the Pharisees return to the attack: «But what did you feel when you came back to life?»

«Nothing. I was alive and healthy as if I had awoken from a long sound sleep.»

«But did you remember that you had died?»

«I remembered that I was very ill, in agony, and that is all.»

«And what do you remember of the other world?»

«Nothing. There is nothing. A black hole, an empty space in my life... Nothing.»

«So, according to you, there is no Limbo, no Purgatory, no Hell?»

«Who says there isn't? Of course there are. But I do not remember them.»

«But are you sure that you were dead?»

The people of Nain lose their temper: «Was he dead? What more do you want? When we put him into the coffin, he was about to start to smell. In any case, with all those balms and bandages even a giant would die!»

«But do you not remember that you were dead?»

«I have told that I don't» the young man is losing his patience and he adds: «But what are you getting at with all these questions? That the whole village was pretending that I was dead, including my mother and my fiancée, who was dying with grief in her bed, including myself, all bandaged up and embalmed, while it was not true? What are you saying? That in Nain we were all children or idiots in a jesting mood? My mother's hair turned white in a few hours. My fiancée had to be treated because sorrow and joy had almost driven her mad. And you doubt it? And why should we have done all that?»

«Why? That's true! Why should we have done it» exclaim those of Nain.

300.5 [5]Jesus does not speak. He plays with the tablecloth as if He were absent. The Pharisees do not know what to say... But Jesus begins to speak all of a sudden, when the conversation on the subject seemed to have come to an end, and He says: «I will tell you why. They (and He points at the Pharisees and scribes) want to prove that your resurrection from the dead was a cleverly contrived game to increase My reputation with the crowds. I, the inventor, you the accomplices to deceive God and our neighbour. No. I leave fraud to worthless people. I do not need witchcraft, or tricks or accomplices to be what I am. Why do you want to deny God the power of giving a soul back to a body? If He creates a soul and gives it when the body is being formed, will He not be able to give it back to the body, when the soul, being restored to the body through the prayer of His Messiah, is an incentive for many people to come to the Truth? Can you deny God the power of miracle? Why do you want to deny it?»

«Are You God?»

«I am Who I am. My miracles and My doctrine testify Who I am.»

«But why does he not remember while the spirits evoked can tell what the next world is?»

«Because this soul speaks the truth, sanctified as it is by the penance of a first death, instead what is spoken by the lips of necromancers is not the truth.»

«But Samuel...»

«Samuel came by the order of God, not of the sorceress, to bring to the traitor of the Law the verdict of the Lord, *Who is not to be derided in His commandments.*»

300.6 [6]«Then why do Your disciples do it?» The arrogant voice of a Pharisee, who stung to the quick raises his voice, draws the attention of the apostles, who are in the opposite room, separated by a corridor a little more that a yard wide, but not isolated by doors or heavy curtains. When they hear themselves being referred to, they stand up and come noiselessly into the corridor to listen.

«In what do they do it? Speak frankly, and if your accusation is true, I will warn them not to do anything against the Law.»

«I know in what they do it, and many others know as well. But since You raise people from the dead and You say that You are more than a prophet, find out for Yourself. We shall certainly not tell You. In any case, You have eyes to see also many other things which Your apostles have done, when they are not to be done, or they did not do, when they are to be done. And You do not mind.»

«Tell Me some of them.»

* «Why do Your disciples infringe the traditions of our ancestors? We saw them today. Also today! Not more than an hour ago! They went into the dining-room to eat without purifying their hands beforehand!» If the Pharisees had said: «and they slaughtered citizens beforehand» they would not have spoken in such a horrified manner.

[7] «You have watched them, of course. There are so many things 300.7
to be seen. Good and beautiful things which make us bless the Lord for creating or permitting such things and for giving us our lives so that we may see them. And yet you do not watch them. And many others do as you do. But you waste your time and your peace running after things which are not good.

You look like jackals, or better still, like hyenas running in the trail of a stench, neglecting the waves of perfumes brought by the wind from gardens full of aromatic herbs. Hyenas do not love lilies and roses, jasmines and camphor, cinnamon and cloves. They are unpleasant smells to them. But the stench of a decomposing corpse in the bottom of a ravine, or on a cart road, or buried under bramble where a murderer threw it, or washed ashore by stormy waves, swollen, violaceous, burst, horrible, oh! that is a delightful smell for hyenas! And as the evening wind condenses and carries all the smells which the sun has distilled from the things it has warmed, they sniff at it to smell that vague inviting scent, and once they discover it and find where it comes from, they run away, with their snouts in the air, showing their uncovered teeth in their quivering jaws, like a hysterical laugh, to go where there is putrefaction. And be it the corpse of a man or a quadruped, or a snake killed by a peasant, or a beech-marten killed by a housewife, or be it a poor mouse, oh! they relish it! And they sink their fangs into the revolting stench, they feast and lick their lips...

* **infringe the traditions**, not the law. The mosaic law prescribed to priests purification of hands for religious acts, as in: *Exodus 30:19-21; 40:30-32*. But it was a tradition imposed by the Jews to wash one's hands before all meals, as can be seen in 160.2 and 414.5/7.

But it is a matter of no interest, if some men improve in holiness day by day! But if one only does wrong, or more omit not a divine commandment, but a human practice — you may call it tradition, precept, as you wish, but it is always a human thing — then it is noticed. And one even runs after a suspicion… to rejoice, if the suspicion is true.

300.8 [8]You who have come here not out of love, or faith or honesty, but for a wicked purpose, tell Me: why do you infringe the commandment of God, for the sake of your tradition? Are you going to tell Me that a tradition is more than a Commandment? And yet God said: "Honour your father and your mother, anyone who *
curses father or mother must die"! You instead say: "Anyone who says to his father and mother: what you should have from me is corban is no longer obliged to give it to his father and mother". *
So with your tradition you have cancelled the commandment of God.

Hypocrites! Isaiah rightly said of you when he prophesied: *
"These people honour Me only with their lips while its heart is far from Me, therefore they honour Me in vain as they teach human doctrine and commandments".

And while you neglect the precepts of God, you keep the traditions of men, the ablutions of amphorae and chalices, of dishes and hands and other such things. While you justify the ingratitude and avarice of a son, by offering him the excuse of a sacrifice so that he may not give a piece of bread to those who gave birth to him and need his help and whom it is his duty to honour, because they are his parents, you are scandalised because one does not wash one's hands. You alter and infringe the word of God in order to obey words invented by you and imposed by you as precepts. You therefore proclaim yourselves more just than God. You arrogate to yourselves the rights of legislators, whereas God alone is the Legislator of His people. You…» and He would continue, but the hostile group goes out, in the hail of accusations, bumping into the apostles and those who were in

* **said**, in: *Exodus 20,12; 21,17*; *Leviticus 20,9*; *Deuteronomy 5,16*.
* **corban** is a Hebrew term indicating offerings made to God in fulfilment of a vow. Often the oath was fictitious and the possessions were not actually granted but only set aside, with the purpose of avoiding to use them for the material care of the parents.
* **Isaiah rightly said of you**, in *Isaiah 29,13*.

the house, guests or women helping the landlady, and who had gathered in the corridor, attracted by Jesus' thundering voice.

300.9 [9]Jesus, Who had stood up, sits down again, beckoning to all those present to enter where He is, and He says to them: «Listen to Me and understand the truth. There is nothing outside man which going into his mouth can make him unclean. It is what comes out of the mouth that makes him unclean. Let those who have ears hear and use their reason to understand and their will to act. And now let us go. People of Nain, persevere in good and may My peace be always with you.»

He stands up, He greets the landlord and landlady in particular and He sets out along the corridor. But He sees the friendly women, who are enraptured looking at Him and He goes towards them saying: «Peace to you as well. May Heaven reward you for assisting Me with such love that I did not regret My Mother's table. I perceived your motherly love in every crumb of bread, in every sauce and bit of roast, in the sweet honey and in the cool scented wine. Love Me always thus, O good women of Nain. But do not work so hard for Me the next time. A piece of bread and a handful of olives, dressed with your motherly smiles and your honest good looks, are quite enough for Me. Be happy in your homes because the gratitude of the Persecuted One is upon you and He is leaving comforted by your love.»

The women, weeping in their happiness, are all on their knees, and in passing by He lightly touches their white or dark-haired heads, one by one, blessing them. He then goes out and sets out again...

The early shades of evening hide the pallor of Jesus, Who is embittered by too *many* things...

301. At Endor in a Sheepfold, the Parable of the Uncrowned "Kings".

13th October 1945.

301.1 [1]Jesus only goes back as far as Endor. He stops at the first house of the village, which is a sheepfold rather than a house. But just because it is such, with low closed stables full of hay, it can shelter the thirteen pilgrims. The landlord, a coarse but good man, hastens to bring a lamp and a small pail of frothy milk, with some small loaves of very dark bread. He then withdraws blessed by Jesus Who remains only with the Twelve.

Jesus offers and hands out the bread, and as they lack bowls or cups, each of them dips his bread into the little pail and
301.2 drinks out of it, when thirsty. Jesus drinks only a little milk. [2]He is serious and silent... So much so, that after the meal, when they have satisfied their appetite, which is always very good, they at last become aware of His quietness.

Andrew is the first to ask: «What is the matter with You, Master? You look sad or tired to me...»

«I do not deny that I am.»

«Why? Because of those Pharisees? You should be accustomed to them by now... I have almost got accustomed myself! And You know how I used to react to them earlier. They always sing the same song!... Snakes can but hiss, in fact, and none of them will ever be able to imitate the singing of a nightingale. One ends up by not paying attention to them» says Peter, both earnestly and to cheer up Jesus.

«And that is how one loses one's control and falls into their coils. I ask you to never get accustomed to the voice of Evil as if it were harmless.»

«Oh! Well! If that is the only reason why You are sad, You are wrong. You can see how the world loves You» says Matthew.

«But is that the only reason why You are so sad? Tell me, my good Master. Or have they told You lies, or made slanderous insinuations or insinuated suspicion, or I do not know what, about us who love You?» asks the Iscariot solicitously and kindly, embracing with one arm Jesus, Who is sitting beside him on the hay.

301.3 [3]Jesus turns towards Judas. His eyes flash like phosphorus in the flickering light of the lamp laid on the ground in the middle of the circle of the apostles sitting on the hay. Jesus stares at Judas of Kerioth and asks him: «And do you know Me to be so silly as to accept as true anybody's insinuations, to the point of being upset by them? They are real facts, Judas of Simon, which upset Me» and His eyes do not stop for one moment piercing, like a probe, the brown eyes of Judas.

«Which real facts are upsetting You, then?» insists the Iscariot in a tone of confidence.

«The ones I see in the depths of hearts and on *dethroned* foreheads.» Jesus lays stress upon the word.

Everybody becomes excited: «Dethroned? Why? What do You mean?»

«A king is dethroned when he is unworthy of remaining on the throne, and the first thing they tear off him is the crown, which is on his forehead, the most noble part of a man, the only animal with his forehead erect towards the sky, as he is animal with regard to matter, but supernatural as a being gifted with a soul. But it is not necessary to be a king on an earthly throne to be dethroned... Every man is king because of his soul, and his throne is in Heaven. But when a man prostitutes his soul and becomes a brute and demon, he then dethrones himself. The world is full of dethroned foreheads which are no longer erect towards Heaven, but are stooped towards the Abyss, weighed down by the word which Satan has carved on them. Do you want to know it? It is the one I read on foreheads. The word is written: "Sold!". And that you may have no doubt as to who the buyer is, I tell you that it is Satan, by himself or through his servants in the world.»

«I have understood! Those Pharisees, for instance, are the servants of a servant who is greater than they are and who is Satan's servant» says Peter earnestly.

Jesus does not reply.

[4] «But... Do You know, Master, that those Pharisees, after 301.4
hearing Your words, were scandalised when they went away? They said so, when they bumped into me while going out... You were very resolute» remarks Bartholomew.

And Jesus replies: «And very truthful. It is not My fault, but theirs, if certain things must be said. And it was charitable of Me to say them. Any plant which was not planted by My Heavenly Father is to be uprooted. And the useless moorland of parasitic, suffocating thorny herbs, which destroy the seed of the holy Truth, was not planted by Him. It is charitable to uproot traditions and precepts which suffocate the Decalogue, misinterpreting it, and making it inert and impossible to abide by. It is charitable to do so for the sake of honest souls. As far as those insolent obstinate persons are concerned, who are deaf to every advice and action of Love, leave them alone and let them be followed by those whose souls and inclinations are like theirs. They are blind men leading blind men. If one blind man leads another, both can but fall into a pit. Let them feed on their own uncleanness, which they call "cleanliness". It cannot contaminate them any further, because it lies on the matrix from which it originates.»

301.5 [5] «What You are saying now is connected with what You said in Daniel's house, is it not? That it is not what goes into the mouth of man that makes him unclean, but what comes out of it» asks Simon the Zealot seriously.

«Yes» replies Jesus briefly.

After a moment's silence, as Jesus' seriousness freezes even the most exuberant characters, Peter asks: «Master, I, and I am not the only one, have not understood the parable very well. Please explain it to us. How is it that what goes in does not make unclean, and what comes out does? If I take a clean amphora and I pour dirty water into it, I will dirty it. So what goes into the amphora makes it unclean. But if from an amphora full of clean water I pour some of it on to the ground, I will not make the amphora unclean, because clean water comes out of it. So?»

301.6 [6] And Jesus says: «We are not amphorae, Simon. We are not amphorae, My friends. And not everything is clean in man! Do even you not understand? Consider the case with which the Pharisees charged you. They stated that you were unclean because you were taking food to your mouths with dusty, sweaty hands, that is, with unclean hands. But where did that food go? From your mouths into your stomachs, from your stomachs into your intestines and from your intestines into the sewer. Can it thus make your *whole* body unclean, and what is contained in your body, if it only goes through the passage destined to fulfil the task of nourishing the flesh, and the flesh only, and then ending in a sewer, as it is right it should? That is not what makes man unclean. What makes man unclean is what is entirely and exclusively *his own*, procreated and brought forth by his *ego*. That is, what he has in his heart, and from his heart rises to his lips and to his head, corrupting his thoughts and words and making him wholly unclean. From the heart come evil intentions, murder, adultery, fornication, theft, false witness, blasphemy. From the heart come avarice, lust, pride, envy, wrath, immoderate desires and sinful idleness. From the heart come incentives to all actions. And if the heart is wicked, they will be as wicked as the heart. *All actions*: from idolatry to insincere grumbling... All these wicked things, which from inside come outside, make man unclean, and not from eating without washing one's hands. The science of God is not a base thing, mud upon which any foot can tread. It is something sublime, which lives among stars, from which it descends with rays of light to perfect the just. Do not, at least you, tear it from Heaven to disgrace it in mud... Go and rest now. I am going out to pray.»

302. In Magdala in Mary's House. Jesus Lets Everybody Go Home for the Feast of Dedication.

14th October 1945.

[1]Rain, rain, rain... The apostles, who are not very happy to walk in the rain, suggest to Jesus that it might be better to take shelter at Nazareth, which is not far... and Peter says: «And then I could leave with the boy...» 302.1

Jesus' «no» is so resolute that no one dares to insist. Jesus is walking ahead of them, all alone... The others are following Him, in two sullen groups.

But Peter cannot resist any longer and he approaches Jesus. «Master, can I stay with You?» he asks in a rather mortified tone.

«You are always dear to Me, Simon. Come.»

Peter cheers up. He trots along beside Jesus, Who goes a long way with His strides, without any effort. After a little while he says: «Master... it would have been lovely to have the boy for the feast...»

Jesus does not reply.

«Master, why do You not make me happy?»

«Simon, you are running the risk of having the boy taken away from you.»

«No! Lord! Why?» Peter is frightened by the threat and looks desolate.

«Because I do not want you to be tied to anything. I told you when I gave you Marjiam. You, instead, are getting stranded in your affection.»

«It is not a sin to love. And to love Marjiam. You love him, too...»

«But My love does not prevent Me from devoting Myself entirely to My mission. Do you not remember My words on human affections and My advice, which was as clear as an order, concerning those who want to put their hands to the plough? Are you getting tired, Simon of Jonah, of being My disciple *heroically*?»

Peter's voice is broken by sobs when he replies: «No, Lord. I remember everything and I am not tired. But I am under the impression that it is the other way round... You are tired of me, of poor Simon who left everything to follow You....»

«You mean: who found everything in following Me.»

«No... Yes... Master... I am a poor man...»

«I know. And that is exactly why I am working on you. To make of the poor man a man, a saint, My Apostle, My Stone. I am hard to make you hard. I do not want you to be as soft as this mud. I want you to be a perfectly squared block: the foundation Stone. Do you not understand that that is love? Do you not re-
302.2 member the Wise Man? He says that he who loves is severe. [2]But *
understand Me! At least you! Can you not see how I am overwhelmed and desolate because of so much misunderstanding, because of too much feigning, of so much indifference and of even more disappointments?»

«Is that... is that how You feel, Master? Oh! Divine Mercy! And I never realized it! What a blockhead I am!... But for how long?... By whom? Tell me...»

«It is of no avail. You would not be able to do anything. I can do nothing Myself ...»

«Could I not do anything to relieve You?»

«I told you: you should understand that My sternness is love and see love in every act of Mine concerning you.»

«Yes, of course. I will not speak any more. My dear Master! I will say no more. Forgive this blockhead. Give me a sign that You really forgive me...»

«A sign! My "yes" should really be enough for you. But I will give you it. Listen: I cannot go to Nazareth because, besides Marjiam, John of Endor and Syntyche are there. And that is not to be known.»

---

* **the Wise Man** is Solomon, who speaks of severity as a sign of love in: *Proverbs 3,12; 13,24.*

«Not even to us? Why?... Ah! Master?! Are You afraid of any of us?»

«Prudence teaches that when something is to be kept secret, two people who are aware of it are too many. Even a careless word can be detrimental. And men are not all and always thoughtful.»

«Really... I am not thoughtful either. But when I want, I can be silent. And I will! I will indeed! I will no longer be Simon of Jonah, if I do not hold my tongue. Thank You, Master, for Your
esteem. It is indeed a great sign of love... [3]So we are now going to 302.3
Tarichea?»

«Yes. Then we will go to Magdala by boat. I must collect the gold of the jewels...»

«You can now see that I am able to hold my tongue! I never said anything to Judas, You know?»

Jesus makes no comment on the interruption. He goes on: «Once I have received the gold, I will leave you all free until the day after the Dedication. If I should want any of you, I will call you to Nazareth. The apostles from Judaea, with the exception of Simon Zealot, will take Lazarus' sisters, their handmaids, and Eliza of Bethzur to their house in Bethany. They will then go to their homes for the Dedication. It will be quite all right if they come back by the end of Shebat, when we shall start going round again. You are the only one to know, is that right, Simon Peter?»

«Yes, I am the only one. But... You will have to tell the others...»

«I will tell them at the right moment. Go now to your companions and be sure of My love.»

Peter obeys and is happy and Jesus becomes absorbed in thought once again.

[4]The waves are breaking against the little beach of Magda- 302.4
la, when the two boats land there in a late November afternoon. They are not big waves, but they are annoying for those landing, as their clothes get wet. But the idea of being sheltered at once in the house of Mary of Magdala makes them put up with the undesired bath without any grumbling.

«Put the boats away and then join us» says Jesus to the servants. And He sets out at once along the shore because they landed in a cove a little outside the town, where there are other boats of fishermen from Magdala.

«Judas of Simon and Thomas, come here with Me» says Jesus calling them. They run up to Him.«I have decided to entrust you with a confidential task, and a pleasant one at the same time. This is the task: you will take Lazarus' sisters to Bethany. And Eliza will go with them. I think highly enough of you to entrust the women disciples to you. And you will take a letter of Mine to Lazarus. Then, when you have fulfilled your task, you will go home for the Dedication... Do not interrupt Me, Judas. We shall all celebrate the Dedication at *home* this year. It is too rainy a winter to travel about. You can see that also sick people are thinning out. So we will take advantage of the situation and make our families happy. I will wait for you at Capernaum by the end of Shebat.»

«But are You staying at Capernaum?» asks Thomas.

«I am not yet sure where I will be staying. Here or there it is the same to Me, providing My Mother is with Me.»

«I would have preferred to celebrate the Dedication with You» says the Iscariot.

«I believe you. But if you love Me, please obey. All the more because your obedience will give you the possibility of helping the disciples, who are once again spread out everywhere. You must help Me with them. In a family it is the elder sons who help the parents to bring up the younger ones. You are the elder brothers of the disciples, and they the younger ones, and you ought to be happy that I rely on you. It proves that I am satisfied with your recent work.»

302.5 [5]Thomas simply says:.«It's too kind of You, Master. But, as far as I am concerned, I will endeavour to do even better, now. But I am sorry to leave You... But time flies... And my old father will be happy to have me for the feast... and my sisters too... My twin sister above all!... She must have had, or is about to have a baby... The first nephew... If it is a boy, and is born when I am there, what name shall I give him?»

«Joseph.»

«And if it is a girl?»

«Mary. There are no sweeter names.»

But Judas, proud of the appointment, is already strutting

about and making plans... He has completely forgotten that he will be leaving Jesus and that shortly before, about the time of the Tabernacles, if I remember rightly, he had protested, like an unbroken horse, against Jesus' order to part from Him for a little while. He forgets also how at the time he suspected that it was Jesus' desire to send him away. He has forgotten everything and he is happy to be considered one who may be entrusted with delicate tasks. He promises: «I will bring You much money for the poor, and he takes out his purse and says: «Here, take this. It is all we have. I have nothing else. Give me provisions for our journey from Bethany home.»

«But we are not leaving this evening» objects Thomas.

«It does not matter. No money is required in Mary's house, so... I am happy that I do not have to handle any more... When I come back I will bring Your Mother some flower seeds. I will get them from my mother. And I want to bring a present for Marjiam...» He is elated. Jesus looks at him...

[6]They are now in the house of Mary of Magdala. They make 302.6
themselves known and go in. The women run joyfully to meet the Master, Who has come to take shelter in their home...

And after supper, when the tired apostles have withdrawn, Jesus, sitting in the centre of a hall, in the circle of the women disciples, informs them of His desire that they should leave as soon as possible. Unlike the apostles, not one of them protests. They bow their heads in assent and then go out to pack their luggage. But Jesus calls back the Magdalene, who is already on the threshold.

«Well, Mary? Why did you whisper to Me, when I arrived: "I must speak to You privately"?»

«Master, I sold the precious stones. At Tiberias. Marcella sold them with the assistance of Isaac. I have the money in my room. I did not want Judas to see...» and she blushes deeply.

Jesus stares at her but does not say anything.

The Magdalene goes out and comes back with a heavy purse which she hands to Jesus:.«Here it is» she says. «They paid a very good price for them.»

«Thank you, Mary.»

«Thank You, Rabboni, for asking this favour of me. Have You anything else to ask me?...»

«No, Mary. And have you anything else to tell Me?»

«No, my Lord. Bless me, Master.»

302.7 «Yes, I bless you... [7]Mary... are you happy to go back to Lazarus? Supposing I were no longer in Palestine, would you go back home willingly?»

«Yes, my Lord. But...»

«Go on, Mary. Do not be afraid to tell me what you think.»

«I would have gone back more willingly, if Simon the Zealot had been in the place of Judas of Kerioth, because he is a great friend of our family.»

«I need him for an important mission.»

«Your brothers, then or John, whose heart is as innocent as a dove. Anyone of them, except him. My Lord, do not look at me so severely... He who has fed on lust, perceives it when it is near... I am not afraid of it. I can hold at bay someone who is much more than Judas. And I am terrified at not being forgiven, and it is my *ego*, and it is Satan who wanders around me, and it is the world... But if Mary of Theophilus is not afraid of anybody, Mary of Jesus is disgusted at the vice which had subdued her, and she... Lord... The man who craves for sensuality disgusts me...»

«You are not alone on the journey, Mary. And I am sure that while he is with you he will not come back... Remember that I must send Syntyche and John to Antioch and he who is not prudent must not know anything about it...»

«That is true. So I will go... Master, when shall we meet again?»

«I do not know, Mary. Perhaps only at Passover. Go in peace, now. I will bless you this evening and every evening, together with your sister and good Lazarus.»

Mary bends to kiss Jesus' feet leaving Him alone in the silent room.

303. Jesus at Nazareth for the Feast of Dedication.

15th October 1945.

303.1 [1]It is a dark, cold, windy December evening. Apart from the leaves torn off the trees which still have a few and which rustle blown by a whistling wind, there is no other noise in the streets of Nazareth, which is as dark as a dead city. No light or noise filters through the bolted doors. It is really a horrible evening.

And yet, the Lamb of God is walking through the deserted streets of Nazareth, on His way home. A tall dark shadow in a dark tunic, He almost vanishes in the dark starless night and His step is just a rustling noise when He treads on a heap of dry leaves, which the wind has laid on the ground, after whirling them around and is ready to pick up again and blow elsewhere.

He arrives near the house of Mary Clopas. He stands for a moment undecided as to whether He should enter the garden and knock at the kitchen door or proceed... He proceeds without stopping. He is now in the little street where His house is. One can already see the tormented olive-trees swaying on the hillock against which the house is placed, dark shadows swaying against the black sky. He quickens His step and arrives at the door. He listens carefully. It is so easy to hear what is happening in that little house! If one presses against the door post there are only a few inches of wood between the outside listener and the speaker within... And yet no voice is heard.

«It is late» He says with a sigh. «I will wait until dawn before knocking.»

[2]But when He is about to go away He hears the rhythmical 303.2
noise of the loom. He smiles and says: «She is up and She is weaving. It is certainly Her... That is Mother's rhythm.» I cannot see His face but I am sure that He is smiling because I can perceive a smile in His voice which was previously sad and now is cheerful.

He knocks. The noise stops for a moment, then there is the sound of a chair being pushed back, and finally the silvery voice asks: «Who is it?»

«It is I, Mother!»

«Son!» A loving cry of joy, even if uttered in a low voice. The noise of the bolt being withdrawn is heard, and the door opens letting out a golden flash into the dark night. Mary falls into Jesus' arms, on the door step, as if He could wait no longer to receive Her and She to throw Herself onto His heart.

«Son! My Son!» Kisses and the sweet words «Mother – Son»... They go in and the door is closed silently.

Mary explains in a low voice: «They are all sleeping. I was awake... Since Judas and James came back saying that You were following them, I have been staying up until late. Are You cold, Jesus? Of course You are, You are frozen. Come. I kept the fire lit. I will put a faggot on it and You will warm Yourself.» And She leads Him by the hand as if He were still the Child Jesus...

The flame shines brightly and crackles in the stirred hearth. Mary looks at Jesus Who holds His hands out to warm them. «How pale You are! You were not like that when we parted... You are becoming thinner and paler, My Child. Once Your complexion was like milk and roses, but now You look like old ivory. What has happened to You recently, Son? Still the Pharisees?»

«Yes... and other worries. But now I am happy, here with You, and I will be all right at once. This year we are celebrating the Dedication here, Mother! I will reach the perfect age here beside You. Are You glad?»

«Yes. But Your perfect age, My darling, is still remote... You are young, and as far as I am concerned, You are always My little Child. Here, the milk is warm. Will You drink it here or in the other room?»

«In the other room, Mother. I am warm now. I will drink it while You cover Your loom.»

303.3 [3] They go back into the little room and Jesus sits on the chest near the table and drinks His milk. Mary looks at Him and smiles. She smiles even more when She takes Jesus' bag and puts it on a shelf. She smiles so much that Jesus asks: «What are You thinking of?»

«I was thinking that You have come just on the anniversary of our departure to Bethlehem... Also then there were bags and cases open or full of clothes and particularly of swaddling clothes... for a Little One, Who might be born, I used to say to Joseph; Who *was to be born*, I said to Myself, in Bethlehem of Judah... I had hidden them in the bottom, because Joseph was afraid of that... He did not yet know that the birth of the Son of God would not be subject, both for Himself and for His Mother, to the common miseries of childbirth. He did not know... and he was afraid of being away from Nazareth with Me in that state. I was sure that I would be a Mother there... You exulted too much in My womb for the joy of Your oncoming Birthday, and of the Birthday of Redemption, so I could not be deceived. Angels whirled around the Lady Who carried You, My God... It was no longer the sublime Archangel, or My most sweet guardian Angel, as in the first months. Now choirs of angels darted from the Heaven of My God to My little Heaven: My womb, where You were... And I heard them sing and exchange brilliant words... words of anxiety to see You, God Incarnate... I heard them when, driven by love, they fled from Paradise to come and worship You, Love of the Father, concealed in My womb. And I endeavoured to learn their words... their songs... their ardour... But no human creature can repeat or have Heavenly things...»

Jesus listens to Her, He is sitting, She is standing near the table, dreaming as much as He is blissful... with one hand resting on the dark wood and the other pressed against Her heart... And Jesus lays His long darker hand on the little white, gentle, holy hand and presses it in His own... And when She becomes silent, almost regretting that She had not been able to learn the words, songs and ardour of the angels, Jesus says: «All the words of the angels, all their songs, all their ardour, could not have made Me happy on the earth, if I had not had Yours, Mother! You said and gave Me what they could not give Me. You did not learn from
them, but they learned from You... [4]Come here, Mother, beside 303.4
Me and tell Me more... Not of the past... but of the present. What were You doing?»

«I was working...»

«I know. But at what? I am certain that You were overworking Yourself for Me. Let Me see...»

Mary becomes redder than the cloth on the loom as Jesus gets up to look at it.

«Purple? Who gave it to You?»

«Judas of Kerioth. I think that he got the fishermen of Sidon to give it to him. He wants Me to make a king's robe for You. Of course, I will make the robe for You. But You do not need purple to be a king.»

«Judas is more stubborn than a mule» is the only comment on the purple gift... He then asks His Mother: «And can You make a full robe with what he gave You?»

«Oh! no, Son! It can be used as a border of a tunic and mantle. But not more than that.»

«Very well. I understand why You are weaving it in low strips. Well... Mother: I like the idea. Keep those strips aside for Me and one day I will tell You to use them for a beautiful tunic. But there is plenty of time. Do not tire Yourself.»

«I work when I am at Nazareth...»

303.5 [5] «That is true... And what have the others done during this time?»

«They have improved their knowledge.»

«That is: *You have improved* their knowledge. What do You think of them?»

«Oh! They are very good. Apart from You, I never had more diligent and kind pupils. I have also endeavoured to make John a little stronger. He is very ill. He will not live long...»

«I know. But it is a good thing for him. In any case, he wishes that himself. He spontaneously understood the value of suffering and of death. And what about Syntyche?»

«It is a pity to have to send her away. She is worth one hundred disciples because of her holiness and her capacity for understanding the supernatural.»

«I realize that. But I must do it.»

«What You do, Son, is always well done.»

«And the boy?»

«He is learning too. But he is very sad these days... He remembers the misfortune of a year ago... Oh! there is not much mirth here!... John and Syntyche sigh thinking of their departure from here, the boy weeps thinking of his dead mother...»

«And what about You?»

«I... You know, Son. There is no sunshine when You are away. There would not be even if the world did love You. But at least there would be a serene sky... Instead...»

«There is weeping. Poor Mother!... Have they asked You questions about John and Syntyche?»

«And who would ask Me? Mary of Alphaeus knows and is silent. Alphaeus of Sarah has already seen John and is not curious. He calls him "the disciple".»

«And the others?»

«With the exception of Mary and Alphaeus, no one comes to see Me. Only a woman occasionally for some work or advice. But the men of Nazareth no longer cross My threshold.»

«Not even Joseph and Simon?»

«... No... Simon sends Me oil, flour, olives, firewood, eggs...

as if he wanted to be forgiven for not understanding You, and he wanted to speak through gifts. But he gives them to Mary, his mother, and he does not come here. In any case, if anyone came, they would only see Me, because Syntyche and John withdraw if someone knocks...»

«A very sad life.»

«Yes. And the boy suffers very much, so much so that Mary of Alphaeus now takes him with her when she does My shopping. But now we shall no longer be sad, My Jesus, because You are here!»

«I am here... Now let us go to bed. Bless Me, Mother, as You used to do when I was a little boy.»

«Bless Me, Son. I am Your disciple.»

They kiss each other... They light another little lamp and go out to go and rest.

304. In Nazareth, The Blessed Virgin Is Mother and Teacher of John of Endor, Syntyche and Marjiam.

16th October 1945.

[1] «Master! Master! Master!» The three shouts of John of En- 304.1
dor, who coming out of his little room to go to the fountain and wash himself, meets Jesus coming from it, awake Marjiam, who runs out of Mary's room wearing only a short sleeveless tunic, still barefooted, with eyes and mouth wide open to see and shout: «Jesus is here!» and runs at full speed to climb up to Jesus' arms. The shouts awaken also Syntyche who sleeps in Joseph's old workshop, and who comes out after a few moments, already dressed but with her dark plaits only half done and hanging loose on her shoulders.

Jesus, with the boy still in His arms, greets John and Syntyche and urges them to go back into the house because the north wind is very strong. And He enters first, carrying the half naked Marjiam, whose teeth are chattering notwithstanding his enthusiasm. He puts the boy near the fire, which is already lit, and where Mary is busy warming some milk and the boy's clothes, so that he may not catch a cold.

The other two do not speak, but they look like the personification of ecstatic joy. Jesus, Who is sitting with the boy in His lap while the Blessed Virgin wraps him up quickly in the warmed garments, looks up and smiling says to them: «I did promise you that I would come. And Simon Zealot will be coming today or tomorrow, too. I sent him on an errand. But he will soon be here and we will be together for many days.»

304.2 [2] Marjiam is soon dressed and his little cheeks, which had turned pale with the cold, are coloured once again. Jesus puts him down and goes into the next room followed by everybody. Mary goes in last holding the boy by the hand. And She reproaches him kindly: «What should I do to you, now? You disobeyed. I said to you: "Stay in bed until I come back", instead you came before...»

«John's shouts awoke me...» replies Marjiam apologetically.

«That is exactly when you should have obeyed. To stay in bed while one sleeps is no obedience and there is no merit in doing so. You should have been able to do it when there was merit, because it exacted your willpower. I would have brought Jesus to you. And you would have had Him all to yourself, without running the risk of catching a cold.»

«I did not know that it was so cold.»

«But I did. It grieves Me to see you disobey.»

«No, Mother. It grieves me more to see You like this... If it had not been for Jesus I would not have got up even if You had forgotten Me in bed without any food, my beautiful Mother!»... Give me a kiss, Mummy. You know that I am a poor boy!...»

Mary takes him in Her arms and kisses him, stopping thus the tears running down his cheeks and making him smile once again with the promise: «I will never, never, never again disobey You!»

304.3 [3] Jesus in the meantime is speaking to the two disciples. He inquires about their progress in Wisdom, and as they state that everything becomes clear to them through Mary's words, He says: «I know. The supernaturally bright Wisdom of God becomes clear light also for the most hard-hearted people, when spoken by Her. But you are not hard-hearted, and thus you fully benefit from Her teaching.»

«You are here now, Son. The teacher becomes a pupil once again.»

«Oh! no! You will continue to be the teacher. I will listen to You as they do. I am only "the Son" these next days. Nothing else. You will be the Mother and Teacher of Christians. You are so even now: I am Your First-born and first pupil, and they, and Simon when he comes, are the others... See, Mother? The world is here. The world of the future in the little pure Israelite who will not even be aware of becoming the "Christian"; the world, the old world of Israel in the Zealot; mankind in John, the Gentiles in Syntyche. And they all come to You, the Holy Mother Who gives the milk of Wisdom and Life to the world and to centuries. How many mouths have desired to suckle at Your breast! And how many will do so in future! Patriarchs and Prophets longed for You, because the nourishment of man was to come from Your fertile womb. And "My followers" will seek You to be forgiven, taught, defended, loved, like as many Marjiams. And blessed are those who will do so! Because it will not be possible to persevere in Christ, unless grace is fortified by Your help, Mother full of Grace.»

Mary looks like a rose in Her dark dress, as She blushes so much at Her Son's praise. A splendid rose in a very humble dress of coarse dark brown wool...

[4] They knock and Mary of Alphaeus, James and Judas come 304.4
in together, the latter laden with pitchers of water and faggots. Their joy to meet again is mutual. And it increases when they learn that the Zealot will be coming soon. That Alphaeus' sons are fond of him is obvious, even without the words spoken by Judas in reply to his mother's remark commenting their joy: «Mother, just in this house and one very sad evening for us, he showed us the love of a father and still has that love for us. We cannot forget it. He is for us "the father". We are for him "his sons". Which sons do not rejoice in seeing a good father?»

Mary of Alphaeus is pensive and sighs... Then, being very practical even in her grief, she asks: «And where will you let him sleep? You have no room. Send him to my house.»

«No, Mary. He will live under My roof. But it is soon settled. Syntyche will sleep with My Mother, I with Marjiam, Simon in the workshop. In fact, we had better prepare at once. Let us go.»

And the men go out into the kitchen garden, while the two Maries go to do their work in the kitchen.

305. Jesus Comforts Marjiam with the Parable of the Nestling Birds.

17th October 1945.

305.1 [1]Jesus goes out of the house, holding the boy by the hand. They do not go to the centre of Nazareth, on the contrary they leave the village going along the same road which Jesus took the first time He left His house for His public life. When they arrive at the first olive-groves, they leave the main road and follow little paths among trees, in search of the warm sun after the stormy days.

Jesus urges Marjiam to run and jump, but the boy replies: «I prefer to stay with You. I am big, now, and I am a disciple.»

Jesus smiles at the... authoritative profession of age and dignity. It is true that it is a *little* adult who is walking beside Him. No one would say that he is more than ten years old. But no one can deny that he is a disciple, and least of all Jesus, Who just says: «But you will be bored being silent while I pray. I brought you here so that you may enjoy yourself.»

«I cannot enjoy myself these days... But it is a great relief
305.2 to me to be beside You... [2]I have *longed* for You so much these days... because... because...» The boy tightens his trembling lips and speaks no more.

Jesus lays a hand on his head saying: «He who believes in My word must not be as sad as those who do not believe. I always speak the truth. Also when I assure you that there is no separation between the souls of the just people who are in Abraham's bosom and the souls of the just people on the earth. I am Resurrection and Life, Marjiam. And I have brought the latter even before fulfilling My mission. You have always told Me that your parents were longing for the coming of the Messiah and they asked God to live long enough to see Him. So they believed in Me. They died in that faith. Therefore they have already been saved by it, and have risen again and are alive through it. Because My faith gives life by giving thirst for justice. Consider how many times they must have resisted temptations to be worthy of meeting the Saviour...»

«But they died without seeing You, Lord... And they died in that manner... I saw them, You know, when they extracted all the dead people of our village from the earth... My mother, my father... my little brothers... What do I care if they said to me to comfort me: "Your relatives are not like these. They did not suffer"? Oh! They did not suffer! So, was it feathers and not rocks that fell on them? And was it air and not earth and water that suffocated them? And did they not suffer thinking of me, when they felt they were dying?...» The boy is shaken by grief. He gesticulates vivaciously standing in front of Jesus, and is almost aggressive...

But Jesus understands his grief, and his need to express it and lets him talk. Jesus is not one of those who says: «Be quiet. You are scandalising me» to those who rave in their grief.

[3] The boy goes on: «And after? What happened after? You know 305.3
what happened! If You had not come, I would have become a beast or I would have died in the wood like a snake. And I would not have gone to join my mother, father and brothers, because I hated Doras and... and I no longer loved God as I did before, when there was my mother who loved me and made me love my neighbour. I almost hated birds, as they filled their crops, had warm feathers and built their nests, whilst I was hungry, my clothes were torn and I was homeless... And I who love birds, would chase them away, as I was seized by wrath comparing myself with them, and then I would weep realising that I had been bad and had deserved Hell...»

«Ah! So you repented of being bad?»

«Yes, my Lord. But how could I be good? My old father was good. But he used to say: "It will soon be all over. I am old...". But I was not old! How many years would I have had to wait before I could work and eat like a man and not like a stray dog? I would have become a thief, if You had not come.»

«You would not, because your mother was praying for you. You can see that I came and took you. That is the proof that God loved you and that your mother was watching over you.»

The boy becomes silent and thoughtful. He seems to be seeking enlightenment from the ground upon which he is treading, walking beside Jesus on the short grass dried up by the north wind of the previous days. He looks up and asks: «But would it not have been a lovelier proof if He had not let my mother die?»

[4] Jesus smiles at the human logic of his young mind. And He 305.4

kindly but earnestly explains: Now, Marjiam. I will make you understand the situation by means of a comparison. You told Me that you like little birds, did you not? Now listen. Were little birds created to fly or to be closed in cages?»

«To fly.»

«Good. And what do the mothers of the little birds do to nourish them?»

«They feed them.»

«Yes. But with what?»

«With seeds, flies, grubs, or crumbs of bread, or bits of fruit which they find flying about.»

«Very well. Now listen. If in springtime you should find a nest on the ground, with little ones in it and their mother on them, what would you do?»

«I would take it.»

«All of it? As it is? Including the mother?»

«All of it. Because it is too unpleasant to be little ones without a mother.»

«But in Deuteronomy it is written that one must take the little ones only, letting the mother free, as it is her mission to proliferate.» *

«But if she is a good mother, she will not go away. She will fly to her little ones. That is what my mother would have done. She would not even have given me to You for good, because I am still a boy. Neither could she have come with me because my brothers were younger than I am. So she would not have let me go.»

«Very well. But listen: according to you, would you love that mother of the little birds and the little ones more if you kept the cage open so that she might come and go with suitable food, or if you kept her in prison as well?»

«Eh!... I would love her more by letting her come and go until the little ones have grown up... and my love would be complete if I kept them and once they have grown up, I let the mother free, because birds were created to fly... Really... to be utterly good... once the little ones have grown up I should let them free as well, and let them fly away... It would be the best love I could have for them... And the most just... Of course! The most just because I

---

* **is written** in *Deuteronomy 22:6-7.*

would do nothing but allow what God wanted for birds to be accomplished...»

«Very clever of you, Marjiam! You have spoken like a wise man. You will be a great teacher of your Lord, and those who listen to you will believe you, because you will speak to them like a wise man!»

«Really, Jesus?» His little face, previously worried and sad, then absorbed in thought, reserved in the effort of judging what was best, settles down and brightens for the joy of the praise.

«Yes, really. [5]Now look! You have judged thus, because you 305.5
are a clever boy. Now consider how God will judge, since He is Perfection itself, with regards to souls and what is best for them. Souls are like birds, enclosed in the cages of bodies. The earth is the place where they are brought with their cages. But they yearn for the freedom of Heaven; for the Sun which is God; for Nourishment suitable to them, which is the contemplation of God. No human love, not even the holy love of a mother for her children or of children for their mother, is so strong as to suffocate such yearning of souls to be rejoined to their Origin, which is God. Likewise God, because of His perfect love for us, finds no reason so strong as to exceed His desire to be rejoined to the soul longing for Him. What happens then? Sometimes He loves it so much that He says to it: "Come! I will free you". And He says so even if there are some children around a mother. He sees everything. He knows everything. What He does, He does well. When He frees a soul — the limited intelligence of men may not think so, but it is true — when He frees a soul, He always does it for a greater welfare of the soul itself and of its relatives. As I have already told you, He then adds to the ministry of the guardian angel the ministry of the soul which He has called to Himself, and which loves its relatives with a love free from human burdens, because it loves them in God. When He frees a soul, He binds Himself to take its place in taking care of the survivors. Has He not done that with you? Has He not made you, little child of Israel, My disciple, My future priest?»

«Yes, my Lord, He has.»

«Now consider this. Your mother will be freed by Me and will not need your suffrages. But had she died after Redemption and were she in need of suffrages, you could pray for her as a priest.

Just think: all you could have done was to spend some money to give an offering to a priest of the Temple so that he would make on her behalf a sacrifice of victims, such as lambs or doves or other fruits of the earth. That in case you had remained the little peasant Jabez near your mother. Instead, you, Marjiam, the priest of Christ, could offer directly for her the true Sacrifice of the perfect Victim, in Whose name all forgiveness is granted!»

«And will I no longer be able to do it?»

«Not for your father, mother and little brothers. But you will
305.6 be able to do it for friends and disciples. [6]Is that not beautiful?»

«Yes, Lord.»

«Well, then, let us go back home and be cheerful once again.»

«Yes...But I did not let You pray!... I am sorry...»

«But we did pray! We considered the truth, we contemplated God in His bounty... All that is prayer. And you did it as a true adult. Come on, now. Let us sing a psalm of praise for the joy which is within us.» And He begins to sing: «"My heart is stirred by a noble theme..."» *

Marjiam joins his silvery voice to the bronze and golden voice of Jesus.

306. Simon the Zealot Arrives at Nazareth. Jesus Works for John of Endor and Syntyche at the Carpente Bench . A Warning on Idleness.

18th October 1945.

306.1 [1]It gets dark early in December, the lights are lit early and families gather in one room. That also happens in the little house in Nazareth, and while the two women work, one at the loom, the other doing needlework, Jesus and John of Endor, sitting near the table, are talking in low voices, and Marjiam is about to finish polishing two chests laid on the floor.

The boy is working vigorously when Jesus stands up and bending over the wood says: «That is enough now. It is smooth enough and tomorrow we will be able to paint it. Put everything away now, because we will be working again tomorrow.» And

* **sing** the *Psalm 45*.

while Marjiam goes out with his polishing tools — stiff spatulas on which rough fish skin is nailed to do the work of our sandpaper, and tools like knives, but certainly not steel, for the same purpose — Jesus lifts with His strong arms one of the chests and takes it into the workshop, where they must have been working because there is sawdust and wood-shavings near one of the benches, which has been placed in the centre of the room for the occasion. Marjiam has put his tools back in their supports and is now picking up the shavings to throw them on the fire, as he says, and would also like to sweep up the sawdust, but John of Endor prefers to do it himself.

Everything has been tidied up when Jesus comes back with
the second chest, which He puts near the first one. [2]The three of 306.2
them are about to come out when they hear someone knock at the door and immediately afterwards the serious voice of the Zealot resounds in a deep greeting to Mary: «Hail, Mother of my Saviour, I bless Your kindness which allows me to live under Your roof.»

«Simon has arrived. We will now learn why he is late. Let us go...» says Jesus.

When they enter the little room where the apostle is with the women, Simon is taking a large bundle off his shoulders.

«Peace to you, Simon...»

«Oh! Blessed Master! I am late, am I not? But I have done everything and well...»

They kiss one another. Simon then continues his story: «I
* went to see the carpenter's widow. Your assistance arrived at the right moment. The old woman is very ill and expenses have thus gone up. The little carpenter does his best to make little items and always remembers You. They all bless You. I then went to see Nara, Samira and Sirah. Their brother is more difficult than ever. But they are peaceful, holy as they are, and they eat their poor bread dressed with tears and forgiveness. They bless You for the assistance sent to them. But they ask You to pray that their harsh brother may be converted. Old Rachel also blesses You for Your alms. Finally I went to Tiberias to shop. I hope I got the right things. The women can now look at them... But I was

* **the carpenter's widow**, in 266.2, 267, 268.1/2, 269.1. **Nara, Samira and Sirah**, nominated further down, are the sisters met in 277.2.

held in Tiberias by some people who thought I was Your forerunner. They sequestrated me for three days... Oh! I may say that it was a golden prison! But it was still a prison... They wanted to know so many things... I told them the truth explaining that You had dismissed us all and that You had retired for the worst period of winter... When they were convinced that it was true, also because they went to Simon of Jonah and Philip without finding You and without learning anything else, they let me go. Even the excuse of the bad weather was of no use, as the weather was lovely. That is why I am late.»

«It does not matter. We have plenty of time to be together. I
306.3 thank you for everything... [3]Mother, look at the contents of the parcel with Syntyche and let Me know whether You think it is enough for what You know...» and while the women are opening the parcel, Jesus sits down and talks to Simon.

«And what have You done, Master?»

«I made two chests, to avoid being idle and because they will be useful. I went for walks, I enjoyed being at home...»

Simon stares at Him... But does not say anything.

The exclamations of Marjiam, who sees lengths of linen and woolen cloths, sandals, veils and belts come out of the parcel, make Jesus and His two companions turn around.

Mary says: «Everything is all right. We will begin to sew at once and everything will soon be ready.»

The boy asks: «Are You getting married, Jesus?»

Everybody laughs and Jesus asks: «What makes you think so?»

«All these things for a man and a woman and the two chests You made. They are for Your trousseau and for Your bride's. Will You let me make her acquaintance?»

«Do you really want to meet My bride?»

«Oh! Yes! She must be beautiful and good! What is her name!...»

«It is a secret for the time being. Because she has two names, like you, who were first Jabez and then Marjiam.»

«And can I not know them?»

«Not just now. You will know them one day.»

«Will You invite me to the wedding?»

«It will not be a feast for children. I will invite you to the wedding party. You will be one of the guests and a witness. All right?»

«How long will it be? In a month's time?»

«Oh! much longer!»

«In that case why did You work so hurriedly as to get blisters on Your hands?»

«I got them because I no longer work with My hands. [4]See, My 306.4
dear child, how painful idleness is? Always. When one resumes working one suffers twice as much because one becomes too delicate. Now, if it hurts one's hands so much, how much will it hurt one's soul? See? This evening I had to ask you to help Me, because My hands were so sore that I could not hold the rasp, whereas only two years ago I could work for fourteen hours without feeling any pain. The same happens to those whose fervour and will become loose. One becomes flacid and feeble and grows weary of everything very easily, as the poisons of spiritual diseases affect those who are weak. On the other hand, it is twice as difficult to do good actions, which previously, when one was always in practice, cost no effort. Oh! It never pays to be idle saying: "After this period of time I will carry on working with fresh energy"! One would never succeed, or would succeed with the greatest difficulty.»

«But You have never been idle!»

«No. I have done other work. But you can see that the idleness of My hands has been deterimental to them.» And Jesus shows His hands which are red and blistered.

Marjiam kisses them saying: «My mother used to do that to me when I hurt myself, because love heals.»

«Yes, love heals *many* things... Well... Come, Simon. You will sleep in the carpenter's room. Come and I will show you where you can put your clothes and...» they go out and it all ends.

307. An Evening at Home in Nazareth. A Discussion on the Nazarenes' Stiffness. A Lesson on Man's Spiritual Weakness from the Original Sin.

19th October 1945.

[1]The loom is idle because Mary and Syntyche are busy sewing 307.1
the cloth brought by the Zealot. The material has been cut into

pieces which have been folded and laid in a tidy pile on the table, colour by colour, and now and again the women take one piece and baste it on the table, so that the men have been pushed back towards the corner of the idle loom; they are close to the women but are not interested in their work.

The apostles James and Judas of Alphaeus are also there and are watching the busy women, without asking any questions, but not without curiosity, I think. The cousins speak of their brothers, and particularly of Simon, who has come with them as far as Jesus' door and then gone away «because his son is not well», says James, to mitigate the sad news and excuse his brother. But Judas is more severe and says: «That is why he should have come. But he also seems to have become dull-witted. Like all the Nazarenes, after all, if we except Alphaeus and the two disciples,
307.2 about whose present whereabouts I wonder. [2]It is clear that nothing else is good in Nazareth, and what was good has all been spat out, as if it tasted unpleasant to our town...»

«Do not say that» begs Jesus. «Do not poison your soul. It is no fault of theirs....»

«Whose fault is it, then?»

«Of many things... Do not be inquisitive. Not everybody in Nazareth is hostile. Children...»

«Because they are children.»

«Women...»

«Because they are women. But neither children nor women will assert Your Kingdom.»

«Why not, Judas? You are wrong. Today's children will be tomorrow's disciples and will propagate the Kingdom all over the world. And women... Why can they not do it?»

«You certainly cannot make apostles of women. At the most they may be women disciples, who will assist disciples, as You said.» *

«You will change your mind about many things in the future, My dear brother. But I will not even attempt to make you change it. I would clash with a mentality which comes to you as the result of centuries of wrong conceptions and preconceptions concerning women. I only ask you to observe and make a note of the dif-

* **as You said**, for example in 153.3, 157.2, 262.9.

ferences you see between disciples and women disciples and to watch how they respond to My teaching. You will see, beginning with your mother, who we can say was the first disciple in order of time and of heroism, and still is, as she bravely makes headway against the whole town which sneers at her because she is faithful to Me, and she resists the voice of her own blood which spares her no reproach because she is faithful to Me, and you will see that women disciples are better than you disciples.»

«I admit that, it is true. But which women disciples are there in Nazareth? Alphaeus' daughters, the mothers of Ishmael and Aser and their sisters. And that is all. Too few. I would rather not come back to Nazareth not to see all that.»

«Poor mother! You would give her deep sorrow» says Mary intervening in the conversation.

«That's true» says James. «She hopes so much to reconcile our brothers to Jesus and to us. I don't think that she wishes anything else. But we shall certainly not do it by staying away. So far I have listened to you by remaining alone. But as from tomorrow I want to go out and approach people... Because if we are to evangelize even Gentiles, shall we not evangelize our own town? I refuse to believe that it is so wicked and cannot be changed.»

Judas Thaddeus does not reply but he is obviously annoyed.

[3] Simon Zealot, who has been silent all the time, intervenes: «I 307.3
do not wish to insinuate a suspicion. But let me ask you a question to relieve your minds. My question is: are you sure that in the stiffness of Nazareth no alien powers are involved, which have come from outside and which work satisfactorily here on a factor which, if men reasoned according to justice, should be the best guarantee that the Master is the Holy Man of God? The knowledge of the perfect life of Jesus, a citizen of Nazareth, should make it very easy for the Nazarenes to accept Him as the promised Messiah. I, and with me many of my age here in Nazareth, have known, more than you have, several alleged Messiahs, at least by fame. And I can assure you that their private lives discredited the most stubborn assertion of their Messianism. Rome persecuted them fiercely as rebels. But apart from their political ideas, which Rome could not allow where she rules, those false Messiahs deserved to be punished for many private reasons. We stirred their blood and supported them because they helped to

satisfy our spirit of rebellion against Rome. We countenanced them because, dull as we are, we thought — until the Master did not clarify the truth, and unfortunately, even so, we still do not believe as we ought to, that is completely — we thought that they were the promised "king". They lulled our dejected souls with hopes of national independence and reconstruction of the kingdom of Israel. But, oh! how miserable! What a fleeting and corrupt kingdom it would have been?! No, in actual fact to call those false Messiahs kings of Israel and founders of the promised Kingdom, was to deeply humiliate the Messianic idea. In the Master a holy life is joined to profound doctrine. And Nazareth is aware of that, as no other town is. Neither do I think of accusing Nazareth of misbelief in His supernatural birth, with which the Nazarenes are not acquainted. But *His* life!... Now, so much hatred, so much impenetrable resistance, so much increased resistance... could it not originate from hostile manoeuvres? We know Jesus' enemies. We know what they are worth. Do you think that they have been inactive or absent only here, when they have preceded us, or marched side by side with us, or followed us everywhere to destroy the work of the Christ? Do not accuse Nazareth of being the only culprit. But weep for it, for it has been misled by Jesus' enemies.»

«What you have said, Simon, is very true. Weep for it...» says Jesus. And He is very sad.

John of Endor remarks: «You are quite right also in stating that a favourable factor changes into an unfavourable one, because the thoughts of man are seldom according to justice. The first obstacle here is the humble birth, the humble childhood, the humble boyhood, the humble youth of our Jesus. Man forgets that real values are concealed under modest appearances whereas non-entities are disguised as great people in order to impose themselves on the crowds.»

«It may be... But nothing will change my opinion of my fellow citizens. Whatever they have been told, they should have judged the Master by His real deeds and not by the words of unknown people.»

307.4 [4] There is a long silence, broken only by the noise of cloth being divided into strips by the Blessed Virgin to make borders. Syntyche has never spoken, but has been most attentive. Her attitude is always one of deep respect and reservedness, and it is not quite so rigid only with Mary and the boy. But the boy has fallen asleep sitting on a little stool at Syntyche's feet, with his head on his folded arm resting on her knees. She does not move and waits for Mary to hand her the strips.

«What an innocent sleep... He is smiling» remarks Mary bending over the sleeping child.

«I wonder what he is dreaming» says Simon smiling.

«He is a very intelligent boy. He learns quickly and he wants lucid explanations. He asks very shrewd questions and wants clear answers on everything. I admit that at times I am embarrassed in giving him an answer. Certain topics are above his age and sometimes they are above my capability to explain them» says John.

«Sure! Like that day... Do you remember, John? You had two vexing pupils on that day! And very ignorant» says Syntyche smiling quietly and looking at the disciple with deep eyes.

John smiles too and says: «Yes. And you had a very poor teacher, who had to call the true Teacher to help him... because in none of the books he had read, had that silly teacher found the answer to give to a child. Which proves that I am still an ignorant teacher.»

«Human science is still ignorance, John. The teacher was not inadequate, but what they had given him in order to be a teacher was not sufficient. Poor human science! How mutilated it looks to me! It makes me think of a deity which was honoured in Greece. Only pagan materialism could believe that the Greeks would possess the goddess of Victory forever, because she was wingless! Not only they stripped Victory of her wings, but they deprived us of our freedom... It would have been better if she had had her wings, in our belief. We could have believed that she was capable of flying and stealing celestial thunderbolts to strike our enemies. But in the state she was, she gave us no hope, but only dejection and sadness. I could not look at her without suffering... And she seemed to be suffering and looked humiliated by her mutilation. She looked like a symbol of sorrow, not of joy... And she was. And man does to Science what he did to Victory. He cuts off its wings, which could achieve supernatural knowledge and thus give him the key to discover many secrets of knowledge and of creation. They believed and believe that they can keep it a prisoner by cutting off its wings... And have thus made it dull and deficient... Winged Science would be Wisdom. As it is, it is only partial understanding.»

307.5 [5]«And did My Mother reply to you on that day?»

«Yes, She did, with perfect lucidity and chaste words, suitable to be heard by a boy and two adults of different sex, so that none of us had to blush.»

«What was it about?»

«The original sin, Master. I wrote Your Mother's explanation, so that I would remember it» says Syntyche, and John of Endor also says: «So did I. I think it will be one of the points we will be asked to clarify, if we go among the Gentiles one day. But I do not think I will be going because...»

«Why, John?»

«Because I will not live long.»

«But would you go willingly?»

«More than many people in Israel, because I am not biased. And also... Yes, also because I have set a bad example among the Gentiles at Cintium and in Anatolia. I would have liked to do some good where I did wrong. The good to be done: take Your word there and make You known... But it would have been too great an honour... I do not deserve it.»

Jesus looks at him smiling but does not say anything in that
307.6 connection. [6]He asks: «And have you no other questions to ask?»

«I have one. It occurred to me the other evening when You were talking to the boy about idleness. I endeavoured to find an answer, but I was not successful. I intended to wait until the Sabbath and ask You when our hands are not active and our souls, in Your hands, are elevated to God» says Syntyche.

«You may ask Me now, while we are awaiting bedtime.»

«This is it, Master. You said that those who become slack in their spiritual work grow feeble and are predisposed to spiritual diseases. Is that right?»

«Yes, woman.»

«Now that appears to me to be in contrast with what I have heard from You and from Your Mother on original sin, its effects in us and the fact that we will be freed from it through You. You taught me that Redemption will cancel the original sin. I do not think that I am wrong if I say that it will not be cancelled in everybody, but only in those who believe in You.»

«Which is true.»

«So I will not take into account the others, but only one of those who have been saved. I will consider him after the effects of Redemption. His soul is no longer stained with original sin. He is therefore once again in the possession of Grace as our First Parents were. Does that, then, not give his soul a strength unassailable by any weakness? You will say: "Man commits personal sins too". I agree. But they will vanish as well through Your Redemption. I will not ask You how. But I suppose that You will leave some means, some symbols... as evidence that Your Redemption has actually taken place; and I do not know how it will happen, although what is referred to You in the Holy Book makes one shudder, and I hope that it will be a symbolical suffering, confined to the morale, although moral grief is not a false impression and is perhaps more dreadful than physical pain. You will leave some means, some symbols. Every religion has them, and at times they are called mysteries... The baptism, at present in force in Israel, is one, is it not?»

«It is. Also in My Religion there will be signs of My Redemption to be applied to souls to purify, strengthen, enlighten, support, nourish and absolve them, but with a different name from the one mentioned by you.»

«So? If they are also absolved of personal sins, they will always be in grace... So how can they be weak and predisposed to spiritual diseases?»

[7] «I will make a comparison for you. Let us take a new born 307.7
baby, who is healthy and strong and was born of very healthy parents. He has no physical hereditary taint. His body is perfect both with regards to its skeleton and its organs and his blood is wholesome. He has therefore all the necessary characteristics to grow strong and sound, also because his mother has plenty of nourishing milk. But in the early days of his life he suffered from a very serious disease, of unknown origin. It was a real deadly disease. He recovers with difficulty by the mercy of God, Who keeps him alive when life was on the point of departing from his little body. Well, do you think that later that boy will be as strong as if he never had had that disease? No, he will

suffer from an everlasting state of weakness. Even if it is not evident, it will still be there and he will be predisposed to diseases with greater ease than if he had never been ill. Some organ of his will not be as wholesome as before. And his blood will not be quite so strong and pure as before. And thus he will catch illnesses more easily. And such illnesses, every time he contracts them, will make him more exposed to be taken ill. The same applies in the spiritual field. The Original sin will be cancelled in those who believe in Me. But their souls will still have an inclination to sin, which they would not have had, had there been no Original sin. It is therefore necessary to continuously watch and take care of one's soul, as a solicitous mother does with her little son, who has been left weak by an infantile disease. So you must not be idle, but always active to grow stronger in virtue. If one falls into sluggishness or tepidity, one will be more easily seduced by Satan. And each serious sin, which is like a serious relapse, will always predispose one to diseases and spiritual death. But if Grace, restored by Redemption, is assisted by an active indefatigable will, it will remain. Or rather, it will increase, because it will be associated with the virtue achieved by man. Holiness and Grace! Which are safe wings to fly to God! Have you understood?»

«Yes, my Lord. You, that is the Most Holy Trinity, give the basic Means to man. Man with his work and care must not destroy it. I understand. Every serious sin destroys Grace, that is, the health of the spirit. The signs which You will leave us, will give health back, that is true. But an obstinate sinner, who does not struggle to avoid sin, will become weaker each time, even if he is
forgiven each time. One must therefore be vigilant in order not to
307.8 perish. Thank You, Master... [8]Marjiam is waking up. It's late...»

«Yes. Let us pray all together and then we will go to rest.»

Jesus stands up imitated by everybody, also by the boy still half asleep. And the «Our Father» resounds loud and harmonious in the little room.

308. Jesus and the Wife of His Cousin Simon of Alphaeus. Marjiam Is the First of the Children Disciples.

20th October 1945.

[1]Jesus with Simon Zealot and Marjiam goes through Nazareth 308.1
towards the country stretching towards Cana. And He crosses His sceptical hostile town along the more central streets, and cuts diagonally across the market square, crowded in the early morning. Many turn to look at Him; very few citizens greet Him, women, particularly elderly ones, smile at Him but, with the exception of few children, no one comes to Him. People whisper after He has gone by. Jesus certainly sees everything, but pretends He does not. He speaks to Simon or to the boy, who is between them, and continues on His way.

[2]They are now at the last houses. A woman, about forty years 308.2
old, is on the door step of one of them. She seems to be waiting for someone. When she sees Jesus, she makes the gesture of moving, then she stops and lowers her head blushing.

«She is a relative of Mine. She is the wife of Simon of Alphaeus» says Jesus to the apostle.

The woman seems to be on tenterhooks, overwhelmed by clashing sentiments. She changes colour, raises and lowers her head, and her face expresses a keen desire to speak, which is restrained by some reason.

«Peace to you, Salome» greets Jesus when He arrives near her.

The woman looks at Him as if she were surprised at the kindness in the voice of her relative and she replies, blushing even more: «Peace to...» A lump in her throat prevents her from ending the sentence. She hides her face in her folded arm and weeps desolately, leaning against the doorpost.

«Why are you weeping thus, Salome? Is there anything I can do to console you? Come here, round the corner, and tell Me what the matter is...» and He takes her by the elbow and leads her into a little lane between her house and her neighbour's kitchen garden. Simon stays at the entrance of the lane with Marjiam who is utterly astonished. «What is the matter, Salome? You know that *I have always loved you. I have always loved you all. And I still love you*. You must believe that and trust Me...»

She stops weeping now and again, as if she wanted to listen

to those words and understand their true meaning, then she resumes weeping more loudly, uttering disconnected words: «Yes, You... We ... But not I... Not even Simon... But he is more foolish than I am ... I said...: "Call Jesus"... But the whole village is against us... against You... me... and my boy...» When she touches the tragical point, her weeping becomes tragical, too. She writhes and moans striking her face as if she were mad with grief.

Jesus grasps her hands saying: «Don't do that. I am here to comfort you. Speak, and I will do everything...»

The woman looks at Him with eyes wide open with astonishment and grief. But hope gives her energy to speak and to speak in an orderly way: «Will You have mercy on me, even if Simon is guilty? Will You?... Oh! Jesus... You save everybody! My boy! Alphaeus, the last one, is ill... he is dying!... You loved Alphaeus. You used to carve toys in wood for him... You lifted him up that he might pick the grapes and figs of Your trees... and before You left... to travel about, You used to teach him so many good things... Now You would not be able... He is as good as dead... He will never eat grapes or figs again. He will never learn anything...» and she weeps her heart out.

«Salome, be good. Tell Me, what is the matter with him?»

«He is seriously ill with stomach trouble. He has been shouting, suffering terribly and delirious for days. Now he does not speak anymore. He is like one whose head has been struck. He moans but does not answer. He can hardly moan. He is deathly
308.3 pale and his body is getting cold. [3]For days I have begged Simon
to come to You. But... Oh! I have always loved him, but now I hate him because he is a fool and for a foolish idea he is allowing my son to die. But, if he dies, I will go away. I will go back to my house. With the other children. He is not capable of being a father at the right moment. And I am defending my children. I will go away. Yes, I will. People can say what they like. But I am going away.»

«Do not say that. Give up your idea of revenge.»

«Of justice. I rebel against them all. See? I had to wait for You, because none of them would say to You: "Come". But I do. And I had to do it as if it were something wrong. And I cannot say to You: "Come in", because Joseph's relatives are in the house and...»

«It is not necessary. Can you promise Me that you will forgive Simon? That you will always be a good wife to him? If you promise Me, I will say to you: "Go home, your son is cured and will smile at you". Can you believe that?»

«I believe in You. Against the whole world, I do believe in You.»

«And can you forgive as you believe?»

«... But... will You really cure him?»

«Not only will I, but I promise you that Simon will cease doubting about Me, and little Alphaeus, your other children, you and your husband will all come back to My house. Mary speaks of you so often...»

«Oh! Mary! Mary! She was there when Alphaeus was born... Yes, Jesus. I will forgive. I will not say anything to him... No. I will say to him: "This is how Jesus replies to your behaviour: giving your son back to you". I can say that!»

«Yes, you can... Go, Salome. Go. Weep no more. Goodbye. Peace to you, good Salome. Go now.» He takes her back to the door, He watches her go in, He smiles seeing that in her anxiety she runs along the vestibule without even closing the door, and He sets it ajar, slowly, and closes it.

[4] He then turns to His two companions and says: «And now let 308.4
us go where we had to go...»

«Do You think that Simon will convert?» asks the Zealot.

«He is not an infidel. He only allows stronger people to dominate him.»

«Well, then! Stronger than a miracle!»

«You can see that you have replied by yourself... [5] I am glad I 308.5
saved the child. I saw him when he was only a few hours old, and he has always been very fond of Me...»

«As I am? And will he become a disciple?» asks Marjiam keenly and he looks rather sceptical that anyone can love Jesus as he does.

«You love Me as a boy and as a disciple. Alphaeus loved Me only as a boy. But later he will love Me also as a disciple. But for the time being he is only a little boy. He will soon be eight years old. You will meet him.»

«So I am the only boy and disciple?»

«You are, at present. You are the head of the boy disciples.

When you are a man remember that you were as good a disciple as men, and so open your arms to all the children who will come to you seeking Me and will say: "I want to be a disciple of Christ". Will you do that?»

«I will» Marjiam promises seriously...

They are now in the open sunny country and they move away from me in the bright sunshine...

309. Marjiam's Abstinence for the Recovery of a Little Girl. Simon of Alphaeus' Repentance.

21st October 1945.

309.1 [1] They are made welcome in a poor house where there is a little grandmother surrounded by a little group of children, from ten down to about two years old. The house is situated in the middle of fields, rather neglected, many of which are meadows with a few surviving fruit-trees.

«Peace to you, Johanna. Are things better today? Did they come and help you?»

«Yes, Master and Jesus. And they told me that they will come back to sow. It will be late, but they tell me that it will grow.»

«Of course it will. What would be a miracle of the earth and of seed will become a miracle of God. So a perfect miracle. Your fields will be the best in this area, and these little birds which are around you will have plenty of corn for their mouths. Do not weep anymore. Next year the situation will improve a lot. But I will still help you. Or better: a good lady whose name is the same as yours, and who is never sated with doing good, will help you. Look: this is for you. It will enable you to make both ends meet until harvest-time.»

The old woman takes the purse and Jesus' hand at the same time and weeping kisses the latter. She then asks: «Tell me who this good lady is, that I may mention her name to the Lord.»

«A disciple of Mine and a sister of yours. Her name is known to Me and to the Father in Heaven.»

«Oh! It's You!...»

«I am poor, Johanna. I give what people give Me. Of My own I have but miracles. And I am sorry that I did not hear of your misfortune before. I came as soon as Susanna told Me. Too late now. But the work of God will shine brighter thus.»

«Late! Yes, it is late! Death was so quick in mowing here! And it took the young ones. Not me, now useless. Not these: immature ones. But those fit to work. Cursed be the moon of Elul, laden with evil influence!»

[2] «Do not curse the planet. It has nothing to do with it... Are 309.2
these little ones good? Come here. See? Also this boy has no father or mother. And he cannot even live with his grandfather. But God does not abandon him. And will not abandon him as long as he is good. Is that right, Marjiam?»

Marjiam nods assent and speaks to the little ones who have gathered around him, they are younger than he is, but some of them are a good bit taller. He says: «Oh! It is true that God does not abandon one. I can say so. My grandfather prayed for me. And your father and mother certainly prayed for you in the next world. And God heard those prayers, because He is Very Good, and He always hears the prayers of just people, whether they are living or dead. Your deceased parents and your dear granny here have certainly prayed for you. Do you love her?»

«Yes, yes...» the peeping of the orphan swarm rises enthusiastically.

Jesus becomes silent in order to listen to the conversation of His little disciple and the orphans.

«That's right. We must not make old people weep. In actual fact we must not make anybody weep, because those who grieve their neighbour grieve God. But old people! The Master is kind to everybody. But He is more than kind and loving with old people and children. Because children are innocent and old people suffer. They have already wept so much! We must love them twice, three times, ten times, for those who no longer love them. Jesus always says that he who does not honour an old person is doubly-wicked, like he who ill-treats a child. Because old people and children cannot defend themselves. So be good to your old mother.»

«Sometimes I do not help her...» says one of the bigger ones.

«Why? After all you eat the bread which she procures for you with her work! Does it not taste of tears when you upset her?
[3]And you, woman, (the *woman* is ten years old at the most and 309.3

she is a very thin pale girl) do you help her?»

The little brothers reply all together: «Oh! Rachel is good! She stays up until late to spin the little wool we have and she became feverish working in the field to prepare it to be sown when our father was dying.»

«God will reward you for that» says Marjiam seriously.

«He has already rewarded me by relieving my granny of her worry.»

Jesus intervenes: «Do you not want anything else?»

«No, Lord.»

«But are you cured?»

«No, Lord. But it does not matter. Even if I die now, my grandmother is assisted. Previously I was sorry to die because I helped her.»

«But death is dreadful, child...»

«As God helps me in life, He will help me in death and I will go to my mother... Oh! don't weep, grandmother! I love you, too, dear grandmother. I will not say that again if it makes you weep. On the contrary, if you wish so, I will ask the Lord to cure me... Don't weep, my little mother...» and she embraces the desolate old woman.

«Cure her, Lord. You made my grandfather happy because of me. Make this old woman happy now.»

Graces are obtained through sacrifices. What sacrifice will you make to obtain it?» asks Jesus seriously.

Marjiam thinks... He seeks the most painful thing to give up... and then he smiles: «I will have no more honey for a whole month.»

«That is not much! The month of Chislev is already far gone...»

«When I say a month I mean the four phases of the moon. And just think... during these days there is the Feast of Lights and honey cakes...»

309.4 «That is true. Well, Rachel will recover, thanks to you. [4]Now let us go. Goodbye, Johanna. I will come back before I go away. Goodbye, Rachel, goodbye, Toby. Be good. Goodbye, you little ones. May My blessing rest upon you all, and My peace be with you.»

They go out followed by the blessing of the old woman and the children.

Marjiam, after being «apostle and victim» begins to jump like a little kid and runs ahead.

Simon remarks with a smile: «His first sermon and his first sacrifice. He is a promising boy, don't You think so, Master?»

«Yes, I do. But he has preached before. Also to Judas of Simon...»

«... and the Lord seems to make children speak to him... Probably to avoid revenge by him...»

«Not revenge... I do not think he would go so far. But strong reactions, yes... He who deserves being reproached, does not love the truth... But it must be spoken...» says Jesus with a sigh.

Simon watches Him, then he asks: «Master, tell me the truth. You have sent him away, and You decided to send everybody home for the Dedication to prevent Judas from being in Galilee just now. I will not ask You and I do not want You to tell me why it is better that the man from Kerioth should not be with us. I only wish to know whether I have guessed right. We all think so, You know? Even Thomas. He said to me: "I will go without reacting because I realize that there is a serious reason behind it". And he added: "The Master is right in doing what He does. There are too many Nahums, Sadocs, Johanans and Eleazars among Judas' friends..." Thomas is not stupid!... And he is not bad, although he is very much a man. He is very sincere in his love for You...»

«I know. And what you all suspected is true. You will soon learn the reason...»

«We are not asking You to tell us.»

«But I will have to ask you to help Me and I must tell you.»

[5] Marjiam runs back and says: «Master, over there, where the 309.5
path ends with the main road, there is Your cousin Simon; he is all sweaty like one who has been running. He asked me: "Where is Jesus?". I replied: "He is here, behind me, with Simon Zealot". He said to me: "Will He be passing here?". "Of course" I replied. "He will pass here to go back home, unless He does what birds do: they fly from all directions to go back to their nests. Do you want Him?" I asked him. He remained uncertain. And yet I am sure that he wants You.»

«Master, he has already seen his wife... Let us do this. Marjiam and I will leave You free. We will go round the back of Nazareth. In any case… we are not in a hurry. And You will go along the main road.»

«Yes, thank you, Simon. I will see you later.»

They part and Jesus quickens His step towards the main road.

309.6 [6]There is Simon, leaning against a trunk, panting and drying his perspiration. As soon as he sees Jesus, he raises his arms… he then drops them and lowers his head dejectedly.

When Jesus arrives near him, He lays a hand on his shoulder asking: «What do you want, Simon? To make Me happy with a word of love, which I have been awaiting for *many* days?»

Simon lowers his head even more and is silent…

«Speak, then. Am I perhaps a stranger to you? No, you really are always My good brother Simon, and I am your little Jesus, Whom you used to carry in your arms, with some difficulty, but with so much love, when we came back to Nazareth.»

The man covers his face with both hands and falls on his knees: «Oh! My Jesus! I am the guilty one, but I have been punished enough…»

«Come on, stand up! We are relatives. What is it that you want?»

«My boy! He is…» a lump in his throat prevents him from speaking.

«Your boy? What about him?»

«He is dying. And Salome's love is dying with him… and I am left with double remorse: I am losing son and wife at the same time… Last night I thought that he was really dead and she looked like a hyena. She shouted at me: "Murderer of your son!". I prayed that that might not happen, and I swore to myself that I would come to You, if the boy recovered a little, also at the cost of being driven away — as I actually deserve — to tell You that You are the only one who can avert my calamity. At dawn the
309.7 boy recovered a little… [7]I ran from my house to Yours, round the back of the town, to avoid any possible hindrance… I knocked at the door. Mary opened and was amazed. She could have ill-treated me. But she only said: "What is the matter with you, poor Simon?". And She caressed me as if I were a child… And that made me weep. And my pride and hesitancy stopped. What Judas told us cannot be true, I mean Judas Your apostle, not my brother. I did not say that to Mary, but I say it to myself, beating my chest,

and casting contumelies on myself ever since. I asked Her: "Is Jesus in? It's for Alphaeus. He is dying…". Mary replied: "Run! He has gone towards Cana with the boy and an apostle. He is on the Cana road. But you must be quick. He went out at dawn. He is about to come back. I will pray that you may find Him". Not one word of reproach, not even one, although I deserve so many!»

«Neither will I reproach you. But I open My arms to you to…»

«Alas! To tell me that Alphaeus is dead!…»

«No. To tell you that I love you.»

«Come, then! Quick!»

«No. It is not necessary.»

«Are You not coming? Ah! Are You not forgiving me? Or is Alphaeus dead? But even if he is, Jesus, since You raise the dead, give me back my son! Oh! Good Jesus!… Holy Jesus! Whom I abandoned!… Jesus… Jesus…» The solitary road is filled with the tears of the man, who, kneeling down, fingers Jesus' mantle convulsively, or kisses His feet, tortured by sorrow, remorse and paternal love…

8 «Did you not go home before coming here?» 309.8

«No. I ran here like a madman… Why? Is there more trouble? Has Salome already run away? Has she become mad? She seemed mad last night…»

«Salome has spoken to Me. She wept, she believed. Go home, Simon. Your son is cured.»

«You!… You!… You have done that for me who offended You by believing that snake? Oh! Lord! I do not deserve so much! Forgive me! Tell me what You want me to do to make amends, to let You know that I love You, to convince You that I suffered in being stand-offish, to tell You that I wanted to speak to You, since You have been here, even before Alphaeus was so ill!… But… but…»

«Never mind. It is all over. I have forgotten about it. Do the same yourself. And forget also the words of Judas of Kerioth. He is a boy. All I want from you is this: that you will never repeat those words to My disciples, to My apostles, and least of all, to My Mother. That is all. Now go home, Simon. Go and be in peace… Do not delay in taking part in the joy which has filled your house. Go.» He kisses him and gently pushes him towards Nazareth.

«Are You not coming with me?»

«I will wait for you with Salome and Alphaeus in My house.

Go. And remember that the present joy comes to you, thanks to your wife who believed the truth.»

«Do You mean that I...»

«No. I mean that I have understood that you have repented. And you repented because of her cry accusing you... God really shouts through the mouths of good people, reproaching and advising!...And I saw the firm humble faith of Salome. Go, I tell you. Do not wait any longer to thank her.»

And Jesus almost pushes him roughly to persuade him to go. And when Simon finally goes away, He blesses him... and then shakes His head in mute soliloquy and tears slowly run down His pale cheeks... One word only hints at the trend of His thought: «Judas!»...

He sets out along the same road taken by the Zealot, behind the boundary of the village, towards His house.

310. Jesus Plans the Departure of John of Endor and Syntyche.

22nd October 1945.

310.1 [1] It is late in the morning when Peter, all alone and unexpected, arrives at the house in Nazareth. He is laden like a porter with baskets and little sacks. But he is so happy that he feels neither weight nor fatigue.

He smiles blissfully at Mary, Who goes to open the door, and He greets Her with joy and veneration at the same time. He then asks: «Where are the Master and Marjiam?»

«They are on the embankment, above the grotto, but towards Alphaeus' house. I think that Marjiam is picking olives and Jesus is certainly meditating. I will call them.»

«I will see to that.»

«Leave all your bundles first.»

«No. They are a surprise for the boy. I like to see him open his eyes wide and rummage eagerly... It makes him so happy, poor boy.»

He goes out into the kitchen garden, he goes under the embankment, he hides in the cavity of the grotto, and he then shouts, altering his voice a little: «Peace to You, Master», and then in his natural voice: «Marjiam!...»

Marjiam's shrill voice, which filled the peaceful air with exclamations, becomes quiet... There is a pause, then the almost girlish voice of the boy asks: «Master, but was that not my father calling me?»

Jesus was perhaps so engrossed in thought that He did not hear anything, and He openly admits it.

Peter calls once again: «Marjiam!» and he laughs his usual hearty laugh.

«Oh! it is him! Father! Father! Where are you?» He leans out to look in the kitchen garden, but does not see anything...

Jesus also comes forward and looks... He sees Mary Who is smiling on the doorstep and John and Syntyche who are also smiling from the room at the end of the kitchen garden near the stone-oven.

But Marjiam comes to a decision: he jumps from the embankment, just near the grotto, and Peter is ready to catch him before he touches the ground. It is touching to see how they greet each other. Jesus, Mary and the two disciples at the end of the kitchen garden watch them smiling, and then they all gather round the little fond group.

[2]Peter frees himself, as best he can, from the grip of the boy 310.2
to bow to Jesus and greet Him once again. Jesus embraces him with the boy, who is still clinging to the apostle and asks: «And mother?»

But Peter replies to Jesus Who asks him: «Why did you come so soon?»

«Did You think I could stay away so long without seeing You? And then... Eh! then there is Porphirea who did not leave Me in peace: "Go and see Marjiam. Take him this. Take him that". She seemed to think that Marjiam was among highwaymen or in a desert. The other night she got up just to make honey cakes and as soon as they were baked, she sent me off....»

«Ah! honey cakes!...» shouts Marjiam. Then he turns silent.

«Yes. They are in here with figs dried in the oven, olives and red apples. And she baked an olive oil loaf for you. And she sent you some cheese made with the milk of your sheep. And there is also a water resistant tunic. And then, and then... I don't know what else there is. What? Are you no longer in a hurry? Are you weeping? Oh! Why?»

«Because I would have preferred you to bring her here, instead of all these things... I am very fond of her, you know?»

«Oh! Divine Mercy! Who would have thought that?! If she were here listening to you, she would melt like butter...»

«Marjiam is right. You could have come with her. She certainly wishes to see him after such a long time. We women are just like that with our children...» says Mary.

«Well... But she will see him before long, won't she, Master?»

«Yes, after the Dedication, when we go away... No... When you come back, after the Dedication, you will come with her. She will stay here with him for a few days, and then they will go back to Bethsaida together.»

«Oh! How lovely! I will be here with two mothers!» The boy is cheerful once again and happy.

310.3 [3] They all go into the house and Peter relieves himself of his bundles.

«Here is some dried, pickled and fresh fish. It will be useful to Your Mother. And here is some of that cream cheese, which You like so much, Master. And here are some eggs for John. I hope they are not broken... No. Good. And some grapes. I got them from Susanna at Cana, where I slept. Then... Ah! Look at this Marjiam! Look how clear it is. It seems to be made with Mary's hair»... And he opens a jar of treacly honey.

«Why so much stuff? You have gone to a lot of trouble, Simon» says Mary looking at the bundles, parcels, vases and jars on the table.

«Trouble? No. I had a good haul and I made a good profit. That, as far as the fish is concerned. With regard to the rest: it is all home made. It costs nothing but gives so much joy to bring it. In any case... We are now at the Dedication... That is the custom. Isn't it? Are you not tasting the honey?»

«I cannot» says Marjiam seriously.

«Why? Are you not well?»

«No. But I cannot take it.»

«But why?»

The boy blushes but does not reply. He looks at Jesus and is silent. Jesus smiles and explains: «Marjiam made a vow to obtain a grace. He cannot eat honey for four weeks.»

«All right. You will eat it after... Take the jar just the same... Just imagine! I didn't think he was... so...»

«So generous, Simon. He who becomes accustomed to penance from his childhood will find the path of virtue easy throughout life» says Jesus, while the boy goes away with the jar in his hands.

Peter watches him go and is amazed. He then asks: «Is the Zealot not in?»

«He has gone to Mary of Alphaeus. But he will soon be back.
You will be sleeping together tonight. [4]Come into the next room, 310.4
Simon Peter.»

They go out while Mary and Syntyche tidy up the room invaded by bundles.

«Master... I have come to see You and the boy. That is true. But also because I have been thinking a lot these days, particularly after the arrival of three poisonous hornets... whom I told more lies than there are fish in the sea. They are now going to Gethsemane as they think that John of Endor is there and then they will be going to Lazarus, hoping to find Syntyche and You there. Let them walk!... But they will come back and... Master, they want to cause You trouble because of those two wretched people...»

«I made all the necessary arrangements months ago. When they come back looking for these two persecuted people, they will not find them anywhere in Palestine. See these chests? I made them for John and Syntyche. Did you notice all those folded garments near the loom? They are for them. Are you surprised?»

«Yes, Master. Where are You sending them?»

«To Antioch.»

Peter whistles meaningfully and then asks: «To whom? And how will they go there?»

«To a house belonging to Lazarus. The last one Lazarus has where his father governed in the name of Rome. And they will go by sea...»

«Ah! I see! Because if John had to go there on foot...»

«By sea. [5]I am glad I can speak to you about it. I was going to 310.5
send Simon to say to you: "Come", to prepare everything. Listen. Two or three days after the Feast of the Dedication we will leave from here few at a time, in order not to attract anybody's attention. The group will be formed by Me, you, your brother,

James and John, My two cousins, John and Syntyche. We will go to Ptolemais! From there you will take them by boat to Tyre. There you will board a ship sailing to Antioch, as if you were proselytes going back home. You will then come back and you will find Me at Achzib. I will be on the mountain top every day. In any case the Spirit will guide you...»

«What? Are You not coming with us?»

«I would be noted too much. I want to give peace to John's soul.»

«And what will I do since I have never been away from here?»

«You are not a child... and soon you will have to go much farther than Antioch. I trust you. You can see that I esteem you very much...»

«And what about Philip and Bartholomew?»

«They will come and meet us at Jotopata and will evangelize while waiting for us. I will write to them and you will take the letter.»

«And... those two over there, do they already know their destiny?»

«No. I want them to celebrate the Feast in peace...»

«H'm. Poor people... Fancy that! People are persecuted by criminals and...»

«Do not foul your mouth, Simon.»

«No, Master... Listen... How will we carry these chests? And John? He looks seriously ill to me.»

«We will take a donkey.»

«No. We will take a cart.»

«And who will drive it?»

«Eh! If Judas of Simon learned to row, Simon of Jonah will learn to drive a cart. It should not be difficult to lead a donkey by the bridle. We will put the chests and those two in the cart... and we will go on foot. Yes, it is better to do that, believe me.»

«And who will give us the cart? Remember that I do not want our departure to be noted.»

Peter thinks... He makes up his mind: «Have You any money?»

«Yes. Still quite a lot of the money we got for Misace's jewels.»

«In that case it is easy. Give me a sum. I will get a donkey and cart from someone and... yes... we will make a present of the donkey to some poor wretch and the cart... we will see... I am glad I came. And must I really come back with my wife?»

«Yes. It is better.»

«Good. [6]But those two poor wretches! I am sorry that we shall 310.6
no longer have John with us. True, we would not have had him for long... But, poor man! He might have died here, like Jonah...»

«They would not have allowed him. The world hates those who redeem themselves.»

«He will feel humiliated...»

«I will find a reason to make him leave with a relieved mind.»

«Which reason?»

«The same as I used to send away Judas of Simon: to work for Me.»

«Ah!... The difference is that in John it will be holiness, whereas in Judas it is only pride.»

«Simon, do not backbite.»

«That is more difficult than to make a fish sing! It is the truth, Master, it is not backbiting... But I think that Simon has come with Your brothers. Let us go...»

«Let us go. Not a word to anybody.»

«Are You telling me? I cannot omit mentioning the truth when I speak, but I can be silent, if I want. And *I do want*! I swore it to myself. Imagine me going to Antioch! To the ends of the earth! Oh! I wish I were already back! I shall sleep no more until it is all over...»

They go out and I see no more.

311. Marjiam's Self-Denial Inspire a Lesson on Renunciation: Nothing is Lost in the Holy Economy of Universal Love.

23rd October 1945.

[1]I do not know whether it is the same day, but I suppose it is, 311.1
because Peter is sitting at the family table in Nazareth. The meal is almost over and Syntyche gets up to put on the table some apples, nuts, grapes and almonds which end the supper, because it is evening and lamps have already been lit.

They are talking about lamps when Syntyche brings the fruit. Peter says: «This year we will light an extra lamp, and then more and more, for you, son. Because we want to light it for you, even if you are here. It is the first time we light one for a boy...» and Simon is moved when he ends: «It would certainly be lovelier, if you were there...»

«Last year, Simon, it was I who sighed for My Son far away, and with Me, Mary of Alphaeus, Salome and also Mary of Simon in her house at Kerioth, and Thomas' mother...»

«Oh! Judas' mother! Her son will be with her this year... but I do not think she will be happier... Never mind... We were at Lazarus'. How many lights!... It looked like a sky of gold and fire. Lazarus has his sister this year... But I am sure of speaking the truth when I say that they will be sighing because You are not
311.2 there. [2]And where will we be next year?»

«I will be very far away...» whispers John.

Peter turns around to look at him, as he is sitting beside John, and he is on the point of asking something, but fortunately he controls himself, because of a meaningful look of Jesus.

Marjiam asks: «Where will you be?»

«By the mercy of the Lord I hope to be in Abraham's bosom...»

«Oh! do you want to die? Do you not want to evangelize? Are you not sorry to die before evangelizing?»

«The word of the Lord is to be announced by holy lips. It is a great favour if He allowed me to hear it and redeem myself through it. I would have liked... But it is late...»

«And yet you will evangelize. You have already done so. So much so that you have attracted people's attention. You will therefore be called just the same an evangelizing disciple, even if you do not travel about preaching the Gospel; and in the next life you will receive the prize reserved for My evangelizers.»

«Your promise makes me desire death... Every minute in life may conceal a snare, and weak as I am, I may not be able to overcome it. If God receives me, being satisfied with what I have done, is that not great bounty, which I must bless?»

«I solemnly tell you that death will be supreme bounty for many, who will thus know to what extent man raves, from a place where peace will comfort them for such knowledge, and will change it into hosanna because it will be linked to the unutterable joy of liberation from Limbo.»

«And where shall we be in future years, Lord?» asks Simon Zealot who has been listening diligently.

«Where it will please the Eternal Father. Do you want to engage the remote future, when we are not certain of the moment in which we live and whether we will be granted to end it? In any case, whatever the place where the future Dedications will be celebrated, it will always be a holy one provided you are there to fulfil the will of God.»

«Provided we are? And what about You?» asks Peter. «I will always be where My beloved ones are.»

Mary has never spoken, but Her eyes have not ceased for one moment to scan the face of Her Son...

[3] She is aroused by Marjiam's remark who says: «Mother, why 311.3
have You not put the honey cakes on the table? Jesus likes them and they are good for John's throat. And my father likes them, too...»

«And you, too» concludes Peter.

«As far as I am concerned... they do not exist. I promised...»

«That is why I did not put them on the table, My dear...» says Mary caressing him, because Marjiam is between Her and Syntyche, on one side of the table, while the four men are on the opposite side.

«No, no. You can bring them. Or rather: You must bring them. And I will hand them out to everybody.»

Syntyche takes a lamp, goes out and comes back with the cakes. Marjiam takes the tray and begins to hand them out. He gives Jesus the most beautiful one, golden and raised like one made by a master confectioner. The next one in perfection is for Mary. Then it is the turn of Peter, Simon and Syntyche. But in order to serve John, the boy gets up and goes beside the old sick teacher and says to him: «I am giving you yours and mine, with a kiss, to thank you for what you teach me.» He then goes back to his place lays the tray in the middle of the table resolutely and folds his arms.

«You make this delicious cake go the wrong way» says Peter when he sees that Marjiam does not take any. And he adds: «At least a little bit. Here, take some of mine, so that you will not die to have some. You are suffering too much ... Jesus will let you have it.»

«But if I did not suffer, I would have no merit, father. I offered this sacrifice exactly because I knew that it would make me suffer. After all... I have been so happy since I made it, that I seem to be full of honey. I taste it in everything, and I even seem to breathe it in the air...»

«That's because you are dying to have some...»

«No. It's because I know that God says to me: "You are doing the right thing, My son".»

«The Master. would have satisfied you, even without this sacrifice. He loves you so much!»

«Yes. But it is not fair that I should take advantage of it, just
because He loves me. In any case, He says that great is the re- *
ward in Heaven even for a cup of water offered in His name. I
think that if it is great for a cup of water given to other people in
His name, it must also be great for a cake or a little honey which
311.4 one gives up out of love for a brother. [4]Am I wrong, Master?»

«No, you have spoken wisely. In fact, I could have granted you what you asked for, in favour of little Rachel, also without your sacrifice, because it was a good thing to do and My Heart desired it. But I did it with greater joy because I was helped by you. The love for our brothers is not confined to human means and limits, but it rises to much higher levels. When it is perfect, it really touches the throne of God and blends with His infinite Charity and Bounty. The communion of saints is just this continuous activity, as God works continuously and in every way, to assist our brothers both in their material and spiritual needs or in both as it is in the case of Marjiam, who relieves Rachel of her illness by obtaining her cure, and at the same time he relieves the dejected spirit of old Johanna and kindles greater and greater trust in the Lord in all the hearts in the family. Even a spoonful of honey, offered as a sacrifice, can help to bring peace and hope to an afflicted soul as a cake or any other food given up out of love, may obtain some bread, offered miraculously, for some starving person who is remote from us and will never be known to us; and an angry word, not uttered out of spirit of sacrifice, although justified, may prevent a remote crime, as to resist the desire to pick a fruit, out of love, may bring about a thought of resipiscence in

* **He says**, in 265.13.

a thief and thwart a theft. Nothing is lost in the holy economy of universal love: neither the heroic sacrifice of a boy before a dish of honey cakes, nor the holocaust of a martyr. In fact, I tell you that the holocaust of a martyr often originates from the heroic upbreeding imparted to him since his childhood for the love of God and his neighbour.»

[5] «So it is really a good thing that I should always make sac- 311.5
rifices. For the time when we will be persecuted» says Marjiam earnestly.

«Persecuted?» asks Peter.

«Yes. Don't you remember that He said so? "You will be per-
* secuted in My name". You told me the first time you came all alone to Bethsaida, in summer, to evangelize.»

«This boy remembers everything» comments Peter admiring him.

The supper is over. Jesus stands up. He prays for everybody and blesses them. And while the women go to tidy up the kitchen, Jesus and the men take seats in a corner of the room, where He begins to carve a piece of wood, which under the amazed eyes of Marjiam, takes the shape of a little sheep...

312. Jesus Informs Dismayed John of Endor that He Will to Go to Antioch. The Year of Jesus' "Mercy" is Over. End of the Second Year of Public Life.

24th October 1945.

[1] It is a wet winter morning. Jesus is already up and is busy in 312.1
His workshop. He is making small items. But in a corner there is a new loom, not a very big one, but well-shaped and polished.

Mary comes in with a cup of steaming hot milk. «Drink this, Jesus. You have been up so long. And it is damp and cold...»

«Yes, but at least I have been able to finish everything... The eight feast days had paralysed My work...» Jesus has sat down on the carpenter's bench, a little sideways, and drinks the milk while Mary looks at the loom and rubs Her hand on it caressingly.

«Are You blessing it, Mother?» asks Jesus smiling.

---

* **You told me**, in 265.7.9.

«No, I am caressing it because You made it. You blessed it by making it. It was a good idea to make it. It will be very useful to Syntyche. She is a very skillful weaver. It will help her to approach women and girls. What else have You made, I see thin shavings, of olive, I think, near the lathe?»

«I have made useful things for John. See? A stylus case and a writing board. And these desks in which he can keep his rolls. I could not have made all these things if Simon of Jonah had not thought of getting a cart. But now we can load these as well... and also through these little things they will feel that I love them...»

«You suffer in sending them away, do You not?»

«I do... For Myself and for them... I have waited up to the present moment to tell them and it is strange that Simon has not yet arrived with Porphirea... I must tell them now... I have had this pain in My heart all these days and even the light of the many lamps looked sad to Me... A suffering which I must now communicate to others... Ah! Mother, I would have liked to have kept it all to Myself...»

«My good Son!» Mary caresses His hand to comfort Him.

312.2 [2] There is silence... Then Jesus carries on speaking: «Is John up?»

«Yes. I heard him cough. He is perhaps in the kitchen taking his milk. Poor John!...» tears stream down Mary's cheeks.

Jesus stands up: «I am going... I must go and tell him. It will be easier with Syntyche... But with him... Mother, go to Marjiam, wake him up and pray while I speak to that man... I feel as if I had to rummage in his bowels. I may kill or paralyse his spiritual vitality... How painful, Father!... I am going...» and He is really depressed when He goes out.

He walks the few steps which separate Him from John's room, which is the same one where Jonah died, that is, Joseph's room. He meets Syntyche, who is coming in with a faggot from the stone oven and who greets Him, completely unaware of the situation. Although engrossed in thought He replies to the Greek woman's greeting and stops to look at a bed of lilies which are beginning to show a tiny tuft of leaves. But I am not sure that He really sees them... He then makes up His mind. He turns around and knocks at John's door, who opens and whose face brightens on seeing Jesus coming to him.

«May I come in for a moment?» asks Jesus.

«Oh! Master! Of course! [3]I was writing what You said last 312.3
night on prudence and obedience. I think You had better have a look at it, because I do not think that I remember everything on prudence.»

Jesus has entered the little room, which has already been tidied up and in which they have put a small table for the convenience of the old master. Jesus bends over the parchments and reads. «Very well, you have repeated it very well.»

«Here, see. I thought this sentence was not quite correct. You always say that it is not necessary to be solicitous about tomorrow and one's body. Now I thought that it was wrong to say that prudence, also with regard to things concerning tomorrow, is a virtue. An error of mine, of course.»

«No. You are not wrong. That is exactly what I said. The exaggerated and fearful anxiety of a selfish person is different from the prudent care of a just person. It is sinful to be avaricious for the future, which, perhaps, we shall never see. But it is not sinful to be thrifty to secure a piece of bread, also for one's relatives when there is a shortage. The selfish care of one's body is sinful, when a person demands that all those around him should worry about him, and avoids all work or sacrifice lest his body should suffer, but it is not sinful to preserve it from wasteful diseases, the result of imprudent behaviour, which diseases are a burden for relatives and a loss of profitable work for ourselves. Life is given by God. It is a gift of His. Consequently we must make holy
use of it, without being imprudent or selfish. [4]See? At times pru- 312.4
dence suggests actions, which foolish people may consider cowardly or inconstant, whereas they are the result of holy prudence in the light of new events, which have occurred. For instance: if I sent you now right in the middle of people who might do you harm... for instance your wife's relatives or the watchmen of the mines where you worked, would I do a good or a bad thing?»

«I... I would not like to pass judgement on You. But I would say that it would be better to send me elsewhere, where there is no danger of my little virtue being put to too hard a test.»

«There you are! You would judge wisely and prudently. That is why I would never send you to Bithynia or Mysia, where you have already been. Neither would I send you to Cintium, although you have a spiritual desire to go there. Your spirit might be overwhelmed by much human harshness and might fall back. Prudence therefore teaches Me not to send you where you would be valueless, whereas I could send you elsewhere with a good profit for Me, for the souls of your neighbours and your own. Is that not right?»

As John is completely unaware of what his destiny has in store for him, he does not catch Jesus' allusions to the possibility of a mission outside of Palestine. Jesus scans his face and sees that he is calm, completely happy to listen to Him, and quick in replying: «Of course, Master, I would be more useful elsewhere. When some days ago I said: "I would like to go among the Gentiles to set a good example where I set a bad one", I reproached myself saying: "Among the Gentiles, yes, because you are not biased as the Israelites. But not at Cintium, nor on the desolate mountains, where I lived as a convict and like a wolf in the lead mines and in the quarries of precious marbles. Not even for the sake of a perfect sacrifice could you go there. Your heart would be upset by recollections of cruelty, and if they recognised you, even if they did not act cruelly against you, they would say: 'Be quiet, murderer. We cannot listen to you so it would be quite useless to go there". That is what I said to myself. And I was right.»

312.5 [5] «You can therefore see that you possess prudence. I possess it, too. That is why I took you away from the hard work of apostolate, as is practised by the others, and I brought you here, to rest and be in peace.»

«Oh! yes! How peaceful it is! If I lived here for a hundred years, it would still be the same. It is a supernatural peace. And if I went away, I would take it with me. I will take it also to the next life... Recollections may still stir my heart and offences may make me suffer, because I am a man. But I will never be able to hate again, because hatred has been sterilised here for good, as far as its most remote ramifications. And I no longer have an aversion to women, whom I considered the filthiest and meanest animals on the earth. Your Mother is out of question. I venerated Her from the first moment I saw Her because I felt that She was different from all women. She is the perfume of woman, but the perfume of holy woman. Who does not love the scent of the purest flowers? But also the other women, the good women disciples, loving and patient under their sorrowful burdens, like Mary Clopas and Eliza; generous like Mary of Magdala, so complete in her change of life; kind and pure like Martha and Johanna; dignified, intelligent, thoughtful and upright, like Syntyche, have reconciled me with women. Syntyche, I admit it, is the one I like best. Affinity of mind and of circumstances make her dear to me: she was a slave, I a convict, and that allows me to be on familiar terms with her which the difference with the others forbids. She is peace and tranquillity to me. I could not tell You exactly what she means to me and what I consider her. As I am old compared to her, I see her as a daughter, the wise and studious daughter I would have liked to have... But I, a sick man whom she cures with so much love, a sad and solitary man who has grieved for and regretted his mother throughout his life, and has sought a mother in every woman, without ever finding one, I now see my dream becoming true in her and I feel the dew of motherly love descend upon my tired head and upon my soul while I am going towards my death... You can see that, as I perceive in Syntyche the soul of a daughter and of a mother, I see in her the perfection of womanhood and for her sake I forgive all the evil I received from women. If, what is an impossible case, that wretch of my wife, whom I killed, should rise from the dead, I feel that I would forgive her because I have now understood the soul of woman, prone to love, generous in giving herself... both in good and in evil.»

«I am glad that you have found all that in Syntyche. She will be a good companion to you for the rest of your days and you will do much good together. Because I will associate you...»

Jesus scans John once again. But there is no sign of aroused attention in the disciple, although he is not a superficial person. Which divine mercy conceals his sentence until the crucial moment? I do not know. I know that John smiles saying: «We shall endeavour to serve You to the best of our ability.»

«Yes. And I am sure that you will do so, without discussing the work or the place, which I will allot to you, even if it should not be what you wish...»

[6] John has a first inkling of what awaits him. His countenance 312.6
and colour change. He becomes serious and pale and his only eye stares attentively and inquisitively at the face of Jesus, Who

continues: «Do you remember, John, when I said to you, to dis- *
pel your doubts about God's forgiveness: "To let you understand Mercy I will employ you in special merciful deeds and I will apply to you the parables of mercy"?»

«Yes. And You did. You have convinced me and You have granted me the possibility to do deeds of mercy, and I would say, the most delicate ones, such as giving alms and teaching a boy, a Philistine and a Greek woman. That made it clear to me that God was aware of my true repentance and thus He entrusted me with innocent souls or the souls of converts, that I might perfect them.»

Jesus embraces John and draws him close to His side, as He is wont to do with the other John, and turning pale because of the grief He has to cause, He says: «Also now God is going to entrust a delicate holy task to you. A task of predilection. Only you who are generous, unreserved and unbiased, wise, and above all
have offered yourself to all renunciations and penances to ex- *
piate the remaining purgation and debt you still had with God, only you can do it. Anybody else would refuse, and quite rightly, because he would be lacking the necessary requisites. Not one of My apostles possesses what you have, to go and preach the ways of the Lord... Further, your name is John. So you will be a Precursor of My Doctrine... you will prepare the way for your Master... and more than that, you will act in place of your Master, Who cannot go *so far*... (John starts and endeavours to free himself from Jesus' arm, in order to look at Him in the face, but he is not successful, because Jesus' hold is kind but authoritative, while His lips give the final blow...) ... He cannot go *so far*... as far as Syria... as far as Antioch...»

312.7 [7] «Lord!» shouts John, freeing himself with violence from Jesus' embrace. «Lord! To Antioch? Tell me that I have misunderstood You! Tell me, please!...» He is standing... His whole attitude is a supplication: his only eye, his face which has turned ashen-grey, his trembling lips, his outstretched shaking hands, his lowered head, which seems to be burdened by the news.

But Jesus cannot say: «You have misunderstood.» He opens His arms, standing up to receive the old teacher on His heart,

---

* **I said to you**, as in 205.1.
* **have offered yourself**, in 250.10.

and He opens His lips to confirm: «Yes, to Antioch. To a house of Lazarus'. With Syntyche. You shall leave tomorrow or the day after.»

John's desolation is really heart-rending. He half-frees himself from the embrace, and face to face, with his thin cheeks wet with tears, he cries: «Ah! You do not want me any longer!! How have I offended You, my Lord?» He gets free of Jesus' grasp and throws himself on the table, in an outburst of heart-rending sobs interrupted by fits of coughing, insensible to Jesus' caresses and he moans: «You are driving me away, You are rejecting me, I will never see You again...»

Jesus is clearly grieved and He prays... He then goes out slowly and sees Mary with Marjiam at the kitchen door. The boy is frightened by John's weeping... A little farther away, there is Syntyche, who is also astonished. «Mother, come here a moment.»

Mary goes at once. She is pale. They go in together. Mary bends over the weeping man as if he were a poor boy, saying: «Good, be good, poor son of Mine! Do not weep like that! You will hurt yourself.»

John raises his convulsed face and shouts: «He is sending me away!... I will die all alone, far away... Oh! He might have waited a few months and let me die here. Why this punishment? How have I sinned? Have I ever troubled You? Why give me all this peace, and then.. and then...» He collapses once again on the table, weeping louder, panting...

Jesus lays a hand on his lean trembling shoulders, saying:
«And can you possibly believe that if I could have, I would not
have kept you here? Oh! John! There are dreadful necessities on
the way of the Lord! And I am the first to suffer thereby, as I
have to bear My sorrow and the sorrow of the whole world. Look
at Me, John. See whether My face is the face of one who hates
you, and is tired of you... Come here, in My arms, and feel how
My heart is throbbing with grief. Understand Me, John, do not
misunderstand Me. This is the last expiation God imposes on
you, to open the gates of Heaven to you. [8]Listen...» and He lifts 312.8
him up and holds him in His arms. «Listen... Mother, go out for a
moment... Listen now, that we are alone. You know who I am. Do
you firmly believe that I am the Redeemer?»

«Of course I do. That is why I wanted to stay with You, for good, until death...» «Death... My death will be a dreadful one!...»

«Mine, I mean. My death...»

«Yours will be placid, comforted by My presence, which will instil the certainty of God's love into you, and consoled by the love of Syntyche, as well as by the joy of having prepared the triumph of the Gospel in Antioch. But Mine! You would see My body reduced to a mass of flesh covered with wounds, covered with spittle, outraged, abandoned to an enraged crowd, put to death hanging from a cross like a criminal... Could you bear all that?»

John, who at each detail of how Jesus will be dealt with during His Passion has groaned: «No, no!», shouts a sharp «no» and adds: «I would begin to hate mankind again... But I will be dead, because You are young and...»

«And I will see but one more Dedication.»

John looks at Him, struck with terror...

«I told you secretly to let you know that that is one of the reasons why I am sending you away. But you will not be the only one. I will send away, beforehand, all those whom I do not want to be upset more than their strength can possibly stand. And do you think that is lack of love?...»

«No, my martyr God... But I have to leave You... and I will die far away from You.»

«In the name of the Truth which I am, I promise you that I will be bent over the pillow of your agony.»

«How can that be, if I am so far away and You say that You cannot come so far? You say that to make my departure less sad...»

«Johanna of Chuza, dying at the foot of Lebanon, saw Me although I was far away and she did not yet know Me and from where I was I brought her back to the poor life of this world. Believe Me, on the day of My death she will regret having survived!... But for you, the joy of My heart during this second year of My teaching, I will do more. I will come to take you to peace, and I will entrust you with the mission to say to those who are waiting: "The hour of the Lord has come. As springtime is coming to the earth, so the springtime of Paradise is rising for us". But that will not be the only time I will come... I will come... you will perceive Me... always... I can and I will do it. You will have the Mas-

ter within you, as you do not have Me even now. Because Love
can be communicated to its beloved ones, and so sensitively as to
touch not only their spirits, but also their senses. [9]Are you more 312.9
tranquil now, John?»

«Yes, my Lord. But how sorrowful!»

«However, you are not rebelling...»

«Rebel? Never! I would lose You completely. I say "my" Our Father: Thy will be done.»

«I knew that you would understand Me...» He kisses John's cheeks, still wet with continuous although calmer tears.

«Will You let me say goodbye to the boy?... That is another grief... I was fond of him...» he weeps bitterly again...

«Yes. I will call him at once... And I will call Syntyche as well. She will suffer, too. You must help her, you, a man...»

«Yes, my Lord.»

Jesus goes out while John weeps and kisses and caresses the walls and furnishings of the little hospitable room.

Mary and Marjiam come in together.

«Oh! Mother! Did You hear? Did You know?»

«I knew. And I was sorry... But I also parted with Jesus... And I am His Mother...»

«That is true!... Marjiam, come here. Do you know that I am going away and we shall not see each other again?...» He wants to be brave. But he takes the boy in his arms, he sits on the edge of the bed and weeps on the dark-haired head of Marjiam, who imitates him at once.

[10]Jesus enters with Syntyche who asks: «Why so much weeping, 312.10
John?»

«He is sending us away, do you not know? Have you not been told yet? He is sending us to Antioch!»

«Well? Did He not say that where there are two people assembled in His name, He will be among them? Come on, John! So far, perhaps, you have chosen your lot yourself, and thus the imposition of another will, even if a loving one, frightens you. I...I am accustomed to accepting the fate imposed on me by other people. And what a destiny!... So I now willingly submit to this new fate. Why not? I did not rebel against despotic slavery, except when it wanted to rule over my soul. And should I now rebel against this sweet slavery of love, which does not injure but elevates our souls and bestows on us the honour of being His servants? Are you afraid of tomorrow because you are not well? I will work for you. Are you afraid of being left alone? But I will never leave you. Be sure of that. I have no other aim in life but to love God and my neighbour. And you are the neighbour whom God entrusts to me. Consider, therefore, whether you are dear to me!»

«You need not work to live, because you will be in Lazarus' house. But I advise you to make use of teaching as a means of approaching people. You, John, as a teacher, and you, Syntyche, with needlework. It will be useful to your apostolate and will give an aim to your daily life.»

«It will be done, Lord» replies Syntyche resolutely,

312.11 [11] John is still holding the boy in his arms and is weeping quietly. Marjiam is caressing him...

«Will you remember me?»

«I will, John, always, and I will pray for you... Indeed... Wait a moment...» He runs out.

Syntyche asks: «How shall we go to Antioch?»

«By sea. Are you afraid?»

«No, Lord. In any case, You are sending us, and that will protect us.»

«You will go with the two Simons, My brothers, Zebedee's sons, Andrew and Matthew. From here to Ptolemais you will go by cart, in which we shall put the chests and a loom which I made for you, Syntyche, with some articles which will be useful to John...»

«I imagined something when I saw the chests and the garments. And I prepared my soul for the separation. It was too beautiful to live here!...» a stifled sob breaks Syntyche's voice. But she collects herself to support John's courage. She asks in a firm voice: «When are we leaving?»

«As soon as the apostles come, tomorrow probably.»

«Well, if You do not mind, I will go and pack the garments in the chests... Give me your rolls, John.» I think that Syntyche is anxious to be alone so that she may weep...

John replies: «Take them... but give me that roll tied with a blue ribbon.»

Marjiam comes in with his jar of honey.

«Here, John, take it. You will eat it instead of me...»

«No, my child! Why?»

«Because Jesus has said that a spoonful of honey offered as a sacrifice can give peace and hope to an afflicted soul. You are afflicted... I am giving you all the honey that you may be completely comforted.»

«But it is too big a sacrifice for you, boy.»

«Oh! no! In Jesus' prayer we say: "Lead us not into temptation, but deliver us from evil". This jar was a temptation to me... and might have been an evil because it might have made me infringe my vow. Now I will not see it anymore... and it is easier... and I am sure that God will help you, because of this new sacrifice. But do not weep anymore. And you, too, Syntyche...»

In fact the Greek woman is now weeping, noiselessly, while taking John's rolls. And Marjiam caresses them in turn, with a keen desire to weep himself. Syntyche goes out laden with rolls and Mary follows her with the jar of honey.

[12] John is left with Jesus, Who is sitting beside him, and with the 312.12
boy in his arms. He is calm, but depressed.

«Put your last writing in the roll» suggests Jesus. «I think that you want to give it to Marjiam...»

«Yes... I have a copy for myself... Here, boy. These are the words of the Master. The words He spoke when you were not here and others as well... I wanted to continue copying them for you, because you have a whole life in front of you... and goodness knows how much you will evangelize... But I cannot do it any more... Now it is I who will be left without His words...» And he begins to weep bitterly once again.

Marjiam is kind and virile in his new gesture. He throws his arms around John's neck and says: «I will write them for you now and I will send them to you... Is that right, Master? It can be done. Can it not?»

«Of course it can. And it will be great charity to do so.»

«I will do it. And when I am not there, Simon Zealot will do it. He loves me and he loves you and he will do it out of charity. So do not weep anymore. And I will come to see you... You will certainly not go very far...»

«Oh! how far! Hundreds of miles... And I will die soon.»

The boy is disappointed and down-hearted. But he collects himself with the beautiful serenity of a child who thinks everything is easy. «If you can go there, so I can come with my father. And... we will write to each other. When one reads the holy scriptures, it is like being with God, isn't it? So when we read a letter, it is like being with the person we love and who wrote it. Come on, let us go into the next room, come with me...»

312.13 «Yes, let us go, John. [13]My brothers will soon be here with the Zealot. I sent for them.»

«Do they know?»

«Not yet. I am waiting to tell them until they are all here...»

«All right, my Lord. Let us go...»

The old man who leaves Joseph's room is really bent with age. And he seems to be saying goodbye to every stem, to every trunk, to the fountain and the grotto, while going towards the workshop where Mary and Syntyche are silently laying things and garments in the chests...

And Simon, Judas and James find them in this way... silent and sad. They watch them... but ask no questions and I wonder whether they realize the truth.

312.14 [14] Jesus says:

«To give the readers a clear indication, I had indicated the place of John's prison expiation, with the name now in use. Someone is objecting to this. An exception is made. So I will now clarify the matter: Bithynia and Mysia, for those who want the ancient names. But this is the Gospel for simple people and little ones, not for doctors, to the majority of whom it is unacceptable and useless. And simple people and the little ones understand "Anatolia" better than "Bithynia or Mysia". Is that not right, little John, who are weeping over John of Endor's grief? But there are *so many* Johns of Endor in the world! They are the forlorn brothers for whom I made you suffer last year. Rest now, little *
John, as you will never be sent far away from the Master, on the contrary you will be closer and closer to Him.

And the second year of preaching and public life ends in this way: the year of Mercy... And I can but repeat the lamentation dictated at the closing of the first year. But it does not implicate My mouthpiece, who continues her work struggling against all

* **for whom I made you suffer**, as can be read in the "dictation" of 29th May 1944, in the volume "The Notebooks. 1944".

kinds of obstacles. It is not really the "great" people but the "little" ones who proceed along the paths of heroism, levelling them through their sacrifices, also for those who are weighed down by too many things. The "little" ones, that is those who are simple, meek, pure in their hearts and intellects: "little children". And I say to you, O little children, and to you, Romualdo, and to you, Mary, and to all those who are like you: "Come to Me so that you may again and always hear the Word Who speaks to you because He loves you and He speaks to you to bless you. My peace be with you".»

The Third Year of the Public Life of Jesus.

313. In Nazareth, Canny Peter Makes the Final Arrangements for a Secret Departure. In the Third Year, Jesus Will Be "Justice".

29th October 1945.

[1] John, James, Matthew and Andrew have already arrived in Nazareth and while waiting for Peter, they are walking around the kitchen garden, playing with Marjiam or talking among themselves. I do not see anybody else, as if Jesus were not in the house and Mary were busy. As there is smoke coming from the stone-oven chimney, I would say that She is in there baking bread. 313.1

The four apostles are glad to be in the Master's house and they show their joy. Marjiam says to them three times: «Do not laugh like that!». His third warning draws the attention of Matthew, who asks: «Why, boy? Are we not right in being happy here? You have enjoyed this place, eh? We are enjoying it now» and pats him fondly on the cheek. Marjiam looks at him very seriously, but he does not reply.

Jesus comes in with His cousins Judas and James, who greet their companions with much affection: they have been separated from them for many days. Mary of Alphaeus, flushed and covered with flour, looks out from the stone-oven and smiles at her big boys.

The last to arrive is the Zealot who says: «I have done everything, Master. Simon will be here shortly.»

«Which Simon? My brother or Simon of Jonah?»

«Your brother, James. He is coming with the whole family to greet you.»

[2] In fact a few minutes later, a knocking at the door and noisy chattering announce the arrival of the family of Simon of Alphaeus, who is the first to enter holding by the hand a little boy about eight years old; behind him there is Salome, surround- 313.2

ed by her group of children. Mary of Alphaeus runs out of the stone-oven and kisses her grandchildren and is very happy to see them there.

«So, are You leaving again?» asks Simon while his children make friends with Marjiam who, I think, is familiar only with Alphaeus, the boy who has been cured.

«Yes. It is time.»

«You will still have wet weather.»

«It does not matter. Springtime is approaching day by day.»

«Are You going to Capernaum?»

«I will certainly go there as well. But not at once. I am now going round Galilee and beyond it.»

«I will come to see You when I hear that You are in Capernaum. And I will bring Your Mother and mine to You.»

«I will be grateful to you. For the time being, do not neglect Her. She will be all alone. Bring your children here. They will not become corrupted here, you may be sure of that...»

Simon blushes at Jesus' allusion to his past thoughts and because of an expressive look cast at him by his wife, who seems to be saying: «Do you hear that? It serves you right.» But Simon changes the subject saying: «Where is Your Mother?»

«She is baking bread. She will soon be here...»

Simon's children, however, wait no longer and they go to the stone-oven following their grandmother. And a little girl, not much taller than Alphaeus, the boy who had been cured, comes out almost immediately saying: «Mary is weeping. Why? Eh! Jesus? Why is Your Mother weeping?»

«Is She weeping? oh! dear! Let me go to Her» says Salome solicitously.

And Jesus explains: «She is weeping because I am going away... But you will come and keep Her company, will you not? She will teach you how to embroider and you will make Her happy. Will you promise Me?»

«I will come, too, now that my father lets me come» says Alphaeus eating a hot bun which has just been given to him.

But although the bun is so hot that he can hardly hold it with his fingers, I think it is ice-cold compared to the heat suffered by Simon of Alphaeus, who blushes with shame at the words of his little boy. Although it is a rather cold winter morning, with a northern breeze blowing away the clouds in the sky and making one's skin tingle, Simon is sweating profusely, as if it were summer time...

But Jesus pretends not to notice it and the apostles pretend they are interested in what Simon's children are saying, and so
the incident is over, [3]and Simon can collect himself and ask Jesus 313.3
why all the apostles are not there.

«Simon of Jonah is about to arrive. The others will join Me at the right moment. It has all been settled.»

«All of them?»

«Yes.»

«Also Judas of Kerioth?»

«Yes...»

«Jesus, come with me for a moment» begs His cousin Simon. And once they have moved away, towards the end of the kitchen garden, Simon asks: «But do You really know who Judas of Simon is?»

«He is an Israelite. Nothing more, nothing less.»

«Oh! You are not going to tell me...» he is on the point of getting excited and raising his voice.

But Jesus calms him, interrupting him and laying a hand on his shoulder, saying: «He is what prevailing ideas and those who approach him have made him. Because, for instance, if he had found an *upright soul and an intelligent mind in everybody here* (and He lays stress on the words) he would not have been anxious to sin. But he did not find them. On the contrary, he found an entirely human element to which he adapted most comfortably his very human *ego*, which dreams and works for Me and sees in Me the king of Israel, in the *human* meaning of the word, as you dream and would like to see Me, and for Whom you would feel inclined to work, and your brother Joseph with you, as well as Levi, the head of the synagogue in Nazareth, and Mattathias and Simon and Matthias and Benjamin, and Jacob and, with the exception of three or four people, everybody in Nazareth. And not only in Nazareth... He has difficulty in perfecting himself, because you all contribute to his perversion. He is the weakest of My apostles. But for the time being, he is but a weak apostle. His impulses are good, his intentions are honest and he loves Me. He loves Me in a devious way, but it is still love. You do not help him

to separate these good qualities from the bad ones that form his *ego*, on the contrary you aggravate them by adding to them your
313.4 own incredulity and human limitations... [4]But let us go home. The others have gone there ahead of us...»

Simon follows Him and looks a little humiliated. They are almost on the threshold when he holds back Jesus and says: «Brother, are You angry with me?»

«No, I am not. But I am endeavouring to perfect you as I do with all the other disciples. Did you not say that you want to be one?»

«Yes, Jesus. But in the past You did not speak thus, not even when You were reproaching... You were kinder...»

«And of what avail was it? I was kinder once. I have been so for two years... Everybody here has become loose resting on My patience and kindness or has sharpened teeth and nails... You have all taken advantage of My love to harm Me. Is it not so?...»

«Yes, it is. It is true. So, will You no longer be good?»

«I will be just. And even so, I shall be such as you do not deserve, you people of Israel who will not acknowledge Me as the promised Messiah.»

313.5 [5]They go into the little room that is so crowded with people that the apostles had to move into the kitchen and into Joseph's workshop, with the exception of Alphaeus' two sons, who have remained with their mother and sister-in-law. The latter are joined by Mary Who comes in holding little Alphaeus by the hand. Mary's face shows clear signs of weeping.

While She is about to reply to Simon, who assures Her that he will come to see Her every day, a cart is proceeding along the little street with such a clanging of harness bells that it draws the attention of Alphaeus' children and the door is opened at the same time as they hear knocking outside. Simon Peter's merry face appears: he is still sitting on the cart, knocking at the door with the handle of the whip... Beside him, shy but smiling, there is Porphirea, sitting on cases and boxes, as on a throne.

Marjiam runs out and climbs on the cart to greet his adoptive mother. The others also come out, including Jesus.

«Master, here I am. I brought my wife, on this cart, as she is not fit for long walks. Mary, may the Lord be with You. And with you, Mary of Alphaeus.» He looks at everybody while getting off the vehicle and helps his wife to get off, and greets them all together.

They would like to help him unload the cart, but he objects resolutely. «Later, later» he says, and without any fuss, he goes to the large door of Joseph's workshop and opens it wide, endeavouring to take the cart in, as it is. But it cannot go in, of course. However the manoeuvre helps to distract the attention of the guests and make them understand that they are not wanted... And in fact Simon of Alphaeus takes leave with all his family...

6 «Oh! now that we are by ourselves, let us attend to our business...» says Simon of Jonah driving back the donkey, which is making a dreadful noise, covered as it is with harness-bells, so much so that James of Zebedee cannot help laughing and asks: «Where did you find it, harnessed like that?» 313.6

But Peter is busy taking the cases from the cart and handing them to John and Andrew, who expect to feel them heavy and are surprised because they are light, and they say so...

«Run into the kitchen garden and do not behave like frightened sparrows» orders Peter, getting off the cart with a little case that is really heavy and is placed in a corner in the little room.

«And now the donkey and the cart. The donkey and the cart? Yes.... That is the problem!... And yet we must put everything inside...»

«Through the kitchen garden, Simon» says Mary in a low voice. «There is an opening in the fence, at the end. You cannot see it, because it is covered by branches... But it is there. Follow the path along the house, between the house and our neighbour's kitchen garden, and I will come and show you where the passage is... Who is coming to remove the bramble covering it?»

«I am... I am...» They all run to the end of the kitchen garden while Peter goes away with his noisy equipage and Mary of Alphaeus closes the door... With a sickle they clear the rustic railing and open a passage through which the donkey and cart come in.

«Oh! Well! And now let us take all this away. They have deafened me!» and Peter hastens to cut the strings that fasten the bells to the harness.

«Why did you leave them on, then?» asks Andrew.

«So that everyone in Nazareth could hear me arrive. And it was a success... I am now taking them off, so that no one in Nazareth may hear us depart. And that is why I loaded the cart with empty cases... We will leave with full ones and no one, should anybody see us, will be surprised seeing a woman sitting beside me on the cases. Our friend, the one who is far away from us just now, boasts that he has a good practical sense. But I have it, too, when I want...»

«Excuse me, brother. Why is all this necessary?» asks Andrew who has given water to the donkey and taken it to the rustic wood-store near the stone-oven.

«Why? Don't you know?... Master, do they not know yet?»

«No, Simon. I was waiting for you. Come into the workshop, all of you. The women are all right where they are. You did the right thing in doing what you did, Simon of Jonah.»

313.7 [7]They go into the workshop, while Porphirea with the boy and the two Maries remain in the house.

«I wanted you here because you must help Me to send John and Syntyche away, very far away. I decided so at the Feast of the Tabernacles. You have clearly seen that it was not possible to keep them with us, neither can we keep them here, without risking their peace. As usual, Lazarus of Bethany is helping Me in this plan. They have already been informed. Simon Peter was told a few days ago. You are being informed now. We are leaving Nazareth tonight, even if it should rain or be windy instead of moonlight of the first quarter. We should have already left. But I suppose that Simon of Jonah must have had difficulties in finding transport...»

«I did, indeed! I was almost giving up hope. But at long last I got it from a slimy Greek in Tiberias... And it will be useful.»

«Yes, it will be very useful, particularly for John of Endor.»

«Where is he? I have not seen him» asks Peter.

«In his room with Syntyche.»

«And... how did he take it?» asks Peter again.

«Very sorrowfully. Also the woman...»

«And You as well, Master. Your forehead is furrowed with a wrinkle, which was not there before, and Your eyes are sad and severe» remarks John.

313.8 «It is true. I am deeply grieved... [8]But let us speak of what we have to do. Listen to Me carefully, because we shall have to part. * We will leave this evening, half way through the first watch. We shall leave like people who run away... because they are guilty. But we are not going away to do anything wrong, neither are we escaping because we have done it. We are going away to prevent other people from harming those who would not be strong enough to bear it. So we are leaving... We will go via Sephoris... We will stop in a house half-way and then leave at dawn. It is a house with many porches for animals. There are shepherds there who are friends of Isaac. I know them. They will give Me hospitality without asking any questions. Then we must reach Jiphthahel by evening and rest there. Do you think the donkey will be able to do it?»

«Certainly! That crafty Greek made me pay for it, but he gave me a good strong animal.»

«Very good. The following morning we will go to Ptolemais, and we will part there. Under the guidance of Peter, who is your leader, and whom you must obey unconditionally, you will go to Tyre by sea. You will find a ship there sailing to Antioch. You will go on board and give this letter to the owner of the ship. The letter is from Lazarus of Theophilus. You will be believed to be his servants, sent to his land at Antioch, or rather to his garden at Antigonea. And *you are to be such for everybody.* Be careful, serious, wise and quiet. When you arrive at Antioch go at once to Philip, Lazarus' steward, and give him this letter...»

«Master, he knows me» says the Zealot. «Very well.»

«But how can he believe that I am a servant?»

«In the case of Philip it is not necessary. He knows that he has to receive and give hospitality to two friends of Lazarus' and help them in every way. That is written in the letter. You have taken them there. Nothing else. He calls you: "his dear friends from Palestine". And that is what you are, united by faith and by the action that you are accomplishing. You will rest there un-

* **half way through the first watch** may correspond in our times to approximately seven or eight o'clock in the evening. The Hebrew day went from one sunset to the other and was divided into two parts. The first part of the day, the night, consisted of four watches, each one of three hours each. The second part of the day, daytime, included the remaining twelve hours. As the two parts of the day were regulated by sunset and sunrise, the length of the night hours (divided up into watches) and daytime varied from one season to another.

til the ship sails again for Tyre after the unloading and loading operations are completed. From Tyre you will come by boat to Ptolemais and join Me at Achzib...»

«Why do You not come with us, Lord?» asks John with a sigh.

«Because I am staying to pray for you, and particularly for
313.9 those two poor people. I am staying to pray. [9]And My third year of public life begins. It begins with a very sad departure; like the first and second ones. It begins with a great prayer and penance, as the first one did... Because this year has the sorrowful hardships of the first year, and even more. I was then preparing to convert the world. I am now preparing for a wider and more powerful action. But listen to Me carefully and bear in mind that if in the first year I was the Man-Master, the Wise Man Who invites to Wisdom with perfect humanity and intellectual perfection, and in the second I was the Saviour and Friend, the Merciful Master Who passes by receiving, forgiving, pitying, bearing, in the third year I will be the Redeemer God and King, the Just Man. Do not, therefore, be surprised if you see new aspects of Me, and if in the Lamb you see flashes of Strength. What has Israel replied to My invitation of love, to My opening My arms saying: "Come: I love and forgive"? It replied with its ever growing deliberate dullness and hardheartedness, with falsehood and deceit. Let it be so. I called every class of Israel, bowing My head to the dust. They spat on Holiness that humbled itself. I invited them to become holy. They replied by becoming demons. I did My duty in everything. They called My duty "sin". I was silent. They called My silence a proof of guilt. I spoke. They called My word blasphemy. Enough of that, now! They gave Me no peace. They granted Me no joy. And My joy consisted in bringing up in the life of the spirit the new-born to Grace. They lie in wait for them, and I have to tear them from My chest, causing them and Myself the grief of parents and children torn from one another, in order to save them from evil-minded Israel. They, the mighty ones in Israel, who call themselves "sanctifiers" and boast of being so, prevent Me, would like to prevent Me from saving souls and from taking delight in those I have saved. I have now had for many months Levi, a publican, as a friend and at My service, and the world can see whether Matthew is scandal or emulation. But the charge stands. And it will stand for Mary of Lazarus and for

all the others I will save. That is enough! I will go My way, which is more and more difficult and wet with tears... I am going... Not one of My tears will fall in vain. They cry to My Father... And later... a much more powerful humour will cry. I am going... Let those who love Me follow Me and be virile: because the severe hour is coming. I will not stop. Nothing will stop Me. Neither will they stop... But woe betide them! Woe to them! Woe to those for whom Love becomes Justice!... The sign of the new time will be of severe Justice for all those who are obstinate in their sin against the words of the Lord and the action of the Word of the Lord!...»

[10] Jesus seems a punishing archangel. His eyes are so bright that 313.10
I would say that they are like flames against the smoky wall... Even His voice seems to be bright, as it has shrill tones of bronze and silver struck violently.

The eight apostles have turned pale and have almost become smaller for fear. Jesus looks at them... full of pity and love. He says: «I am not referring to you, My friends. These threats are not for you. You are My apostles and I chose you.» His voice has become kind and deep. He concludes: «Let us go into the house. Let us make the two persecuted disciples feel that we love them more than ourselves, and I would remind you that they believe they are leaving to prepare My way in Antioch. Come...»

314. Dinner in the House of Nazareth Before the Painful Departure.

30th October 1945.

[1] It is evening. Another farewell evening for the little house in 314.1
Nazareth and its inhabitants. Another supper during which grief makes people silent and unwilling to eat. Jesus, John, Syntyche, Peter, John, Simon and Matthew are sitting at the table. It was not possible for the others to sit there. The table in Nazareth is so small! It was made just for a small family of honest people, who at the most can invite a pilgrim or an afflicted person to sit at it in order to give them refreshment of love rather than of food! Marjiam might have been able to sit at it tonight, as he is a very thin boy and takes up little room... But Marjiam is very serious

and silent and is eating in a corner, sitting on a little stool at the feet of Porphirea, whom Mary has sat on the seat of Her loom and who, meek and reserved as she is, is eating the food which they have given her, looking with eyes full of pity at the two about to depart, who endeavour to swallow their food with lowered heads to conceal their faces reddened by weeping. The others, that is, the two sons of Alphaeus, Andrew and James of Zebedee have settled in the kitchen, near a kind of kneading trough. But they can be seen through the open door.

314.2 [2] The Blessed Virgin and Mary of Alphaeus come and go serving this one and that one, with motherly care although they are worried and sad. And if the Blessed Virgin caresses with Her smile, so sad this evening, those whom She approaches, Mary of Alphaeus, less reserved and more informal, adds actions and words to her smiles, and more than once she encourages with a caress or a kiss, according to whoever benefits by it, this one or that one to take the food most suitable to their needs and in consideration of the imminent journey. I think that out of loving pity for John, who is exhausted and has become even thinner during the days of expectation, she would give herself as food to him, so anxious she is to convince him he should eat this or that dish, the flavour and beneficial properties of which she praises. But notwithstanding her... enticement, the food remains almost intact on John's plate and Mary of Alphaeus is distressed like a mother who sees her unweaned babe refuse her breast.

«But you cannot leave like that, son!» she exclaims. And in her motherly love she does not consider that John is about her own age and that the name «son» is not appropriate. But she sees in him only a suffering human being and thus does not find any other name to comfort him... «It will do you no good to travel on an empty stomach, on that shaking cart, in the cold dampness of the night. And then! Goodness knows what you will eat during the dreadful long journey!... Eternal mercy! At sea for so many miles! I would be frightened to death. And along Phoenician coasts and later!... even worse! And the owner of the ship will certainly be a Philistine, or a Phoenician or from some other hellish country... and will have no mercy on you... So, while you are still close to a mother who loves you, eat a little bit of this exquisite fish. Just to please Simon of Jonah who prepared it at

Bethsaida with so much love and taught me how to cook it for
you and Jesus, so that it may nourish you. [3]You definitely do not 314.3
want it?... Well... Oh! You will eat this!»... and she runs into the kitchen and comes back with a tureen full of a steaming pudding. I do not know what it is... It is certainly a kind of flour or corn mashed with milk: «Look, I made this because I remembered that one day you spoke of it as a sweet reminder of your childhood... It is good and will do you good. Come on, just a little.»

John lets her put some spoonfuls of the soft meal in his plate and tries to swallow it, but tears stream down his face adding their salt to the food, while he lowers his head even more towards his plate.

All the others do ample justice to the dish, which is perhaps exquisite. Their faces have brightened up in seeing it and Marjiam has stood up... but then he felt that he had to ask the Blessed Virgin: «May I eat some? There are still another five days to the end of my vow...»

«Yes, son. You may have some» says Mary caressing him.

But the boy is still uncertain and Mary, to appease the scruple of the little disciple, asks Her Son: «Jesus, Marjiam wants to know whether he can eat the pudding of barley meal... because of the honey which makes it a sweet dish, You know...»

«Of course you can, Marjiam. I dispense you this evening from your sacrifice, providing John eats his honey pudding as well. See how keen the boy is to have it? Help him, so that he may have some» and Jesus, Who is near John, takes his hand and holds it while John obediently strives to finish his helping.

[4]Mary of Alphaeus is now happier. And she makes a fresh as- 314.4
sault with a lovely dish of steaming pears, baked in the oven. She comes back in from the kitchen garden with her tray and says: «It's raining. It has just begun. What a nuisance!»

«No! On the contrary! There will be no one in the streets. It is always sad to say goodbye when one leaves... It is better to go away sailing before the wind, without running into sandbanks or rocks which make one stop or slow down. And curious people are just like sandbanks and rocks...» says Peter who sees sails and sailing in every action.

«Thank you, Mary. But I do not want anything else» says

John in an attempt to refuse fruit.

«Ah! Not these! Mary cooked them. Are you going to despise the food that She prepared? Look how well She prepared them! With spices in the little cavity... dressed with butter... They are food fit for a king. A julep. She turned brown Herself standing near the fire to glaze them like that. And they are good for your throat and your cough... They warm and cure you. Mary, tell him how they helped my Alphaeus when he was ill. But he wanted You to cook them. Of course! Your hands are holy and bestow health!... The food that You prepare is blessed indeed!... My Alphaeus was calmer after eating Your pears... he breathed more freely... My poor husband!...» and Mary takes advantage of her recollection to be able to weep at last and to go out to weep. Perhaps I am evil-minded, but I do not think that Mary would have shed a tear for her «poor Alphaeus» that evening, had she not felt pity for the two who were about to leave... Mary of Alphaeus was so deeply grieved for John and Syntyche and so distressed at the departure of Jesus, James and Judas, that she burst into tears in order not to suffocate.

314.5 [5] Mary now replaces her and lays a hand on the shoulder of Syntyche, who is sitting opposite Jesus, between Simon and Matthew. «Come on. Eat up. Are you going to leave and let Me worry also because you have gone away on almost empty stomachs?»

«I have eaten, Mother» says Syntyche looking up and showing her tired face marked by several days' weeping. She then lowers her head towards her shoulder, on which Mary's hand is resting, and rubs her cheek on the little hand to be caressed. With Her other hand Mary caresses her hair and draws towards Herself the head of Syntyche, whose face now rests on Her breast.

«Eat, John. It will really do you good. You must not get cold. Simon of Jonah, you will see that every evening he has some hot milk with honey, or at least some hot water and honey. Remember that.»

«I will see to that, as well, Mother. You may rest assured» says Syntyche.

«I am sure in fact. But you will do that when you are settled in Antioch. Simon of Jonah will see to it, for the time being. And remember, Simon, to give him much olive oil. That is why I gave you the little oil jar. Watch that it does not get broken. And if you see that he has difficulty in breathing, do as I told you, using the other little vase of balm. Take enough of it to rub his chest, shoulders and kidneys. Warm it first so that you can touch it without burning yourself, then rub it on and cover him immediately with the woollen bands I gave you. I prepared the balm for that special purpose. And you, Syntyche, remember its composition, so that you can make more. You will always be able to find lilies, camphor, dittany, resin and cloves with laurel, artemisia and the rest. I hear that Lazarus has gardens of essence plants at Antigonea.»

«And they are wonderful» says the Zealot who has seen them.

And he adds: «I do not want to give any advice. But I say that
that place should be more healthy for John, both for his spirit
and his body, than Antioch. It is sheltered from winds, light air
comes from thickets of resin plants on the slopes of a little hill,
which protects from sea winds but allows benign sea salts to
spread there, it is serene and quiet and yet cheerful because of
the large variety of flowers and birds that live there in peace...
You will see yourselves what suits you best. [6]Syntyche is so sensi- 314.6
ble! It is better to rely upon women in certain matters. Is it not?»

«In fact I entrust My John just to Syntyche's good sense and kind heart» says Jesus.

«And so do I» says John of Endor. «I... I... I have no more vigour... and... I will never be of any use...»

«Do not say that, John! When autumn strips trees of their leaves, it does not mean that they are already inert. On the contrary they work with concealed energy to prepare the triumph of the next fructification. It is the same with you. You have been stripped by the cold wind of your pain. But in actual fact in the depths of your soul you are already working for new ministries. Your very grief will be a spur to be active. I am sure of that. And then you, always you, will be the one to help me, a poor woman, who has still so much to learn to become *something* of Jesus.»

«Oh! What do you expect me to be?! There is nothing I can do... I am finished!»

«No. It is not right to say that! Only a dying man can say: "I am a finished man". Nobody else. Do you think that you have nothing else to do? You still have to do what you told me one day: to complete the sacrifice. How can you, but by suffering? It is silly, John, to quote wise authors to you, a school master, but I would remind you of Gorgias of Leontina (or Leontine). He taught that *one does not expiate, in this Life or in the next one, but through sorrow and suffering.* And I would remind you also of our great Socrates: "To disobey who is above us, be it god or a man, is evil and shameful". Now, if it was right to do so for an unjust judgement, passed by unjust men, what will it be if done by order of the most holy Man and of our God? Obedience is a great thing, simply because it is obedience. So, most great is the obedience to a holy order, which I consider, and you must consider with me, a great mercy. You always say that your life is approaching its end and that you do not yet feel that you have cancelled your debt with Justice. So why do you not consider this deep grief as a means of cancelling your debt, and do so in the short time you still have? A great grief to achieve a great peace! Believe me, it is worth suffering it. The only important thing in life is to have conquered Virtue when we arrive at the hour of our death.»

«You encourage me, Syntyche... Please always do so.»

«I will. I promise you here. But comply with me, as a man and as a Christian.»

314.7 [7] The meal is over. Mary collects the pears which have been left and puts them in a vase, which She hands to Andrew, who goes out and comes back in saying: «It is raining harder and harder. I would say that it is better...»

«Yes. It is always an agony to wait. I am going at once to prepare the donkey. And you can come as well, with the chests and everything else. You, too, Porphirea. Quick! You are so patient that even the donkey is subdued and allows you to dress it (he says exactly that) without reacting. Afterwards Andrew will do it, as he is like you. Quick, all of you!» And Peter pushes everybody, with the exception of Mary, Jesus, John of Endor and Syntyche, out of the room and the kitchen.

«Master! Oh! Master, help me! The hour has come... and I feel that my heart is breaking! It has really come! Oh! why, good Jesus, did You not let me die here, after I had received the dreadful news of my sentence and I had striven to accept it?!» And John collapses on Jesus' chest, weeping distressingly.

Mary and Syntyche endeavour to calm him, and Mary, although always so reserved, detaches him from Jesus, embracing and calling him: «My dear son, My darling son»...

[8]Syntyche in the meantime kneels at Jesus' feet saying: «Bless me, consecrate me, that I may be fortified. Lord, Saviour and King, I, here, in the presence of Your Mother, swear and profess that I will follow Your doctrine and serve You until I breathe my last. I swear and profess that I will devote myself to Your doctrine and its followers for Your sake, my Master and Saviour. I swear and profess that there will be no other purpose in my life and that everything that is world and flesh is definitely dead, as far as I am concerned, whilst, with the help of God and of the prayers of Your Mother, I hope to defeat the Demon so that he may not lead me into error and I may not be condemned at the hour of Your Judgement. I swear and profess that allurements and threats will not bend me and I will remember everything, unless God allows otherwise. But I hope in Him and I believe in His bounty, whereby I am sure that He will not leave me at the mercy of obscure powers, stronger than my own. Consecrate Your servant, O Lord, that she may be protected from the snares of every enemy.» 314.8

Jesus lays His hands on her head, as also priests do, and prays over her.

Mary leads John beside Syntyche and makes him kneel saying: «Bless this one, too, Son, that he may serve You with holiness and peace.»

And Jesus repeats the gesture on the lowered head of poor John. He then lifts him and makes Syntyche stand up, and putting their hands in the hands of Mary He says: «And let Her be the last one to caress you here» and He goes out quickly, I do not know where.

«Mother, goodbye! I will never forget these days» moans John. «Neither will I forget you, dear son.»

«I, too, Mother... Goodbye. Let me kiss You once more... Oh! after so many years I had satisfied my desire for maternal kisses!... But no longer now...» Syntyche weeps in the arms of Mary Who kisses her.

John sobs unreservedly. Mary embraces him also, She now has both of them in Her arms, the true Mother of Christians, and with Her most pure lips She touches John's wrinkled face lightly: a chaste, but so loving kiss. And with Her kiss there are tears of the Blessed Virgin on the emaciated cheek...

314.9 [9]Peter comes in: «It's ready. Come on...» and he cannot say anything else because he is deeply moved.

Marjiam, who follows his father like a shadow, clings on to Syntyche's neck and kisses her, he then embraces John and kisses him repeatedly... But he is weeping as well.

They go out. Mary is holding Syntyche by the hand, and John has taken Marjiam's. «Our mantles...» says Syntyche and she makes the gesture of going back to the house.

«They are here. Quick, take them...» Peter feigns coarseness as he does not want to show that he is moved, but with the back of his hand he wipes off his tears standing behind the two who are wrapping themselves in their mantles.

Over there, beyond the hedge, the little swinging lamp of the cart gives a yellowish light in the dark air... The rain rustles among the olive leaves and resounds in the fountain full of water... A dove, awakened by the light of the lamps, which the apostles are shielding under their mantles, holding them low to illuminate the paths full of puddles, is cooing lamentingly...

Jesus is already near the cart over which a blanket has been spread to act as a roof.

«Come on, quick, it's raining hard!» urges Peter. And while James of Zebedee replaces Porphirea at the bridle, Peter, without ceremony, lifts Syntyche off the ground and puts her on the cart, and with greater speed he grasps John of Endor and throws him on. He gets on himself and gives the poor donkey such a strong blow with the whip, that it bounces forward almost running over James. And Peter insists until they are on the main road, a good distance from houses... A last farewell cry reaches the persons who are leaving and who weep unreservedly...

Peter stops the donkey outside Nazareth, waiting for Jesus and the others, who soon join him walking fast in the increasing rain.

They take a road among the vegetable gardens, to go again to the north of the town without crossing it. But Nazareth is dark and asleep in the ice-cold rain of a winter night... and I think that the noise of the donkey's hooves, hardly audible on the wet beaten ground, cannot be heard even by those who are awake...

The group proceeds in dead silence. Only the sobs of the two can be heard, mingled with the sound of rain on olive leaves.

315. The Journey Towards Jiphthahel. John of Endor's Grief.

31st October 1945.

[1]It must have rained all night. But at dawn a dry wind has blown the clouds southwards, beyond the hills of Nazareth. Thus a timid winter sun dares to peep out and light with its beam a diamond on every olive leaf. But they are gala dresses which the olive-trees soon lose, because the wind shakes them off the leaves, which seem to be weeping diamond chips, which get lost among the dewy grass or on the muddy road. 315.1

Peter is preparing the cart and donkey with the help of James and Andrew. The others have not appeared as yet. But they soon come out, one after the other, from a kitchen, probably because they say to the three who are outside: «You can go now and have something to eat.» And they go and come out shortly afterwards with Jesus.

«I have put the cover on again because of the wind» explains Peter. «If You really want to go to Jiphthahel, we shall have it in our faces... and it will be biting. I do not understand why we do not take the direct road to Sicaminon and then the one along the coast... It is longer but not so hard. Did You hear what the shepherd said, the man I encouraged to speak? He said: "Jotopata in the winter months is isolated. There is only one road to go there, but it is not possible to go there with lambs... You cannot carry anything on your shoulders because there are passes where you proceed more with your hands than with your feet, and lambs cannot swim. There are two rivers, which are often flooded, and the very road is a torrent that flows on a rocky bed. I go there after the Tabernacles and in full spring, and I do good business, because they buy supplies for months". That is what he said... And we... with this thing... (and he kicks the wheel of the cart)... and with this donkey... bah!!...»

«The direct road from Sephoris to Sicaminon is better. But it is very busy. Remember that we must not leave traces of John...»

«The Master is right. And we may find Isaac with some disciples... At Sicaminon in any case!...» says the Zealot.

«Let us go then...»

«I am going to call those two... » says Andrew.

And while he does so, Jesus takes leave of an old woman and a boy who are coming out of a sheepfold with buckets of milk. Also some bearded shepherds arrive and Jesus thanks them for the hospitality given to Him during the rainy night.

315.2 [2] John and Syntyche are already in the cart, which sets out along the road, driven by Peter. Jesus with the Zealot and Matthew at His sides, followed by Andrew, James, John and the two sons of Alphaeus, quickens His step to reach it.

The wind bites their faces and swells their mantles. The cover stretched over the arches of the cart snaps like a sail notwithstanding the rain of the night that has made it heavy: « Never mind, it will soon dry!» moans Peter looking at it. Providing the lungs of that poor man do not dry up!... Wait, Simon of Jonah... This is what you do.» And he stops the donkey, takes his mantle off, gets on the cart and wraps John carefully in it.

«Why? I already have one....»

«Because pulling the donkey I am already as warm as I would be in a bread oven. And I am used to being naked on the boat, particularly when there is a storm. The cold spurs me and I am quicker. Come on, make sure you are well covered. Mary made so many recommendations to me in Nazareth, that if you were taken ill, I would not be able to face Her any longer...»

315.3 [3] He gets off the cart, takes the bridle again and spurs the donkey. But he soon has to call his brother and also James to help the donkey get out of a muddy spot in which a wheel had sunk. And they proceed, pushing the cart in turns to help the donkey that digs its strong feet in the mire and draws the cart. The poor animal is panting and puffing with fatigue and greediness because Peter entices it to move on by offering it bits of bread and cores of apples, which, however, he lets it have only when they stop for a moment.

«You are cheating, Simon of Jonah» says Matthew jokingly after watching Peter's manoeuvring.

«No. I am getting it to do its duty, and I am doing it *kindly*. If I did not do that, I would have to use the whip. And I do not like that. I do not strike my boat when she is wayward, although she is of wood. Why should I flog the donkey, which is flesh? This is my boat now... it is in water... it is indeed! So I am dealing with it as I deal with my boat. I am not Doras, you know? I wanted to name it Doras, before I bought it. Then I heard its name, and I liked it. So I did not change it...»

«What is its name?» they ask curiously.

«Guess!» and Peter laughs through his beard.

The strangest names are mentioned including those of the fiercest Pharisees and Sadducees etc. etc. But Peter always shakes his head. They give up.

«Antonius is its name! Isn't it a beautiful name? That cursed Roman! Obviously also the Greek who sold me the donkey must have had a grudge against Antonius!»

They all laugh while John of Endor explains: «He is probably one from whom money was extorted after Caesar's death. Is he old?»

«He is about seventy... and must have done all kinds of jobs... He now owns a hotel at Tiberias...»

[4]They are at the cross-roads of Sephoris with the Nazareth- 315.4
Ptolemais, Nazareth-Sicaminon, Nazareth-Jotopata roads (I would point out that they pronounce J as a very soft G). On the consular milestone there are the three indications of Ptolemais, Sicaminon, Jotopata.

«Are we going to Sephoris, Master?»

«It is quite useless. Let us go to Jiphthahel without stopping. We shall eat something while walking. We must be there before evening.»

They proceed crossing two little torrents in flood, and begin to climb the slopes of a range of hills lying south-northwards
* with a large steep mass to the north stretching eastwards.

* **eastwards.** The sketch by M.V. shows the four cardinal points and, to the North, *Jiphthahel.*

«Jiphthahel is over there» says Jesus.

«I cannot see anything» remarks Peter.

«It is to the north. The coast is very steep in our direction, as well as to the east and the west.»

«So we must go all the way around that mountain?»

«No. There is a road at the foot of the highest mountain, in the valley. It is a short cut, but the road is very steep.»

«Have You been there?»

«No. But I know.»

The road is steep indeed! So much so that, when they arrive there, they are frightened. Night seems to fall all at once, so dark it is at the bottom of the valley, which is so horrifying and precipitous that it reminds me of Dantesque Malebolge; it is a road cut in the rock, so steep that it almost ascends in steps, a narrow wild road, enclosed between a furious torrent and an even more rugged mountain side that becomes steeper as one proceeds north-wards.

If the light increases little by little as one ascends higher, fatigue also increases, and in fact they unload the cart of personal baggage and Syntyche also gets off to make the cart as light as possible. John of Endor, who after his few words has not opened his mouth but to cough, would like to get off as well. But they do not let him and he remains where he is, while all the others push or pull cart and donkey sweating at each gradient of the road. But no one complains. On the contrary they all pretend to be satisfied with the exercise in order not to embarrass the two disciples for whom they do it and who have more than once expressed their regret for so much work.

The road turns at a right angle ┐, then there is another corner, a shorter one, which ends in a town perched on such a steep slope that, as John of Zebedee says, it seems on the point of sliding down to the valley with all its houses.

«It is, instead, very solid. All one with the rock.»

«Like Ramoth then...» says Syntyche who remembers the place.

«Even more. The rock here is part of the houses, not just their foundation. It reminds one more of Gamala. Do you remember it?»

«Yes, and we remember those pigs as well...» says Andrew.

«It was from there that we departed to go to Tarichea, the Tabor and Endor...» says Simon Zealot.

5 «It is my fate to let you have painful recollections and hard work...» says John of Endor with a sigh. 315.5

«Never! You have given us faithful friendship and nothing else, my friend» says Judas of Alphaeus impulsively. And everybody joins him to confirm his statement.

«And yet... I have not been loved... No one tells me... But I can meditate and put together various facts, as in a picture. This departure was not foreseen and it was not a spontaneous decision...»

«Why do you say that, John?» asks Jesus kindly, although He is afflicted.

«Because it is true. I was not wanted. I was chosen to go far away, no one else, not even the great disciples.»

«And what about Syntyche, then?» asks James of Alphaeus, grieved at the lucidity of thought of the man of Endor.

«Syntyche is coming so as not to send me away alone... to conceal the truth pitifully...»

«No, John!...»

«Yes, Master. See? I could also tell You the name of my torturer. Do You know where I can read it? Just by looking at these good eight ones I read it! Only by considering the absence of the others I can read it! The one through whom I was found by You is also the one who would like me to be found by Beelzebub. And he drove me to this hour, and he drove You to it, Master, because You suffer as much as I do, perhaps more, and he drove me to this hour to make me fall back into despair and hatred. Because he is bad, cruel, envious. And much more. Judas of Kerioth is the dark soul amongst Your servants, who are all as clear as light...»

«Do not say that, John. He is not the only one missing. They were, all away for the Dedication, with the exception of the Zealot, who has no family. One cannot come from Kerioth in this season in a few stages. It is about two hundred miles walk. And it was fair that he should go and see his mother, like Thomas. I spared also Nathanael, because he is old, and Philip, to give him as a companion to Nathanael.»

«Yes. Three more are absent... But, O good Jesus! You know men's hearts, because You are the Holy One. But You are not the only one to know them! Also the wicked know the wicked, because they know one another. I was wicked, and I saw myself again, with my worst instincts, in Judas. But I forgive him. For one reason only I forgive him for sending me to die so far away: because it was just through him that I came to You. And may God forgive him for the rest… for *all* the rest.»

Jesus does not deny… He is silent. The apostles look at one another while pushing the cart on the slippery road.

315.6 [6] It is almost night when they reach the town, where unknown amongst unknown people, they put up at a hotel situated on the southern end of the town. It is on the edge of a gorge, which makes one giddy looking down it, as it so steep and deep. At the bottom: a noise and nothing else in the shadow of peace already in the valley, where a torrent roars.

316. Jesus' Farewell to John of Endor and Syntyche.

1st November 1945.

316.1 [1] It is along the same road, which in any case is the only one in this village that looks like an eagle's nest on a solitary mountain top, that they set out again the following day, tormented by cold wet weather hindering their march. John of Endor is also compelled to get off the cart, because a downhill road is more dangerous than an uphill one, and if the donkey by itself would be in no danger, the weight of the cart, thrust forward by the slope, makes the situation very awkward for the poor animal. The apostles also are in trouble today, as they perspire not pushing but holding back the vehicle, which might crash down causing a disaster or, at least, the loss of the load.

The road is dreadful for about one third of its total length, the last stretch towards the valley. It then forks, and the branch running westwards becomes more comfortable and level. They stop to rest wiping their perspiration and Peter rewards the donkey, which is shaking its ears trembling and panting, obviously engrossed in deep meditation on the painful situation of donkeys and the whims of men who choose certain roads. Apparently Simon of Jonah ascribes to such considerations the thoughtful expression of the animal and to raise its spirits he hangs from its neck a bag of small beans, and while the donkey crushes the hard food with greedy relish, the men also eat bread and cheese and drink milk of which their little flasks are full.

The meal is over. But Peter wants to give some water to «his Antonius that deserves more honour than Caesar» he says, and taking a bucket from the cart he fetches some water from a torrent flowing towards the sea.

[2] «We can go now... And we would like to trot the donkey because I think that the country is flat beyond that hill... But we cannot. However, we shall proceed fast. Come on, John, and you, woman. Get on and let us go.» 316.2

«I am getting on as well, Simon, and I will drive. You will all follow us...» says Jesus as soon as the two are in the cart.

«Why? Are You not well? You look so pale!...»

«No, Simon. I want to speak to them alone...» and He points at the two who have also turned pale as they realise that the moment of farewell has come.

«Ah! All right. Get on and we will follow You.»

Jesus sits on the plank used as a seat by the driver and says: «Come here beside Me, John. And you, Syntyche, come near Me...»

John sits on the Lord's left and Syntyche at His feet, almost on the edge of the cart, with her back to the road, and her face raised towards Jesus. In her present position, sitting on her heels, relaxed as if she were burdened by a weight exhausting her, her hands abandoned on her lap and clasped to hold them still as they were trembling, with her tired face and most beautiful dark violet eyes dimmed by the many tears shed, in the shade of her veil and mantle lowered over her forehead, she seems a desolate Pieta.

Not to mention John!... I think that if his scaffold were at the bottom of the road, he would not be so upset.

The donkey is now ambling and is so obedient and sensible that Jesus is not compelled to keep a close watch of it. And Jesus takes advantage of the situation to drop the reins and take John's hand and lay the other one on Syntyche's head.

[3] «My children, I thank you for all the joy you have given Me. 316.3
This has been for Me a year strewn with flowers of joy, because I was able to take your souls and hold them in front of Me, to

hide the ugly things of the world, to scent the air corrupted by the sins of the world, to instill kindness into Myself and confirm My hope that My mission is not useless. Marjiam, you, My John, Ermasteus, you, Syntyche, Mary of Lazarus, Alexander Misace and others... The triumphal flowers of the Saviour, Whom only people with upright hearts can perceive as such... Why are you shaking your head, John?»

«Because You are good and You are putting me amongst people with right hearts. But my sin is always present to me...»

«Your sin is the fruit of the flesh stirred by two wicked people. Your heart's righteousness is the sub-layer of your honest *ego*, desirous of honest things, but unfortunate because they were taken away from you by death or by wickedness, but even so your *ego* was not less alive under the burden of so much grief. It was sufficient for the voice of the Saviour to penetrate into the depth of your heart where your *ego* was languishing, and you sprang to your feet, shaking every burden off you, to come to Me. Is it not so? So you are righteous of heart. More, much more than others who do not have *your* sin, but have many worse ones, because they were premeditated and stubbornly preserved alive...

May you, therefore, you the flowers of My triumph as Saviour, be blessed. In this dull hostile world, which sates the Saviour with bitterness and disgust, you have represented love. Thank you! In the most grievous hours of this year I bore you in mind to be comforted and supported. In the more grievous ones, which I am to suffer, I will bear you even more in mind. Until My death. And you will be with Me forever. I promise you.

316.4 [4] I entrust you with My dearest interests, that is, the preparation of My Church in Asia Minor, where I cannot go because the place of My mission is here, in Palestine, and also because the backward mentality of the mighty ones in Israel would injure Me in every possible way, if I went elsewhere. I wish I had more Johns and more Syntyches for other countries, so that My apostles would find the soil already ploughed to spread the seed in the hour to come!

Be kind and patient, and strong at the same time, in order to penetrate and tolerate. You will come across dullness and mockery. Do not let that discourage you. Say: "We are eating the same bread and drinking the same chalice as our Jesus is". You are not worth more than your Master and you cannot expect to have a better lot. This is the greatest fortune: to share the lot of the Master. I give you one order only: do not be disheartened, do not endeavour to give yourselves an answer to why you have been sent away; you are not being sent into exile, as John is inclined to think, on the contrary you are being placed on the threshold of your Fatherland before everybody else, because you are perfected servants, as no one else is. Heaven has come down upon you like a maternal veil and the King of Heaven is already welcoming you to His bosom, and will protect you under His bright wings of love, as the first-born of the numberless swarm of the servants of God, of the Word of God, Who in the name of the Father and of the Eternal Spirit blesses you now and forever.

And pray for Me, the Son of Man, Who is going towards all the tortures of the Redeemer. Oh! My Humanity is about to be crushed by the most bitter experience!... Pray for Me. I will need your prayers... They will be caresses... They will be professions of love... They will help Me, that I may not go to the extent of saying: "The whole of Mankind is made of demons"...

[5]Goodbye, John! Kiss Me goodbye... Do not weep... I would 316.5
have kept you with Me, at the cost of tearing bits of flesh off My body, had I not seen all the good that this separation will bring about both for you and for Me. Eternal good... Goodbye, Syntyche. Yes, you may kiss My hands, but bear in mind that, if the difference of sex prevents Me from kissing you as a sister, I give My brotherly kiss to your soul... And let your souls wait for Me. I will come. I will be close to your work and to your souls. I certainly will, because if My love for man has closed My divine Nature in mortal flesh, it did not limit its freedom. And as God I am free to go to those who deserve to have God with them. Goodbye, My children. The Lord is with you...»

And He tears Himself away from the convulsive grip of John, who had grasped His shoulders, and of Syntyche, who was clinging to His knees, and He jumps from the cart, waving goodbye to His apostles, running away along the road He came, as fast as
a chased deer... [6]The donkey has stopped, feeling that the reins 316.6
which were previously on Jesus' knees, had dropped completely. The eight astonished apostles have also stopped and are looking at the Master Who is moving farther and farther away.

«He was weeping...» whispers John.

«And He was as pale as a dead body...» whispers James of Alphaeus.

«He has not even taken His sack... There it is on the cart...» remarks the other James.

«And what will He do now?» asks Matthew.

Judas of Alphaeus shouts at the top of his powerful voice: «Jesus! Jesus! Jesus!...» The echo of the hills replies far away: «Jesus! Jesus! Jesus!...» But the green trees at a bend of the road conceal the Master, Who does not even look back to see who is calling Him... «He has gone... All we can do is to go as well...» says Peter desolately, getting on the cart and taking the reins to spur the donkey.

And the cart starts off and its squeaking is mingled with the rhythmical sound of the iron shoes of the donkey and the anguished weeping of the two disciples, who forlorn on the bottom of the cart are moaning: «We will never see Him again, never, never again...»

317. Jesus' Sorrow, Prayer and Penance for Judas' Redemption.

2nd November 1945.

317.1 [1] Jesus is once again at the foot of the massive height on which Jiphthahel is built. But He is not on the main road (let us call it so) or mule-track, along which the cart came. He is instead on a little footpath fit for ibexes, so steep it is, strewn with large stone splinters and deep crevices, and seems to be stuck onto the mountain side; I would say that it is engraved on the vertical face of the mountain, which looks as if it were scratched by a huge claw. At its edge there is a precipice, a sheer deep drop, at the bottom of which an angry torrent foams along. To slip there means to fall hopelessly, bouncing from one bush to another of bramble or other wild plants, which have grown between the crevices of the rocks, I do not know how, as they have not come up vertically, as is normal with plants, but obliquely and even horizontally, compelled by their ubication. To slip there means to be torn to pieces by the thorns of such plants, or to have one's back broken by the impact on rigid tree trunks protruding over the abyss. To slip there means to be lacerated by the sharp-edged stones sticking out from the face of the precipice. To slip there means to drop bleeding and in pieces into the foamy water of the angry torrent and be drowned, and lie submerged on a bed of pointed rocks and be lashed by the impetuous water. And yet Jesus is walking along that path, that scratch in the rock, which is even more dangerous because of the dampness that rises steaming from the torrent, or drops from the overhanging surface and from the plants growing on that vertical face, which I would say is lightly concave.

* I will make an effort to illustrate this infernal place.

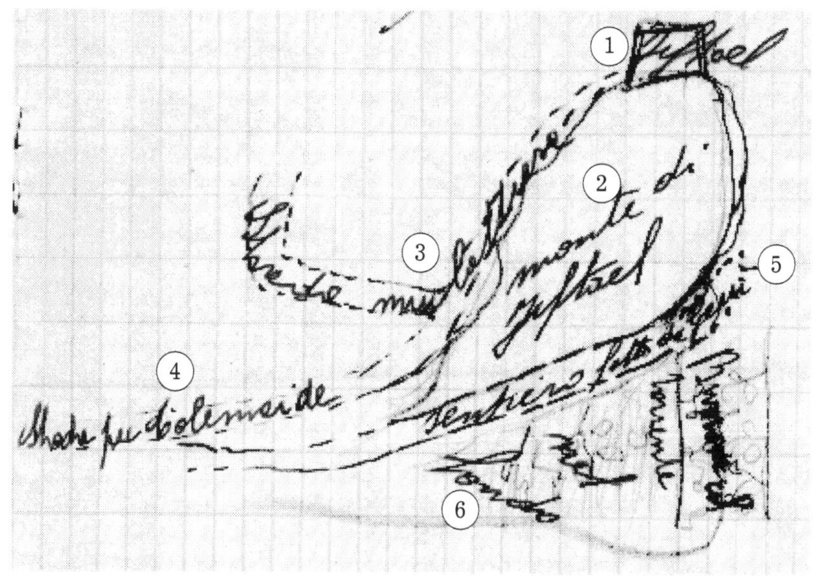

He proceeds slowly, cautiously, watching each step on the sharp stones, some of which are wobbly. At times He is compelled to squeeze against the mountain side when the path narrows; and to pass over some particularly dangerous spots, He has to get hold of branches hanging from the rocks. He goes round the western side thus and reaches the southern one, where the mountain, after a perpendicular drop from the summit, becomes

---

* **place**. M.V.'s map shows: 1. *Jiphthahel*; 2. *mount of Jiphthahel*; 3. *mule-track*; 4. *road to Ptolemais*; 5. *path covered by Jesus*; 6. *precipice with the torrent at the bottom.*

more concave than elsewhere, allowing the path thus to widen a little, but reducing its height, so that Jesus now and again must lower His head to avoid knocking it against the rocks.

317.2 [2] Perhaps He intends to stop there, where the path ends abruptly, because of a landslide. But when He sees that under the cliff there is a cave, a fissure in the mountain rather than a cave, He lets Himself down among the fallen stones. He goes in. There is a cleft at first, then a large grotto inside, as if the mountain had been hollowed out a long time ago by man, for some unknown reason. One can clearly see that the natural curves of the rock have been enlarged by man, who, on the side opposite the entrance, opened a narrow corridor, at the end of which there is a streak of light, and remote forests can be seen, which proves that the corridor cuts through the mountain spur from the southern side to the eastern one.

Jesus slips into the narrow semi-dark tunnel and goes along it until He reaches its opening, which is above the road on which He came with the apostles and the cart to go up to Jiphthahel. The mountains surrounding the lake of Galilee are in front of Him, beyond the valley, and to the north-east the great Hermon shines in its snowy mantle. Rough steps have been dug on the mountain side, which is not so steep here, neither upwards nor downwards and the steps lead to the mule-track, which is in the valley, and also to the mountain top where Jiphthahel is.

Jesus is satisfied with His exploration. He goes back into the large cave and looks for a sheltered place where He heaps up dry leaves that the wind has blown inside. A very poor pallet, a thin layer of dry leaves laid between His body and the bare icy soil... He drops on it and remains inert, lying with His hands under His head, staring at the rocky vault, absorbed, I would say bewildered, like one who bears a strain or is struck by sorrow greater than one's strength.

317.3 [3] Then tears, without sobs, begin to drop slowly from His eyes and stream down both sides of His face, disappearing in His hair, near His ears, and ending among the dry leaves... He weeps in this way, for a long time, without speaking or moving... He then sits up, and with His head between His raised knees, embraced by His clasped hands He calls His far away Mother, with all His soul: «Mother! Mother! Mother of Mine! My eternal sweetness!

Oh! Mother, I wish You were near Me! Why do I not always have You, the only comfort of God?»

Only the hollow cave replies to His words and His sobs with the whisper of a faint echo, and it seems to be weeping and sobbing itself through its edges and rocks and the few and still small stalactites hanging in a corner, the one which is probably most exposed to the internal activity of water.

Jesus continues weeping, although more calmly, as if the simple invocation of His Mother consoled Him and His weeping slowly changes into a monologue. «They have gone... Why? Whose fault is it? Why did I have to grieve them thus? And grieve Myself, since the world fills each day of Mine with affliction?... Judas!»...

I wonder where Jesus' thought wanders when He lifts His head from His knees and looks in front of Himself with wide open eyes and the tense face of a person engrossed in the vision of future spiritual events or in deep meditation. He no longer weeps. But he is evidently suffering. He then seems to be replying to an invisible interlocutor. And He stands up to do so.

«I am a man, Father. I am the Man. The virtue of friendship, which was wounded and torn from Me, is writhing and moaning sorrowfully... I know that I must suffer *everything*. I know as God and as God *I want it* for the good of the world. As man also I know, because My divine spirit informs My humanity. And also as man *I want it*, for the good of the world. But how grievous it is, O Father! This hour is much more sorrowful than the one I lived with Your spirit and Mine in the desert... And much stronger is the present temptation not to love and not to bear at My side the slimy tortuous being, whose name is Judas, the cause of the deep sorrow with which I am sated and which tortures the souls to
whom I had given peace. [4]Father, I perceive it. You are becoming 317.4
more and more severe as I approach the end of My expiation on behalf of Mankind. Your kindness is moving farther and farther away from Me, and Your countenance appears more and more severe to My spirit, which is rejected more and more into the depth, where Mankind, struck by Your punishment, has been moaning for millennia. It was pleasant to suffer, pleasant was the way at the beginning of My life, it was pleasant also when from the son of a carpenter I became the Master of the world, tearing Myself away from a Mother to give You, Father, to man who had fallen.

It was still pleasant to Me, as compared with the present hour, to struggle with the Enemy, in the Temptation in the desert. I faced him with the boldness of a hero with intact strength... Oh! Father!... My strength is now encumbered by the indifference of too many people and the knowledge of too many things... I knew that Satan would go, when the temptation was over, and he did go, and the angels came to comfort Your Son for being a man, subject to the temptation of the Demon. But the temptation will not cease now, after this hour, in which the Friend suffers because of the friends sent away, and because of the perjured friend who injures Him both when he is near and far away. It will not cease. Your angels will not come to comfort Me in this hour and after it. But the world will come with all its hatred, its mockery and incomprehension. And the traitor who sold himself to Satan will come and he, the perjurer, will be more and more tortuous and slimy. Father!!...» It is really a cry of anguish, of fear and of invocation and Jesus is agitated and reminds me of the hour at Gethsemane.

«Father! I know. I can see... While I suffer here and will suffer, and I offer My suffering to You for his conversion and for those who have been torn away from My arms and who are going towards their destiny with broken hearts, he is selling himself to become greater than I am: the Son of Man! I am, am I not, the Son of Man? Yes, but I am not the only one. Children were born of mankind, of prolific Eve, and if I am Abel, the Innocent One, Cain is not missing among the children of Mankind. And if I am the First-Born, because I am what the children of man should have been, without stain in Your eyes, he, who was born in sin, is the first of what men have become after eating the poisoned fruit. And now, not satisfied with having in himself the disgusting blasphemous incentives of falsehood, anti-charity, of thirst for blood, of greed for money, of pride and lust, he is raving to be the man who becomes a demon, whilst he is a man who could become an angel... "And Lucifer wanted to be like God and was
therefore driven out of Paradise and changed into a demon and *
317.5 he dwelt in Hell". [5]But Father! Oh! Father! I love him... I still love
him. He is a man... He is one of those for whom I left You... Save him, because of My humiliation... grant Me to redeem him, Most

* **demon...** The following quote seems to be taken, with different words, by *Isaiah 14:12-15*.

High Lord! I offer this penance more for him than for anybody
else! Oh! I am aware of the incongruity of what I am asking, be-
cause I know everything!... But, Father, do not consider Me Your
Word for a moment. Look only at the Humanity of the Just One...
and let Me be for a moment only the "Man" in Your grace, the
Man who is not aware of the future, who can deceive himself...
the Man who not being aware of ineluctable fate can pray with
absolute hope to wring a miracle out of You. A miracle! A mira-
cle of Jesus of Nazareth, for Jesus of Mary of Nazareth, Our eter-
nal Beloved One! A miracle that violates what has been set down
and cancels it! The salvation of Judas! He has lived beside Me,
he has drunk in My words, has shared food with Me, has slept
on My chest... No, do not let him be My satan!... I am not asking
You not to be betrayed... That must happen, and will happen...
so that all falsehood may be cancelled by My sorrow of being be-
trayed, as all avarice may be expiated by My grief for being sold,
as amends may be made for all blasphemy through My torment
at being cursed, and faith may be given to those who are and will
be without faith, through My torture at not being believed, and
all the sins of flesh may be cleansed by My being scourged... But
I beg You: not him, not Judas, My friend, My apostle! I would like
no one to be a traitor... No one... Not even the remotest inhabit-
ant of the hyperborean ice fields or of the torrid zone... I would
like You alone to be the Sacrificer... as You already have been in
* the past when You set fire to the holocausts by means of Your
flames... But since I am to die by the hand of man, and since the
traitor friend will be a more brutal executioner than the real ex-
ecutioner, the putrid traitor who will have in himself the stench
of Satan, and is already inhaling it to be like Me in power... that
is what he thinks in his pride and lust... since I am to die by the
hand of man, Father, do not let him whom I called friend and I
loved as such, be My Traitor. Increase My torment, Father, but
give Me Judas' soul... I am putting this prayer on the altar of
My victim Person... Accept it, Father!... [6]Heaven is closed and si- 317.6
lent!... Is this therefore the horror that I shall have with Me un-
til My Death? Heaven is silent and closed!... Is this therefore the
silence and the prison in which I shall breathe My last? Heaven

* **set fire**, as in: *Leviticus 9:24*; *Judges 6:21*; *1 King 18:38*; *1 Chronicles 21:26*; *2 Chronicles 7:1*.

is closed and silent!... Is this therefore the supreme torture of the Martyr?... Father, may Your will be done, not Mine... But because of My suffering, oh! grant Me at least this: give peace and illusion to Judas' other martyr, to John of Endor, Father... He is really better than many. He has already gone a long way, such as few are or will be able to go. Redemption has already been completed for him. Give him, therefore, Your total complete peace, so that I may have him in My Glory, when everything will be completed also for Me in Your honour and obedience... Father!...»

Jesus has slowly fallen on His knees and is now weeping with His face on the ground, and while He prays the light of the short winter day fades precociously in the dark cavern, and the roar of the torrent seems to grow louder as the shade in the valley becomes darker...

318. From Ptolemais to Tyre by Boat. The Voyage of the Eight Apostles with John of Endor and Syntyche Begins.

3rd November 1945.

318.1 [1] The town of Ptolemais looks as if it is to remain overwhelmed by a low leaden sky, without a gleam of azure, without any change in its dullness. There is not a cloud, a cirrus, a nimbus sailing all alone in the closed vault of heaven. The firmament looks like a solid convex heavy lid on the point of crashing on a case. A huge lid of dirty, sooty, dull, oppressive tin. The white houses of the town seem to be made of chalk, of coarse rough chalk that looks desolate in this light... the green of evergreens seems dull and sad, the faces of people look worn or ghastly and the shades of their clothes colourless. The town is stifled with heavy sirocco.

The sea matches the sky with similar deadly dullness. An infinite, still, lonely sea. It is not even leaden, it would be wrong to describe it as such. It is a limitless expanse, and I would say ripple free, of an oily substance as grey, I suppose, as lakes of crude petroleum must be, or rather, if it were possible, lakes of silver mixed with soot and ashes, to make a pomade with a special brightness of quartziferous scales, which however is so deadly dull that it does not seem to shine. Its gleaming is noticed only through the discomfort it causes to one's eyes, dazzled by such flickering of blackish mother-of-pearl, which tires them without delighting them. There is not a wave as far as the eyes can see. One can see as far as the horizon, where the dead sea touches the dead sky, without seeing a wave stir; but one realises that the water is not solidified because there is an underwater gurgle, which is hardly perceptible on the surface through the dark glittering of the water. The sea is so still that at the shore the water is as motionless as the water in a vat, without the slightest indication of waves or surf. And the sand bears clean marks of dampness at a metre or little more from the water, proving thus that for many hours there has been no movement of waves on the shore. There is dead calm.

The few boats in the harbour do not stir. They are so still that they seem to be nailed on a solid substance, and the few strips of cloth stretched out on the high decks, ensigns or garments, whatever they may be, are hanging motionless.

[2]The apostles with the two bound for Antioch are coming from 318.2
a lane in the working-class district near the harbour. I do not know what has happened to the donkey and the cart. They are not there. Peter and Andrew are carrying one chest, James and John the other one, while Judas of Alphaeus is carrying on his shoulder the dismantled loom and Matthew, James of Alphaeus and Simon Zealot are laden with all the bags, including Jesus'. Syntyche is holding only a basket with some food. John of Endor is not carrying anything. They walk fast among the people coming back mostly from the market with their shopping, while seamen are hastening towards the port to load or unload ships or repair them, according to their requirements.

Simon of Jonah is proceeding resolutely. He must be already aware of where to go, because he does not look around. He is flushed while holding the chest, on one side, by a loop of a rope which serves as a handle, and Andrew does likewise on the other side. And one can see, both in them and in their companions, their efforts in carrying their weights, as the muscles of their calves and arms bulge, in fact, in order to move freely, they are wearing only short sleeveless undertunics and are thus like porters hurrying from warehouses to ships or vice versa, doing their work. They thus pass by completely unnoticed.

318.3 [3]Peter does not go to the large quay, but along a squeaky footbridge he goes to the little one, a little arched pier forming another much narrower dock for fishing boats. He looks around and cries out.

A man replies, standing up in a stout rather large boat. «Do you really want to go? Mind you, sails are of no use today. You will have to row.»

«It will warm me up and give me an appetite.»

«But are you really capable of sailing?»

«Hey! man! I could not say "mummy" yet, and my father had already put line and sail ropes in my hands. I sharpened my milk-teeth on them»

«It's because... you know... this boat is all my wealth... you know?...»

«You already told me yesterday... Don't you know any other song?»

«I know that if you go to the bottom, I will be ruined and...»

«I will be ruined, because I shall lose my life, not you!»

«But this is all I own, it's my bread, my joy and the joy of my wife, it's my little girl's dowry, and...»

«Ugh! Listen, don't get on my nerves, which are already seized with a cramp... a cramp! more dreadful than a swimmer's. I have given you so much that I could say: "I bought your boat", I did not haggle over the price requested by you, you sea-thief, I proved to you that I am more familiar with oars and sails than you are, and everything was settled. Now, if the leek-salad you had last night — and your mouth stinks like a bilge — has given you nightmares and remorse, I don't care. The business was done in the presence of two witnesses, one was yours and the other one mine, and that's all. Get out of there, you shaggy crab, and let me get in.»

«But I... at least some guarantee... If you die, who will pay for my ship?»

«Your ship? Are you calling this hollowed pumpkin a ship? You miserable proud man! But I will reassure you, providing you make up your mind: I will give you another hundred drachmas. With this lot and what you wanted as rent you can buy three more of such moles... No, just a moment. No money. You would be equally capable of saying that I am mad and asking for more when I come back. Because I will come back, you may rest assured. Even if I have to come back to teach you a lesson by boxing your ears if you have given me a boat with a faulty keel. I will pledge the donkey and cart to you... No! Not even that! I will not trust you with my Antonius. You might change trade and from a boatman become a carter, and slink off while I am away. And my Antonius is worth your boat ten times over. It is better if I give you some money. But mind you, it is a pledge and you will give it back to me when I come back. Is that clear? Hey, you of the boat! Who is from Ptolemais?»

Three faces appear from a nearby boat: «We are.»

«Come here.»

«No, it's not necessary. Let us settle the matter between ourselves» begs the boatman.

Peter scans his face, ponders upon it, and when he sees that the other man leaves the boat and hastens to put on board the loom that Judas had left on the ground, he whispers: «I see!». He shouts to those in the other boat: «It's no longer necessary. Stay where you are» and taking some coins out of a small purse, he counts them and kisses them saying: «Goodbye, my dear!» and he hands them to the boatman.

«Why did you kiss them?» asks the amazed man.

«Just a... rite. Goodbye, you thief! Come on, all of you. And you, man, at least hold the boat. You will count them later and will find that they are right. I do not want to be your companion in hell, you know? I am not a thief. Heave ho! Heave ho!» and he pulls the first chest on board. He then helps the others to stow theirs, as well as the bags and everything else, balancing the weight and arranging the various items so as to be free to manoeuvre. And after the objects he arranges the passengers. «You can see that I know how to do it, you blood-sucker! Let go and go to your destiny.» And with Andrew he presses an oar against the little pier to depart from it.

[4] When the boat is in the flow of the current he hands the rud- 318.4
der over to Matthew saying: «You used to come and catch us when we were out fishing, in order to fleece us properly and you can handle it fairly well» and he sits on the first bench at the prow, with his back to the bows, and Andrew sits beside him. James and John of Zebedee are sitting in front of them and are

rowing with strong regular strokes.

The boat is sailing fast and smoothly, although it has a heavy load, skimming the sides of large ships, from the boards of which words can be heard praising their perfect rowing. Then there is the open sea, beyond the water-breakers... The whole of Ptolemais appears before the eyes of the departing group, as the town is stretched along the beach with the port to the south. There is dead silence in the boat. Only the squeaking of the oars in the rowlocks can be heard.

After a long while, when Ptolemais has already been left behind, Peter says: «However, if there had been a little wind... But nothing! Not a breath of it!...»

«Providing it does not rain!...» says James of Zebedee.

«H'm! It looks very much like it...»

There is silence for a long time while the men row hard.

Then Andrew asks: «Why did you kiss the coins?»

«Because those who part always greet one another. I will never see them again. And I am sorry. I would have preferred to give them to some poor wretch... Never mind! The boat is really a good one, it is strong and well built. It is the best one in Ptolemais. That is why I gave in to the demands of the owner. Also to avoid many questions about our destination. That is why I said to him: "To make purchases at the white Garden"... Ah! It's beginning to rain. Cover yourselves up, you who are in a position to do so, and you, Syntyche, give John his egg. It's time... Much more so because with a sea like this, nothing will upset his stomach... And what will Jesus be doing? I wonder what He is doing! With no clothes, no money! Where will He be now?»

«He will certainly be praying for us» replies John of Zebedee.

«Very well. But where?...»

Nobody can say where. And the boat proceeds heavily, laboriously, under a leaden sky, on the grey bitumenous sea, in a drizzling rain as fine as fog and as boring as protracted tickling. The mountains, which after a flat area are now close to the sea, look livid in the foggy air. The sea nearby continues to irritate one's eyes with its strange phosphorence, and farther away it fades into a hazy veil.

318.5 [5] «We will stop at that village to rest and eat» says Peter who rows untiringly. The others agree.

They reach the village. A little group of fishermen's houses built on a mountain spur protruding towards the sea.

«It is not possible to land here. There is no bottom...» grumbles Peter. «Well, we shall eat where we are.»

In fact the oarsmen eat with appetite, whereas the two exiles take some food unwillingly. It begins and stops raining alternately.

The village is deserted as if there were no inhabitants in it. And yet flights of doves from one house to another and clothes hanging out on roof-terraces prove that there are people in it. At last a half-naked man appears in the street and goes towards a little beached boat.

«Hey, man! Are you a fisherman?» shouts Peter holding his hands like a speaking-trumpet.

«Yes.» His assent is heard feebly owing to the distance.

«What will the weather be like?»

«Long sea shortly. If you are not from this place, I tell you to go round the cape at once. Over there it is not so rough, particularly if you keep close to the shore, which you can do, as the sea is deep. But go at once...»

«Yes, I will. Peace to you!»

«Peace and good luck to you.»

«Let's go then» says Peter to his companions. «And may God be with us.»

«He certainly is. Jesus is certainly praying for us» replies Andrew who resumes rowing.

But the sea is, in fact, already long and the waves push and drag the poor boat alternately, while the rain becomes thicker... and a blustery wind joins in to torture the poor people in the boat. Simon of Jonah gratifies it with all the most picturesque epithets, because it is a wicked wind that cannot be used to sail and it pushes the boat towards the rocks of the cape, which is now close at hand. The boat proceeds with difficulty in the curve of the little gulf, which is as black as ink. They row with difficulty, flushing, sweating, clenching their teeth, without wasting the least particle of strength in words. The others, sitting opposite them — I can see their backs — are silent in the boring rain: John and Syntyche in the centre, near the sail mast, Alphaeus' sons behind them, Matthew and Simon are last, struggling to hold the rudder straight against each breaker.

318.6 [6]It is a difficult task to go round the cape. But they succeed at last... And the oarsmen, who must be exhausted, have a little rest. They consult each other as to whether they should take shelter in a little village beyond the cape. But the idea prevails that «the Master is to be obeyed even against common sense. And He said that they must arrive at Tyre in one day». So they go on...

The sea calms all of a sudden. They notice the phenomenon and James of Alphaeus says: «The reward of obedience.»

«Yes, Satan has gone because he did not succeed in making us disobey» confirms Peter.

«But we shall arrive at Tyre at night. We have been greatly delayed...» says Matthew.

«It does not matter. We shall go to bed and we shall look for the ship tomorrow» replies Simon Zealot.

«But shall we find it?»

«Jesus said so. So we shall find it» says Thaddeus confidently.

«We can hoist the sail, brother» remarks Andrew. «The wind is favourable and we will move fast.»

The wind in fact fills the sail, although not very much, but enough to make rowing less necessary and the boat glides, as if it had been lightened, towards Tyre, the promontory of which, or rather its isthmus, is white to the north, in the last light of the day.

And night falls fast. And it is strange, after so much dullness of sky, to see stars appear in an unforeseeable clear sky and the Great Bear shine brightly in its stars, while the sea is illuminated by placid moonlight, which is so white that it seems to be dawning after a painful day, without an intervening night...

318.7 [7]John of Zebedee looks at the sky and smiles and he suddenly begins to sing, pulling his oar with his song and modulating his words to the rhythm of rowing:

«Hail, Star of the Morning,
Jasmine of the night,
Golden Moon of my Heaven,
Holy Mother of Jesus.

The sailor hopes in You,
Who suffers and dies dreams of You,

Shine, holy pious Star,
Upon those who love You, Mary!...»

He sings out happily in a tenor voice.

«What are you doing? We are talking of Jesus and you are singing of Mary?» asks his brother.

«He is in Her and She is in Him. But He is because She was... Let me sing...» And he starts singing with his whole heart, leading all the others...

They thus reach Tyre where they land without any difficulty in the little port, south of the isthmus, lit up by lamps hanging from many boats, with the help also of people present there.

While Peter and James of Zebedee remain in the boat to look after the chests, the others, with a man from another boat, go to a hotel to rest.

319. Departure from Tyre on the Ship of the Cretan Nicomedes.

4th November 1945.

[1]Tyre awakes among gusts of mistral. The sea is sparkling 319.1
with bright white-blue little waves, under a blue sky and white cirri moving up there, as the foaming waves move down here. The sun is enjoying a clear day after so much dull bad weather.

«I see» says Peter, standing up in the boat where he slept. «It's time to go. And "it" (and he points at the sea, which is rough even within the entrance of the port) sprayed us with lustral water...

H'm! Let us go and fulfil the second part of the sacrifice... Tell me, James... Don't you think that we are taking two victims to be sacrificed? I do.»

«So do I, Simon. And... I thank the Master for thinking highly of us. But... I would have preferred not to see so much grief. And I would never have thought I was to see all this...»

«Neither would I... But... You know? I say that the Master would not have done this, if the Sanhedrin had not poked their noses into the matter...»

«He in fact said so... But who told the Sanhedrin? That is what I would like to know»

«Who? Eternal God, make me be silent and do not let me think! I made this vow to get rid of the suspicion that tortures me. Help me, James, not to think. Speak of something else.»

«Of what? Of the weather?»

«Yes, it's better.»

«The trouble is that I know nothing about the sea...»

«I think that we are going to be tossed...» says Peter looking at the sea.

«No! Only small waves. It's nothing. It was worse yesterday.
It will be lovely to look at this moderate sea from the upper deck
319.2 of the ship. John will like it... It will make him sing. [2]Which ship
will it be?»

He stands up as well, looking at the ships on the other side, the high superstructures of which become visible particularly when their boat is raised by the up-and-down motion of the waves. They examine the various ships, guessing... The port is becoming alive with people.

Peter asks a boatman, or the like, who is bustling on the dock: «Can you tell me whether in the port over there, there is the ship of... wait a moment till I read his name... (and he takes a tied parchment out of his belt), here it is: Nicomedes Philadelphius of Philip, a Cretan from Paleocaster...»

«Oh! The great navigator! Who does not know him? I think that he is known not only from the Pearl Gulf to the pillars of Hercules, but also as far as the cold seas, where they say that night lasts for months! You are a sailor, how come you do not know him?»

«No. I don't know him, but I shall soon meet him, because I am looking for him on behalf of our friend Lazarus of Theophilus, formerly governor in Syria.»

«Ah! When I was a sailor — I am old now — he was in Antioch... Wonderful times... Your friend? And you are looking for Nicomedes, the Cretan? You need not worry, then. See that ship over there, the highest one, with flying colours? That's his ship. He will sail before the sixth hour. He is not afraid of the sea!...»

«In fact there is no need to be afraid of it. It's not really rough.» But a high wave gives him the lie, drenching both of them from head to foot.

«Yesterday it was too calm, today too rough. It's really mad. I prefer the lake...» grumbles Peter drying his face.

«I advise you to go into the basin. Everybody goes there.»

«But we are leaving. We are going in the ship of... of... wait: Nicomedes, and all the rest!» says Peter who cannot remember the strange names of the Cretan.

«You are not going to load your boat also on the ship?»

«Of course not!»

«Well, there is room in the basin for boats and men to look after them until you come back. A coin a day until you come back. I suppose you are coming back...»

«Certainly. We are going and will come back after seeing the state of Lazarus' garden, that's all.»

«Ah! You are his stewards?»

«Yes, and something more...»

«Well. Come with me. I will show you the place. It's really made for those who leave their boats there, like you...»

«Wait... [3]Here are the others. We will be with you in a mo- 319.3
ment.» And Peter jumps on the quay and runs to meet his com-
panions who are approaching.

«Did you sleep well, brother?» asks Andrew kindly.

«Like a baby in a cradle. And I was lulled to sleep with a lullaby...»

«I think that you had also a good wash» says Thaddeus smiling.

«Yes! The sea... is so kind that it washed my face to wake me up.»

«It looks very rough to me» remarks Matthew.

«Oh! But if you knew with whom we are going! One who is known even to the fish of the ice-cold seas.»

«Have you already seen him?»

«No, but I was told by one who says that there is a place for boats, a depot... Come, we will unload the chests and will go, because Nicodemus, no, Nicomedes, the Cretan, will be sailing soon.»

«In the Cyprus channel we shall be tossed about in good style» says John of Endor.

«Shall we?» asks Matthew anxiously.

«Yes. But God will help us.»

[4]They are near their boat once again. 319.4

«Here we are, man. We are unloading this luggage and then we will go, since you are so kind.»

«We help one another...» says the man from Tyre.

«Of course! We help one another, we ought to help one another. We ought to love one another, because that is the Law of God...»

«I am told that a new Prophet has risen in Israel and that is what He preaches. Is it true?»

«Is it true! That and much more! And the miracles that He works! Come on, Andrew, heave ho! heave ho! a little to your right. Right, when the wave lifts the boat... There you are, it's up!... I was saying, man: and what miracles! Dead people rise from death, sick people are cured, the blind see, thieves repent and even... See? If He were here, He would say to the sea: "Be still" and the sea would calm down... Can you manage, John? Wait, I'll come and help you. Hold the boat still and close... Up, up... a little more... Simon, take the handle... Watch your hand, Judas! Up, up... Thank-you, man... Watch you don't fall into the water, you sons of Alphaeus... Up... Here we are! Praised be the Lord! We had less trouble in stowing them than in pulling them up... But my arms are sore after yesterday's exercise... So, I was saying about the sea...»

«But is it true?»

«True? I was there and saw it!»

«Were you? Oh!... But where was it?»

«On the lake of Gennesaret. Come in the boat, while going to the basin, I will tell you...» and he goes away with the man and James, rowing in the canal towards the basin.

319.5 [5] «And Peter says that he does not know how to do...» remarks the Zealot. «Instead he has a talent for telling things in a simple way and he is more efficient than anybody else.»

«What I like so much in him is his honesty» says the man from Endor.

«And his perseverance» adds Matthew.

«And his humility. He does not pride himself on being our "head"! He works more than anybody and worries more about us than about himself...» says James of Alphaeus.

«And he is so virtuous in his feelings. A good brother. Nothing more...» concludes Syntyche.

«So it is all settled: you will be considered as brother and sister?» the Zealot asks the two disciples after some time.

«Yes, it is better so. And it is not a lie, it is spiritual truth. He
is my elder brother, of different marriage, but of the same father.
The Father is God, the different marriages: Israel and Greece;
and John is older, as one can see, by age, and — and one cannot
see it but it is true — by being a disciple before me. [6]Here is Si- 319.6
mon coming back...»

«It's all done. Let's go.»

Through the narrow isthmus they pass into the other port carrying the chests on their shoulders. The man from Tyre, familiar as he is with the place, takes them through the narrow passages between piles of bales of goods under very wide sheds, to the powerful ship of the Cretan, who is preparing to depart. He shouts to those on board to lower the gangway that they had already lifted.

«It's not possible. We have finished loading» shouts the head of the crew.

«He has letters to hand to you» says the man pointing to Simon of Jonah.

«Letters? From whom?»

«From Lazarus of Theophilus, the former governor of Antioch.»

«Ah! I will tell the boss.»

Simon says to the other Simon and to Matthew: «You will speak now. I am too coarse to speak to a man like him...»

«No. You are the head and you will speak because you are doing very well. We will help you, eventually. But there will be no need.»

«Where is the man with the letters? Let him come up» says a man as swarthy as an Egyptian: he is thin, handsome, agile, severe looking, about forty years old, or a little older, and looks down from the high ship's side. And he orders the gangway to be lowered.

Simon of Jonah, who has put on his tunic and mantle while waiting for a reply, goes up with a dignified bearing. The Zealot and Matthew follow him.

«Peace to you, man» greets Peter seriously.

«Hail. Where is the letter?» asks the Cretan.

«Here it is.»

The Cretan breaks the seal, unfolds the roll and reads.

«The messengers of Theophilus' family are welcome! The Cretans have not forgotten that he was good and kind. But be quick. Have you much to load?»

«What you see on the quay.»

«And how many are you...»

«Ten.»

«Good. We will find accommodation for the woman. You will adapt yourselves as best you can. Quick. We must set sail before the wind becomes stronger and that will happen after the sixth hour.»

With rending whistling he orders the chests to be loaded and stowed. Then the apostles and the two disciples go on board. The gangway is lifted, the ship's side is closed, the moorings are picked up, the sails are hoisted. And the ship sets out rolling steeply while leaving the harbour. Then the sails stretch out creaking, as the wind fills them, and pitching heavily the ship puts out to sea sailing fast towards Antioch...

Notwithstanding the very strong wind, John and Syntyche, one close to the other, holding on to a tackle, aft, are looking at the coast, the land of Palestine move away, and they weep...

320. Storm and Miracles on the Ship.

5th November 1945.

320.1 [1]The Mediterranean is an enraged expanse of green-blue water, with very high foam-crested billows clashing one against the other. There is no thick fog today. But the sea water, pulverised by the continuous pounding of breakers, is turned into a burning salty dust that penetrates even into people's clothes, reddens eyes, irritates throats, and seems to spread like a veil of salt powder everywhere, both in the air, making it opaque as thin fog does, and on things that seem sprayed with bright flour: the minute salt crystals. That happens, however, where there is no pounding of billows, or where the waves do not wash the deck from one side to the other, crashing on to it, rushing over the ship's side, then falling again into the sea, with the roar of a waterfall, through bilge drain holes in the opposite side. And the ship rises and plunges into the water, a twig at the mercy of the ocean, a mere nothing compared to it, squeaking and moaning from the bilges to the tops of the masts.The sea is really the master and the ship its plaything...

With the exception of those manoeuvring the boat, no one is on the deck. There are no goods either, only the lifeboats. And the crewmen, first of all the Cretan Nicomedes, half-naked, rolling like the ship, run here and there, refitting and securing, a difficult task because of the flooded slippery deck. The locked hatchways make it impossible to see what is happening below deck. But I am sure that they cannot be very happy down there!...

I cannot make out where they are, because there is nothing but sea around and a remote coast, which appears to be a mountainous one, with real mountains, not hills. I would say that they have been sailing for more than one day, because it is certainly morning, as the sun, which appears and disappears among thick clouds, is shining from the east.

I think that the ship is making little progress, notwithstanding that it is tossed about so much. And the sea seems to become more and more precipitous.

With a frightening crash a part of a mast, the precise name of which I do not know, breaks off, and in falling, dragged by an avalanche of water which collapses on the deck together with a real whirlwind, knocks down part of the ship's side.

[2]Those below must feel that the ship is foundering... And that 320.2
is proved, after a moment, when a hatch is half-opened and Peter's grey haired head juts out. He looks around, sees, and closes the hatch just in time to prevent a torrent of water from falling through it. But later, in a moment of calm, he opens it again and jumps out. He clings to supports and watches all hell let loose, and he whistles and mumbles commenting on the situation.

Nicomedes sees him: «Away! Go away!» he shouts. «Close that hatch. If the ship becomes heavier, it will sink. We are lucky if I do not have to throw the cargo overboard... Never seen a storm like this! I'm telling you, get away! I don't want landlubbers in my way. This is no place for gardeners, and...» He cannot continue because another wave sweeps the deck drenching all those on it. «See?» he shouts to Peter who is dripping wet.

«I see. But it doesn't surprise me. I am not capable only of looking after gardens. I was born on water, of a lake, that's true... But even a lake!... Before being a gardener I was a fisherman and I know...»

Peter is very calm and he knows how to be with the rolling of the ship perfectly well with his sturdy legs wide apart. The Cretan watches him while he moves to go near him.

«Are you not afraid?» he asks him.

«I wouldn't dream of it!»

«And the others?»

«Three are fishermen like me, that is, they were... The others, with the exception of the sick man, are strong.»

«Also the woman?... Watch! Look out! Hold on!»

Another avalanche of water invades the deck. Peter waits until it is over. and then says: «I could have done with this coolness last summer... Never mind! You were asking what the woman is doing. She is praying... and you had better do the same. But where are we now, exactly? In the Cyprus channel?»

«I wish we were! I would sail to the island and wait for the elements to calm. We are just off Colonia Julia, or Beritus, if you prefer so. Now we will get the worst of it... Those are the Lebanon mountains.»

«Could you not go in there, where the village is?»

«It's not a good port, reefs and rocks. It's not possible. Watch!...»

320.3 [3] Another whirlwind and another piece of a mast falls striking a man, who is not washed overboard only because the wave carries him against an obstacle.

«Go below deck! Go! See?»

«I see, I see... but that man?...»

«If he is not dead he'll come round. I cannot look after him... You can see!...» In fact the Cretan has to have eyes in the back of his head for the sake of everybody's life.

«Give him to me. The woman will look after him...»

«Anything you want, but go away!...»

Peter creeps as far as the motionless man, gets hold of his foot and pulls him towards himself. He looks at him, whistles... He grumbles: «His head is split like a ripe pomegranate. The Lord should be here... Oh! if He were! Lord Jesus! My Master, why have You left us?» There is deep sorrow in his voice... He loads the dying man on his shoulder, being drenched himself with blood, and goes back to the hatch.

The Cretan shouts to him: «It's quite useless. Nothing to be done. See!...»

But Peter, loaded as he is, makes a gesture as if to say: «We shall see» and he presses against a pole to resist a new wave. He then opens the hatch and shouts: «James, John, come here!» and with their help he lowers the wounded man, then descends himself securing the hatch.

In the smoky light of hanging lamps they see that Peter is bleeding: «Are you wounded?» they ask him.

«No, not I. It's his blood... But... you may as well pray because... [4]Syntyche, look here. You told me once that you know 320.4
how to cure wounded people. Look at this head...»

Syntyche leaves John of Endor, whom she was supporting as he is suffering a great deal, and goes to the table on which they have laid the poor man, and she looks...

«A bad wound! I have seen the like twice, in two slaves, one was struck by his master, the other by a stone at Caprarola. I would need water, a lot of water to clean it and stop the blood...»

«If you want just water!... There is even too much! Come, James, with the tub. We will handle it better in two.»

They go and come back dripping wet. And Syntyche with wet cloths washes and applies compresses to the nape of his neck... But the wound is a nasty one. The bone is bare from the temple to the nape. And yet the man opens his eyes vaguely and grumbles while gasping for breath. He is seized by the instinctive fear of death.

«Good! Be good! You will recover» says the Greek woman comforting him with motherly love and she speaks to him in Greek as Greek is his language.

The man, although stunned, is amazed and looks at her with a faint smile upon hearing his mother tongue and searches for Syntyche's hand... man who becomes a child as soon as he suffers and looks for a woman who is always a mother in such cases.

«I am going to try with Mary's ointment» says Syntyche when the wound bleeds less.

«But that is for pains...» objects Matthew, who has turned

deadly pale, I do not know whether because of the rough sea or at the sight of blood, or because of both. «Oh! Mary prepared it, with Her own hands! I will use it, praying... Will you pray, too. It can do no harm. Oil is always a medicine...»

She goes to Peter's sack, takes a vase out of it, a bronze vase I would say, opens it and takes a little ointment, which she warms on a lamp in the same lid of the vase. She pours it on a folded piece of linen cloth and applies it to the wounded head. She then bandages it tightly with linen strips. She places a folded mantle under the head of the wounded man who seems to doze off and she sits near him praying; the others also pray.

320.5 [5]The storm is still raging on the deck and the ship is pitching awfully. After some time a hatch is opened and a sailor rushes in.

«What's the matter?» asks Peter.

«We are in danger. I have come to get incense and offerings for a sacrifice...»

«Forget about such nonsense!»

«But Nicomedes wants to sacrifice to Venus! We are in her sea...»

«Which is as frantic as she is» grumbles Peter in a low voice. Then a little louder: «You, come with me. Let's go on deck. Perhaps there is work to be done... Are you afraid to stay with the wounded man and those two?» The two are Matthew and John of Endor, who are worn out by seasickness.

«No. You may go» replies Syntyche.

While getting on deck they run into the Cretan who is endeavouring to light the incense and who attacks them furiously to send them below, shouting: «Can't you see that without a miracle we shall be shipwrecked? It's the first time! The first time since I have been sailing!»

«Just listen: he will now say that we have cast a spell!» whispers Judas of Alphaeus.

In fact the man shouts louder: «Cursed Israelites, what have you got on you? You dogs, you have cast a spell on me! Go away? I am now going to offer a sacrifice to new-born Venus...»

«No, not at all. We will sacrifice...»

«Go away! You are pagans, you are demons, you are...»

«Do you hear that? I swear to you that if you let us do what we want to do, you will see the miracle.»

«No. Go away!» and he lights the incense and he throws into the sea, as best he can, some liquids that he had previously offered and tasted, as well as some powders, which I do not recognise. But the waves put the incense out and the sea, instead of calming, rages more and more, washing away all the paraphernalia of the rite and nearly sweeping away Nicomedes as well...

«Your goddess is giving you a beautiful answer! [6]It's our turn 320.6
now. We have One as well, purer than that one made of foam, but then... Sing, John, as you did yesterday, and we will follow you, and let us see!»

«Yes, let us see! But if it comes to the worst, I will throw you overboard as propitiatory victims.»

«All right. Come on, John!»

And John strikes up his song, followed by all the others, including Peter, who usually does not sing, as he is always out of tune. The Cretan is watching them, with folded arms and a smile that is half angry and half ironical. After the song, they pray with their arms stretched out. It must be the «Our Father» but it is in Hebrew and I do not understand it. They then sing louder. They thus alternate songs with prayers without fear or interruptions, although they are struck by the waves. They do not even hold on to supports, and yet they are so self-confident as if they were one thing with the wood of the deck. And the violence of the waves really begins to abate slowly. It does not cease completely, as the wind does not drop entirely. But the storm is not as furious as before, neither do the waves wash the deck.

The face of the Cretan is a poem of amazement... Peter casts sidelong glances at him and continues praying. John smiles and sings louder... The others follow him exceeding the roar of the waves more and more clearly as the sea calms down into a normal motion and the wind begins to blow favourably.

«Well? What do you think of it?...»

«But what did you say? What formula is it?»

«That of the True God and of His holy Handmaid. You may hoist your sails and sort things out, here... Is that not an island?»

«Yes, it's Cyprus... And the sea is even calmer in its channel... How strange! But that star that you worship, who is it? Venus, isn't it?»

«You should say: that you venerate. We worship God only. But She has nothing to do with Venus. She is Mary. Mary of Nazareth, the Hebraic Mary, the Mother of Jesus, the Messiah of Israel.»

«And that other thing, what was it? That wasn't Hebrew...»

«No, it was our dialect, the dialect of our lake, of our fatherland. But we cannot tell you, a pagan. It's a speech addressed to
320.7 Jehovah, and only believers can learn it. [7]Goodbye, Nicomedes. And don't regret what has gone to the bottom. A... spell less to cause you misfortune. Goodbye, eh? Are you dumbfounded?»

«No... But... Excuse me... I insulted you!»

«Oh! It does not matter! The effects of... Venus' cult... Come on, boys, let's go to the others...» and smiling happily Peter goes towards the hatchway.

The Cretan follows them: «Listen! And what about the man? Is he dead?»

«Not at all! We may give him back to you safe and sound very shortly... Just another trick of our... spells...»

«Oh! Please excuse me! But tell me, where can one learn them in order to be helped? I am prepared to pay for that...»

«Goodbye, Nicomedes! It's a long story... and it's not allowed... Sacred things are not to be given to heathens. Goodbye! Fare you well, my friend!»

And Peter, followed by all the others, goes below deck, smiling. Also the sea is now a pleasant sight, a fair mistral now favours navigation while the sun is setting and a slice of the waxing moon looms in the east...

321. Disembarking in Seleucia and Farewell to Nicomedes.

6th November 1945.

321.1 [1]The town of Seleucia appears in a beautiful sunset like a huge white mass on the edge of the blue water of the sea, which is placid and pleasantly bright, while the breeze plays among the little waves under a cloudless sky that blends its cobalt blue with the purple of sunset. The ship is heading under sail towards the remote town and is so flooded by the splendour of the setting sun, that she seems ablaze with lights of joy for the arrival now close at hand.

On the deck, among sailors no longer busy or worried, there are passengers who see that their destination is approaching. The injured sailor is sitting beside John of Endor, who is much more emaciated than when he left. The man's head is still dressed with a light bandage and he is as pale as ivory because of the blood he has lost. But he is smiling and he speaks to those who saved him and to his companions who, as they pass, congratulate him on his return to deck.

[2]The Cretan also sees him and, entrusting his post for a mo- 321.2
ment to the coxswain, he comes to greet his «very good Demetes», who has come back on deck for the first time after being hurt. «And thanks to all of you» he says to the apostles. «I did not think he could survive after being struck by the heavy beam and by the iron, which made it even heavier. Demetes, these people have really brought you back to life, because you were as good as dead, and not once, but twice. The first time when you were lying like a bale of goods on the deck, and because of the blood you were losing and of the waves that would have washed you overboard, you would have died and gone down to the kingdom of Neptune among Nereids and Tritons. The second time because they cured you with their wonderful ointments. Let me see your wound.»

The man undoes the bandage and shows a smooth healed scar, like a red mark from his temple to his nape, just under his hair, which appears to be cut, probably by Syntyche, to keep it out of the wound. Nicomedes touches the mark lightly: «Even the bone is healed! Marine Venus did love you! And she wanted you only on the surface of the sea and on the shores of Greece. May Eros be gracious to you, now that we land, and assist you to forget your misfortune and the terror of Thanatos as you were already in his grip.»

Peter's face displays his feeling on hearing so many mythological embellishments. Leaning against a mast, with his hands behind his back, he does not speak, but everything speaks in him fastening a biting epithet on heathen Nicomedes and his heathenism, and expressing his disgust at the whole of Gentilism.

The others are not less disgusted... Judas of Alphaeus is frowning as he normally does when in a bad temper, his brother is moving around showing a great interest in the sea. James of

Zebedee decides that the best thing to do is to leave them all and go below deck to get the bags and the loom, Matthew is toying with his belt and the Zealot imitates him, busying himself exceedingly with his sandals, as if they were something new, and John of Zebedee is hypnotised contemplating the sea.

The contempt and annoyance of the eight apostles is so obvious — and the mutism of the two disciples sitting near the wounded man is just as clear — that the Cretan becomes aware of it and he apologises: «It's our religion, you know? As you believe in yours we all believe in ours...»

321.3 No one replies [3]and the Cretan wisely decides to leave his gods in peace and descend from Olympus on the earth, or rather on the sea on his ship, inviting the apostles to go on to the prow to have a good view of the town that they are approaching. «There it is, see? Have you ever been here?»

«I was here, once, but I came by land» says the Zealot seriously and dryly.

«Very well! So you know that Seleucia is the real port of Antioch. The sea-town is at the mouth of the river Orontes, which is also gracefully suitable to receive boats that can go up the river as far as Antioch when the water is deep. The town you see, the larger one, is Seleucia. The other one, to the south, is not a town, but the ruins of a devastated place. They are deceiving, but it is a dead place. That chain is the Pierios, after which the town is called Seleucia Pieria. The mountain top farther inland, beyond the plain, is mount Casius, and it dominates like a giant the plain of Antioch. The other chain to the north is the Amanus. Oh! You will see the work the Romans have done in Seleucia and in Antioch! They could not have done anything greater. A port with three basins, which is one of the best, canals, jetties and breakwaters. There is not so much in Palestine. But Syria is better than other provinces in the Empire...»

His words fall in death like silence. Even Syntyche, who being Greek is less squeamish than the others, sets her lips, and her face becomes more than ever as sharp as a face sculptured on a medal or a bas-relief: the face of a goddess disdainful of earthly contacts.

The Cretan notices it and he apologises: «What do you expect! After all I make my money from the Romans!...»

Syntyche's reply is as sharp as a sabre-cut: «And gold blunts the sword of national honour and freedom», and she says so in such a way and in such pure Latin that the man is dumbfounded...

Then he dares to ask: «But are you not Greek?»

«I am Greek. But you love the Romans. I am speaking to you in the language of your masters, not in mine, which is the language of our martyred Fatherland.»

The Cretan is embarrassed while the apostles silently rejoice at the lesson given to the praiser of Rome. [4]And the Cretan 321.4
changes the subject and asks by which means they will be going from Seleucia to Antioch.

«On foot, man» replies Peter.

«But it is evening. And it will be night by the time you land...»

«There will be a place where we can sleep.»

«Of course. But you can sleep here until tomorrow.»

Judas Thaddeus, who has seen that they have already prepared everything necessary for a sacrifice to the gods, to be offered likely at their arrival in the port, says: «It is not necessary. We thank you for your kindness, but we prefer to land. Is that right, Simon?»

«Yes, it is. We also have our prayers to say, and it is... either you and your gods, or us and our God.»

«Do as you like. I would have liked to do a good turn to Theophilus' son.»

«And we would have liked to do one to the Son of God, convincing you that there is only one God. But you are a rock that will not move. As you can see, we are on the same standing. But perhaps we shall meet again one day and you may not be so persistent...» says the Zealot seriously.

Nicomedes makes a gesture as if he wished to say: «Perhaps!». A gesture of ironic carelessness concerning the invitation to acknowledge the true God and forsake the false one. He then goes to the pilot's place as the harbour is close at hand.

«Let us go below and get the chests. Let us do it by ourselves. I am dying to get away from this pagan stench» says Peter. And they all go below with the exception of Syntyche and John.

[5]The two exiles are close to each other and are watching the 321.5
water-breakers that are coming closer and closer.

«Syntyche, another step towards the unknown, another tug from the happy past, another agony, Syntyche... I cannot bear it any longer...»

Syntyche takes his hand. She is very pale and sorrowful. But she is still the strong woman who knows how to encourage people. «Yes, John, another tug, another agony. But do not say: another step towards the unknown... It is not right. We know what our mission is here. Jesus told us. So we are not going towards the unknown, on the contrary we blend more and more with what we know, with the Will of God. It is not even right to say: "another tug". We are being united to His will. A tug separates. We are being united. So we are not being pulled apart. We are only parting with the sensitive delights of our love for Him, our Master, reserving super-sensitive delights for ourselves, transferring love and duty to a supernatural level. Are you convinced that it is so? You are? Well, you must not even say: "another agony". Agony presupposes impending death. But by reaching a spiritual level to make it our abode, our atmosphere and our food, we do not die, "*we live*". Because what is spiritual, is eternal. We therefore rise to a more lively life, an anticipation of the great Life in Heaven. So, cheer up! Forget that you are the man-John, and remember that you are destined to Heaven. Reason, act, think and hope only as a citizen of that immortal Fatherland...»

321.6 [6] The others come back with their loads, when the ship is entering the large port of Seleucia majestically.

«And now let us make off as quickly as possible, to the first hotel we come across. There must be some in the neighbourhood, and tomorrow... by boat or by cart we will go to our destination.»

The ship docks by directions given by whistling and the gangway is lowered.

Nicomedes approaches the departing passengers.

«Goodbye, man. And thank you» says Peter on behalf of everybody.

«Goodbye, Israelites. And I thank you. If you go along that street you will find lodgings at once. Goodbye.»

The apostles come down on this side, and he goes in the opposite direction, and while Peter and the others, laden like porters, go to rest, the heathen begins his useless rite...

322. From Seleucia to Antioch on a Cart.

[No date].

[1] «You will certainly find a cart at the market. If you want mine, 322.1
I will give it to you, in memory of Theophilus. If I am a happy
man, I owe it to him. He defended me because he was a just man.
And one cannot forget certain things» says the old hotel-keeper
standing before the apostles in the early morning sunshine.

«The trouble is that we would be keeping your cart for several days... And in any case who would drive it? I can manage with a donkey... But a horse...»

«But it's the same, man! I won't give you a fiery colt, but a wise draught horse, as good as a lamb. And you will go in a short time and without any difficulty. You will be at Antioch by the ninth hour, also because the horse is familiar with the road and will go by itself. You will give it back to me when you want, without any interest on my side, as I am interested only in doing something pleasant to Theophilus' son, and you can tell him that I am always indebted to him, that I remember him and I am his servant.»

«What shall we do?» Peter asks his companions.

«Whatever you think is better. You decide and we will obey.»

«Shall we try with the horse? I am thinking of John... and also to be quick... I feel as if I am taking a man to the scaffold and I am dying to see it all over...»

«You are right» they all say.

«Well, I will take it, man.»

«And I am delighted to give it to you. I am going to prepare the vehicle.»

[2] The hotel-keeper goes away. Peter can now get the load off 322.2
his chest: «I have lost half of my lifetime in the past few days.
* How grievous! I wish I had Elijah's charriot, the mantle taken
by Elisha, anything that is quick in doing things... And above
all, at the cost of suffering death myself, I would have liked to
give something that might comfort those poor wretches, making them forget... I don't know!... In a few words, something that would not make them suffer so much... But if I find out who is

---

* **charriot**, as in: *2 King 2:11*; **mantle**, as in: *2 King 2:14*.

the main cause of all this grief, I am no longer Simon of Jonah, if I don't wring his neck like a wet cloth. I don't mean... killing him. No! But I'll squeeze him as he squeezed joy and life out of those two poor people...»

«You are right. It is very sorrowful. But Jesus says that we must forgive affronts...» says James of Alphaeus.

«Had they given offence to me, I would forgive... And I could. I am strong and sound, and if anybody offends me, I have enough strength to react against grief. But poor John! No, I cannot forget an affront to the man redeemed by the Lord, to a man who is dying broken-hearted...»

«I am thinking of the moment when we shall be saying goodbye to him...» says Andrew with a sigh.

«So am I. It's a fixed idea and it torments me more and more as that moment draws near...» whispers Matthew.

«Let us do it as quickly as possible, for goodness sake» says Peter.

«No, Simon. Forgive me, if I point out to you that you are wrong in wanting that. Your love for your neighbour is becoming devious and that must not happen to you, as you are always righteous» says the Zealot calmly laying a hand on Peter's shoulder.

«Why, Simon? You are learned and kind. Show me where I am wrong, and if I see that I am at fault, I will say to you: "You are right".»

«Your love is becoming unwholesome because it is changing into selfishness.»

«How? I am grieved over them, and I am selfish?»

«Yes, brother, because by excess of love — every excess is disorder and thus leads to sin — you are becoming cowardly. *You* do not want to suffer seeing other people suffer. That is selfishness, my brother in the name of the Lord.»

«That is true! You are right! And I thank you for telling me. That is what should be done among good companions. Well. I will no longer be in a hurry... But tell me the truth, is it not a pitiful situation?»

«It is indeed...» they all say.

322.3 [3] «How shall we leave them?»

«I would say that we should leave them after Philip has given them hospitality... we could remain for some time in Antioch, hiding ourselves, calling on Philip to find out how they are adjusting themselves...» suggests Andrew.

«No. Such sudden parting would make them suffer too much» says James of Alphaeus.

«Well, let us take part of Andrew's suggestion. We will remain in Antioch, but in Philip's house. And for a few days we will go and visit them, but less and less frequently, until we stop going» says the other James.

«We would renew their sorrow and disappoint them bitterly. No. It must not be done» says Thaddeus.

«What shall we do, Simon?»

«Ah! As far as I am concerned, I would rather be in their position than have to say: "I bid you goodbye"» says Peter who is down-hearted.

«I suggest this. Let us go with them to Philip's house and remain there. Then we will all go to Antigonea. It is a pleasant place... And we will stay there. When they have become acclimatised, we will withdraw, in a sorrowful but manly manner. That is what I would say. Unless Simon Peter has received different instructions from the Master» says Simon Zealot.

«Me? No. He said to me: "Do everything well, with love, without being sluggish, but without rushing, in the way which you think is best". So far I think I have done so. There is only one thing: I said I was a fisherman!... But If I had not said that, he would not have allowed me on the deck.»

«Don't have silly scruples, Simon. They are snares of the demon to upset you» says Thaddeus comforting him.

«Yes. Quite right! I think he is around us as never before, creating obstacles and endeavouring to frighten us to drive us to cowardly actions» says the apostle John, and he concludes in a low voice:.«I think he wanted to drive those two to despair by keeping them in Palestine... and now that they are avoiding his snares, he is avenging himself on us... I feel that he is around me like a snake hiding in the grass... And I have felt him like that for months... But here is the hotel-keeper coming from one side and John with Syntyche from the other. I will tell you the rest later when we are alone, if it is of interest to you.»

In fact a sturdy cart drawn by a strong horse is coming forward on one side of the yard, driven by the host, while the two disciples are coming towards them on the other side.

«Is it time to go?» asks Syntyche.

«Yes, it is. Are you well covered, John. Is your pain improving?»

«Yes. I am wrapped in woollen garments and the ointment has helped me.»

«Get on, then, and we shall be with you in a moment.»

322.4 [4]... And when they have finished loading, and everyone is in the cart, they go out through the wide door, after being repeatedly assured by the host of the docility of the horse. They cross a square as pointed out to them and take a road near the walls until they go out through a gate and they then proceed along a deep canal first and later along the river. It is a fine well kept road, running towards north-east, following the turns of the river. On the other side there are mountains, the slopes, creeks and gorges of which are very green, and in the most sunny spots one can see the swollen gems of many shrubs in the undergrowth thickets.

«How many myrtles!» exclaims Syntyche.

«And laurels!» adds Matthew.

«Near Antioch there is a place sacred to Apollo» says John of Endor.

«Perhaps the winds have blown the seeds as far as here...»

«Perhaps. But the whole area here is full of lovely plants» says the Zealot.

«Since you have been here, do you think that we shall pass near Daphne?»

«We must. You will see one of the most beautiful valleys in the world. Apart from the obscene cult, which has degenerated into dirty orgies, it is a valley of earthly paradise, and if Faith enters it, it will become a true paradise. Oh! how much good you will be able to do here! I wish you hearts as fertile as the soil...» says the Zealot to arouse consoling thoughts in the two disciples. John lowers his head and Syntyche sighs.

322.5 [5]The horse trots with a rhythmical step and Peter does not speak, tense as he is in the strain of driving, although the horse proceeds safely without any need of guidance or spur. They travel thus quite fast until they stop at a bridge to eat and let the horse rest. The midday sun is shining and all the beauty of a most beautiful country is visible.

«But... I prefer this to the sea...» says Peter looking around.

«What a storm!»

«The Lord prayed for us. I felt that He was near us when we were praying on the deck. As close as if He were among us...» says John smiling.

«I wonder where He is. I have no peace thinking that He has no clothes... And if He gets wet? And what will He eat? He is quite capable of fasting...»

«You may rest assured that He does so to help us» says James of Alphaeus confidently.

«And for other reasons as well. Our brother has been very depressed for some time. I think that He mortifies Himself continuously to defeat the world» says Thaddeus.

«You mean the demon who is in the world» says James of Zebedee.

«It's the same thing.»

«But He will not succeed. My heart is weighed down with fear...» says Andrew with a sigh.

«Oh! Now that we are far away, things will improve!» says John of Endor rather bitterly.

«Don't you believe that! You and Syntyche were nothing compared to the "great faults" of the Messiah according to the mighty ones in Israel» says Thaddeus sharply.

«Are you sure? Over and above all my troubles, I have also this aching pain in my heart: that I have harmed Jesus by coming to Him. If I were sure that it is not so, I would not suffer so much» says John of Endor.

«Do you think that I am sincere, John?» asks Thaddeus.

«Yes, I do.»

«Then, in the name of God and mine I assure you that you have given Jesus but one sorrow: that of having to send you here on a mission. You have nothing to do with *all* His past, present and future griefs.»

The first smile, after sad days of gloomy melancholy, brightens the hollow cheeks of John of Endor, who says: «What a relief you give me! The day seems brighter to me, my disease less troublesome, and my heart is more comforted... Thank you, Judas of Alphaeus, thank you!»

322.6 [6]They get into the cart again and after crossing the bridge they go along the other bank of the river, following the road that goes straight to Antioch, through a very fertile area.

«There you are! Daphne is in that poetic valley with its temple and thickets. And over there, in the plain, there is Antioch and its towers on the walls. We will enter the gate near the river. Lazarus' house is not very far from the walls. His most beautiful houses have been sold. This one is left, once it was the place where Theophilus' servants and clients stopped and rested and it has many stables and granaries. Philip lives in it. A good, old soul faithful to Lazarus. You will be at home there. And we will go to Antigonea where the house is in which Eucheria lived with her children, who were very young then...»

«This town is well fortified, isn't it?» asks Peter, who is now relaxing, as he has realized that his test as a charioteer has been successful.

«Yes, very. Walls of great height and width, over one hundred towers, which, as you can see, look like giants standing on the walls, with impassable moats at their feet. And mount Silpius has also lent its tops to assist the defence system, as a buttress in the weakest part of the walls... Here is the gate. It is better if you stop and go in holding the horse by the bit. I will guide you as I know the way...»

They go through the gate watched by Romans.

The apostle John says: «I wonder whether the soldier of the Fish Gate is here... Jesus would be happy to know...»

«We will look for him. But go on now» orders Peter, who is obviously worried at the idea of going to an unknown house.

John obeys without speaking; he only looks carefully at every soldier he sees.

322.7 [7]After a short distance, there is a strongly built but simple house, that is, a high wall with no windows. There is only a large door in the central part of the wall.

«Here we are. Stop» says the Zealot.

«Oh! Simon! Be good! Will you speak now?!»

«Yes, I will, if it is going to make you happy» and the Zealot knocks at the heavy door. He makes himself known as a messenger from Lazarus. He goes in by himself. He comes out with an old dignified man, who bows profusely and orders a servant to open the gate and let the cart go in. And he apologises for letting them all go in there and not through the main door.

The cart stops in a large yard with porches, well kept, with a huge plane-tree in each of the four corners and two in the centre sheltering a well and watering trough for horses.

«Take care of the horse» the steward orders the servant. He then says to the guests: «Please come with me and may the Lord be blessed for sending me His servants and the friends of my master. Your servant is at your disposal, please give me your orders.»

Peter blushes because the steward's words and bows are addressed mainly to him, and he does not know what to say... The Zealot comes to his rescue.

«The disciples of the Messiah of Israel, of whom Lazarus of Theophilus speaks to you, and who from now on will live in your house to serve the Lord, need nothing but rest. Will you show them their rooms?»

«Oh? There are rooms always ready for pilgrims, as in the days of my mistress. Come...» And followed by everybody he goes along a corridor into a little yard at the end of which is the real house. He opens the door, goes along a passage, then he turns to the right. There is a staircase. They go upstairs, where there is another corridor with rooms on both sides.

«Here you are. And may your stay be a pleasant one. I am now going to order water and some linen. May God be with you» says the old man and he goes away.

They open the windows of the rooms they choose. The walls and towers of Antioch are opposite the rooms on one side; the peaceful yard adorned with creeping rose-bushes, which are now bare because of the season, can be seen from the rooms on the other side of the corridor.

And at last, after so much travelling, a house, a room, a bed... A resting place for some, the final destination for others...

323. The Stay at Antigonea. Hermione, the Good Proselyte Wife from Alexandroscene.

7th November 1945.

323.1 [1] «My son Ptolmai has come to the market. He is going back to Antigonea today at the sixth hour. It is a mild day. Do you still wish to go as you had planned?» asks old Philip while serving hot milk to his guests.

«We shall certainly go. When did you say?»

«At the sixth hour. You can come back tomorrow, if you wish, or the evening before the Sabbath, if you prefer so. All the Hebrew servants and those who have embraced our faith come for the Sabbath service.»

323.2 «We will do that. [2]And that place may still be chosen as the residence for these two.»

«I will be pleased even if I lose them. Because it is a wholesome place, and you could do much good among the servants, some of whom are still the ones left by our master. Some are there through the bounty of our blessed mistress who ransomed them from cruel masters. So they are not all Israelites. But by now they are not pagans either. I am referring to the women. All the men have been circumcised. Do not disdain them… But they are still very far from the Justice of Israel. The saints of the Temple would be scandalised at them, as they are perfect…»

«Of course! They would indeed! Well! They will now be able to improve by breathing in wisdom and goodness from the messengers of the Lord… Have you heard how much you have to do?» concludes Peter, addressing the two.

«We will do it. We will not disappoint the Master» promises Syntyche. And she goes out to prepare what is necessary to take.

John of Endor asks Philip: «Do you think that at Antigonea I could do some good also to other people, as a teacher?»

«Much good. Old Plautus died three months ago and the children of the Gentiles have no school now. With regard to the Jews, there is no master for them because all our people keep away from that place, which is close to Daphne. It would take one like… like Theophilus… Without rigidity for… for…»

«Yes, without Pharisaism, you mean» concludes Peter promptly.

«That's it... yes... I do not want to criticise... But I think... It's of no use cursing... It would be better if they helped... As our mistress used to do... she brought more people to the Law with her smiles and in a better way than a rabbi.»

[3]«That is why the Master sent me here! I am the man with the right qualifications... Oh! I will do His will. Until I breathe my last breath. I now believe, I firmly believe that my mission is nothing but a mission of predilection. I am going to tell Syntyche. You will see that we will stay there... I am going to tell her» and he goes out, full of life as he had not been for a long time. 323.3

«Most High Lord, I thank You and bless You! He will still suffer, but not so much as before... Ah! What a relief?» exclaims Peter. He then feels that it is his duty to give Philip some kind of explanation, as best he can, of his joy: «You must realise that John was made the object of the attacks of the... "rigid ones" in Israel... You call them "rigid ones"...»

«Ah! I see! He was persecuted for political reasons like... like...» and he looks at the Zealot.

«Yes, like me and more, and for other reasons as well. Because he provokes them not only because he is of a different caste, but also because he belongs to the Messiah. So — and let this be said once for all — both he and Syntyche are entrusted to your loyalty... Do you understand?»

«Yes, I do. And I know how to behave.»

«What will you say they are?»

«Two teachers recommended by Lazarus of Theophilus, he is a teacher for boys, and she for girls. I see that she embroiders and has a loom... A considerable amount of needle work is done and sold in Antioch by foreigners. But it is rough and coarse stuff. Yesterday I saw that she had a piece of work which reminded me of my good mistress... They will be in great demand...»

«Once again may the Lord be praised» says Peter.

«Yes. That will soothe our grief in parting.»

«Are you going to leave already?»

«We must. We have been delayed by the storm. At the beginning of Shebat we must be with the Master. He is already waiting for us, because we are late» explains Thaddeus.

[4]They part, each attending to his own business, that is, Philip 323.4

goes where a woman calls him, the apostles to a high ground, in the sunshine.

«We could leave the day after the Sabbath. What do you say?» asks James of Alphaeus.

«As far as I am concerned!... I don't mind!... Every morning I get up tormented by the idea that Jesus is alone, without clothes, without anyone looking after Him, and every night I go to bed with the same idea. But we shall decide today.»

«Tell me. But was the Master aware of everything? I have been wondering for days how He knew that we were going to meet the Cretan, how he could foresee John's and Syntyche's work, how... That is... many things» says Andrew.

«Actually I think that the Cretan stops at Seleucia on fixed dates. And perhaps Lazarus told Jesus, and so He decided to leave without waiting until Passover...» explains the Zealot.

«Indeed! That's right. And how will John manage at Passover?» asks James of Alphaeus.

«Like every other Israelite...» says Matthew.

«No. That would mean falling into the wolf's mouth!»

«Not at all! Who is going to find him out among so many people?»

«The Iscar... Oh! What have I said! Forget about it. It's only a trick of my mind...» Peter is flushed and sad, because he has spoken.

Judas of Alphaeus lays a hand on his shoulder and smiling with his severe smile, he says: «Never mind! We are all thinking of the same thing. But we won't tell anybody. And let us bless the Eternal Father for diverting John's mind from this thought.»

They are all silent, engrossed in thought. But as they are true Israelites, the thought of how the exiled disciple will be able to celebrate Passover in Jerusalem worries them... and they begin to speak about it again.

«I think that Jesus will see to it. Perhaps John already knows. We have only got to ask him» says Matthew.

«No, don't. Don't put desires and thorns where peace is just springing up» begs the apostle John.

«Yes. It is better to ask the Master Himself» confirms James of Alphaeus.

«When shall we see Him? What do you think?» asks Andrew.

«Oh! If we leave the day after the Sabbath, by the end of the moon we shall certainly be at Ptolemais...» says James of Zebedee.

«If we find a ship...» remarks Judas Thaddeus.

And his brother adds: «And if there is no storm.»

«There are always ships leaving for Palestine. And if we pay, we will call at Ptolemais, even if the ship is heading for Joppa. Have you any money left, Simon?» the Zealot asks Peter.

«Yes, I have, although that thief, the Cretan, fleeced me in no uncertain manner, notwithstanding his protestations that he wanted to do a favour to Lazarus. But I have to pay for the custody of the boat and the keeping of Antonius... I do not want to touch the money given to me for John and Syntyche. It is sacred. At the cost of starving, I will leave it as it is.»

«That is the right thing. That man is very ill. He thinks that he will be able to teach. I think he will be ill all the time, and soon...» states the Zealot.

«I am of the same opinion. Syntyche will be busier preparing ointments than working» confirms James of Zebedee.

«What do you think of that ointment? What a wonderful thing! Syntyche told me that she wants to make it here and use it to become familiar with local families» says John.

«A very good idea! A sick person who is cured always becomes a disciple and relatives follow suit» states Matthew.

«Oh! no! Certainly not» exclaims Peter.

«What? Do you mean that miracles do not attract people to the Lord?» Andrew asks him together with two or three companions.

«Oh! little babies! One might say that you have just come down from Heaven! But don't you see what they do to Jesus? Did Eli of Capernaum turn? Or Doras? Or Oshea of Korazim? Or Melkia of Bethsaida? And — excuse me you from Nazareth — the whole of Nazareth, after the five, six, ten miracles worked there, up to the last one for your nephew?» asks Peter.

Nobody replies, because it is the bitter truth.

«We have not found the Roman soldier yet. Jesus led us to understand...» says John after a little while.

«We will tell those who are staying. It will be another opportunity for them» replies the Zealot.

323.5 [5]Philip comes back: «My son is ready. He finished early. He is with his mother who is preparing gifts for her grandchildren.» *

«Your daughter-in-law is good, isn't she?»

«She is. She consoled me for the loss of my Joseph. She is like a daughter to me. She was Eucheria's maid, and was brought up by her. Come and have something to eat before leaving. The others are already taking something.»...

... And they trot towards Antigonea, preceded by the cart of Ptolmai, Philip's grandson... They soon reach the little town. Situated as it is among fertile gardens, shielded from winds by chains of mountains around it, far enough not to oppress it, but sufficiently close to protect it and pour on to it the scents of their woods of resinous and essential plants, full of sunshine, it cheers up one's sight and heart only by going through it.

323.6 [6]Lazarus' gardens are in the southern part of the town and are preceded by a path, which is now bare, along which are the houses of the gardeners. Low but well kept houses, from the doors of which children and women appear watching curiously and greet smiling. The different races can be told by the different faces.

As soon as he enters the gate, where the estate begins, Ptolmai cracks his whip in a special way when passing in front of each house; it must be a signal. And the inhabitants of each house, after hearing it, go into their houses and then come out, closing the doors and walking along the path, behind the two carts, as the horses are ambling and they stop at the centre of radial paths stretching in every direction like the spokes of a wheel, among numberless fields arranged as flower beds, some of which are bare, some full of evergreens, protected by laurels, acacias or similar trees and by other trees which ooze odoriferous milk like juices and resins through cuts in their trunks. The air contains a mixed scent of balsamic, resinous, aromatic fragrances. There

---

* **My son**, is called Ptolmai by the old Philip, his grandfather, father of his father Joseph. The Hebrews also used to call their nephews *son*, as they also used to call their grandparents *father* and *mother*, and the title of *brother* or *sister* was also extended to cousins and brother-in-laws. It was unusual to say *uncle* and *aunty* (as in 100.12). The work by Valtorta includes both ways of calling different degrees of kinship, those of Jesus times and those of our times (especially "aunty" in 95.5/6).

are beehives everywhere, as well as irrigation vats where snow-white doves are drinking. And in special areas white hens are scratching about on the bare ground, which has just been hoed, while some girls are watching over them.

[7]Ptolmai cracks his whip repeatedly, until all the subjects of the little kingdom have gathered round the arrivals. He then begins his little speech: «Listen. Phillip, our head and the father of my father, has sent and recommends these holy people from Israel, who have come here by the will of our master, and may God be always with him and his family. We have been complaining because there was no rabbi here to speak to us. Now the bounty of God and of our master, who although so far is so affectionate to us — may God give him the welfare that he gives his servants — have procured for us what our hearts desire so keenly. The Messiah promised to peoples has risen in Israel. They had told us at the Feasts in the Temple and in the house of Lazarus. But now the time of grace has really come because the King of Israel has taken care of His lowest servants and has sent His ministers to bring us His words. These are His disciples and two of them will live with us, either here or in Antioch, teaching us the Wisdom of Heaven and the science that is necessary on the earth. John, a schoolmaster and a disciple of Christ, will teach our children the former and the latter wisdom. Syntyche, a disciple and a teacher of needlework will teach our girls the science of the love of God and the art of needlework. Welcome them as a blessing from Heaven and love them as Lazarus of Theophilus and Eucheria loves them — glory to their souls and peace — and as the daughters of Theophilus love them: Martha and Mary, our beloved mistresses and disciples of Jesus of Nazareth, the Rabbi of Israel, the promised King.» 323.7

The little group of men, wearing short tunics and holding garden tools in their earthy hands, and of women and children of every age, listen in utter astonishment, they then whisper and finally bow their heads very low.

Ptolmai begins to introduce them: «Simon of Jonah, the head of the messengers of the Lord; Simon the Cananean, a friend of our master; James and Judas, brothers of the Lord; James and John, Andrew and Matthew» and then to the apostles and disciples: «Anne, my wife, of the tribe of Judas, as my mother was,

because we are pure Israelites and we came here with Eucheria of Judas. Joseph, the son consecrated to the Lord, and Theocheria, our first-born, who is called after our just masters, a wise daughter who loves God as a true Israelite. Nicolaus and Dositeus. Nicolaus is a Nazirite; Dositeus, our third born, has been married for several years (he says that with a big sigh) to Hermi-
323.8 one. [8]Come here, woman...»

A very young swarthy woman comes forward holding an unweaned babe in her arms.

«Here she is. She is the daughter of a proselyte and a Greek *
mother. My son saw her at Alexandroscene in Phoenicia, when he was there on business... and wanted her... and Lazarus did not object, on the contrary he said to me: "Better so than debauched". And it is better. But I wanted someone with Jewish blood...»

Poor Hermione has lowered her head as if she were accused. Dositeus trembles with anger and suffers. Anne, his mother, looks at him with sorrowful eyes...

Although the youngest of all the apostles, John feels that it is necessary to raise the humiliated spirits and says: «In the Kingdom of the Lord there are no longer Greeks or Israelites, Romans or Phoenicians, but only the children of God. When you learn the Word of God from those who have come here, your heart will rise to a new light and this woman will no longer be "the foreigner", but the disciple of our Lord Jesus, like yourself and all the rest.»

Hermione raises her mortified head and smiles gratefully at John and the same expression of gratitude can be seen on the faces of Dositeus and Anne.

Ptolmai replies seriously: «God grant it, because apart from her origin, I cannot blame my daughter-in-law for anything.
323.9 [9]The child in her arms is Alphaeus, her last born, called after her father, a proselyte. The little girl with sky-blue eyes and ebony curls is Myrthica, who was called after Hermione's mother, and this one, the first born, is Lazarus, as our master wanted, and the other one is Hermas.»

«The fifth must be called Ptolmai and the sixth Anne, to tell the Lord and the world that your heart has opened to new under-

---

* **proselyte**: it was so called the pagan converted to the Hebrew religion and circumcised.

standing» says John again.

Ptolmai bows without speaking. He then resumes the introductions: «These are two brothers from Israel: Miriam and Silvian, of the tribe of Naphtali. And these are Elbonides, a Danite, and Simeon, a Judaean. And here are the proselytes, Romans or sons of Romans, whom Eucheria's charity redeemed from slavery and heathenism: Lucius, Marcellus, Solon the son of Elateus.»

«A Greek name» remarks Syntyche.

«From Thessalonica. The slave of a servant of Rome» — and there is manifest contempt in saying "servant of Rome" — «Eucheria took him with his dying father, in troubled times, and if his father died a heathen, Solon is a proselyte... Priscilla, come forward with your children...»

A tall thin woman with an aquiline nose comes forward pushing a girl and a boy, with two lovely little girls hanging to her skirt.

«This is Solon's wife, a freed woman of a Roman lady now dead, and this is Marius, Cornelia, and the twins Mary and Martilla: Priscilla is experienced in essences. Amiclea, come with your children. She is the daughter of proselytes. And her boys Cassius and Theodorus are also proselytes. Tecla, don't hide yourself. She is Marcellus' wife. She is grieved because she is sterile. She is the daughter of proselytes, too. And these are the
farmers. [10]Let us go to the gardens now. Come.» 323.10

And he leads them through the vast estate followed by the gardeners who explain the various cultivations and work while the girls go back to their hens, which have taken advantage of their absence to trespass on to other ground.

Ptolmai explains: «They are brought here to free the soil from grubs before sowing the yearly cultivations.»

John of Endor smiles at the cackling hens and says: «They look like those I had once...» and he bends throwing bread crumbs taken from his sack, until he is surrounded by pullets and he laughs because a cheeky one snatches the bread from his fingers.

«That's not so bad!» exclaims Peter nudging Matthew and pointing to John who is playing with the chicken and to Syntyche who is speaking Greek to Solon and Hermione.

They then go back to the house of Ptolmai who explains: «This is the place. But if you want to teach, we can make room.

Are you staying here or...»

«Yes, Syntyche! Here! It's nicer! Antioch oppresses me with recollections...» John begs his companion in a low voice.

«Of course... As you wish. Providing you are well. It is all the same to me. I no longer look back... Only forward... Cheer up, John! We shall be all right here. Children, flowers, doves, hens for us, poor human beings. And for our souls... the joy of serving the Lord. What do you all say?» she asks addressing all the apostles.

«We are of the same opinion as you, woman.»

«Well, that is settled.»

«Very well. We will leave with relieved minds...»

«Oh! Don't go away! I will not see you again! Why so early? Why?...» John falls into a state of depression.

«But we are not going away now! We are staying until you are...» Peter does not know what to say John will be, and to hide his tears he embraces weeping John endeavouring to console him in this way...

324. The Eight Apostles Begged to Preach Before Departing. Goodbye to John of Endor and Syntyche. Farewell to Antioch.

8th November 1945.

324.1 [1] The apostles are once again in the house at Antioch with the two disciples and all the men from Antigonea, who are not wearing their work clothes, but have on their long best garments. I thus understand that it is the Sabbath.

Philip begs the apostles to speak to everybody at least once before their departure, which is now imminent.

«About what?»

«About anything you like. You have heard our conversation during the past days. You may speak accordingly.»

The apostles look at one another. Whose duty is it? Peter's, of course. He is the head! But Peter would rather not speak but surrender the honour to James of Alphaeus or to John of Zebedee. And only when he sees that they are inflexible, he makes up his mind to speak.

«Today in the synagogue we heard the explanation of chapter 52 of Isaiah. A learned comment according to the world, a defective one according to Wisdom. But the commentator is not to be blamed, because he gave what he could within the limits of his own wisdom: without the knowledge of the Messiah and of the new Time brought by Him. But let us not find fault with him, let us instead pray that he may achieve the knowledge of these two graces and accept them without difficulty. You told me that at Passover you heard some people speak of the Master with faith, some with sneering words. And that only because of the great faith that fills the hearts of the house of Lazarus, all their hearts, you were able to bear the unease that the innuendoes of other people caused to your hearts, particularly because these other people were rabbis of Israel. But to be learned does not mean to be holy or to possess the Truth. And this is the Truth: Jesus of Nazareth is the promised Messiah, the Saviour of Whom the Prophets speak, and the last of them want to rest in Abraham's bosom only recently, after his glorious martyrdom, which he suffered for the sake of justice. John the Baptist said, and those who heard his words are here now: "This is the Lamb of God that takes away the sins of the world". His words were believed by the most humble of those present, because humility helps to reach Faith, whereas it is difficult for proud people — laden as they are with unnecessary things — to reach the mountain top where chaste bright Faith dwells. Those humble people, both because they were such and because they believed, deserved to be the first in the army of the Lord Jesus. You can thus see how necessary humility is in order to attain instant faith, and how faith is rewarded, particularly when one believes against adverse appearances. I exhort and stimulate you to possess these two qualities and you will then be in the army of the Lord and will conquer the Kingdom of Heaven... [2]It is your turn, Simon Zealot. I 324.2
have spoken. Please continue.»

The Zealot, caught out so suddenly and so clearly pointed out as the second speaker, can but move forward without delay or complaint. And he says:

«I will continue the sermon of Simon Peter, the head of us all by the will of the Lord. And I will continue taking up the subject of chapter 52 of Isaiah, as seen by one who knows the Incar-

nate Truth, Whose servant he is for good. It says: "Awake, clothe yourself in strength, Zion, put on your richest clothes, city of the Holy One". And that is how it should really be. Because when a promise is fulfilled, peace is made, punishment comes to an end, and the time of joy comes; hearts and towns should put on their best clothes and raise their mortified foreheads, realizing that they are no longer hated, defeated, beaten, but are instead loved and freed. We are not here to institute proceedings against Jerusalem. Charity, the first of all virtues, forbids it. Let us not watch the hearts of other people, let us, instead, look at our own. Let us clothe our hearts in strength by means of that faith of which Simon has spoken and let us put on our richest clothes because our age-old faith in the Messiah is now crowned by the real fact. The Holy Messiah, the Word of God is really among us. And both souls and bodies have evidence of this: the former hear the words of Wisdom, which fortify them and infuse holiness and peace, the latter, thanks to the Holy One, to Whom everything is granted by the Father, are released from the most dreadful diseases, even from death, so that the hills and valleys of Israel, our Fatherland, may resound with hosannas to the Son of David and to the Most High Who has sent His Word, as He had promised the Patriarchs and Prophets. I, who am speaking to you, was a leper, destined to die, after years of unrelenting distress, in the brutal solitude familiar to lepers. A man said to me: "Go to Him, to the Rabbi of Nazareth, and you will be cured". I had faith. I went. I was cured. In my body. In my heart. The former was freed from the disease that separates lepers from other men. The latter was freed from the hatred that separates from God. And with a new spirit, from a troubled, sick exile I became His servant, called to the happy mission of going among men, loving them in His Name, teaching them the one and only necessary knowledge: that Jesus of Nazareth is the Saviour and that blessed are those
324.3 who believe in Him. [3]It's your turn to speak now, O James of Alphaeus.»

«I am the brother of the Nazarene. My father and His were brothers, born of the same mother. And yet I cannot say that I am His brother, but His servant. Because the paternity of Joseph, my father's brother, was a spiritual paternity and I solemnly tell you that the Most High, Whom we worship, is the true Father of our

Master Jesus. God allowed the Second Person of God One and Triune to become incarnate and to come upon the earth, remaining however God and always united to the Persons Who dwell in Heaven. Because God, Who is infinitely Almighty can do that. And He does it out of Love, which is His nature. Jesus of Nazareth is our brother, men, because he was born of a woman, and is like us in His humanity. He is our Master because He is the Wise One, He is the very Word of God and has come to speak to us to take us to God. And He is our God, being One with the Father and the Holy Spirit, with Whom He is always united in love, power and nature. May this Truth, which the Just One, my relative, was granted to know through clear evidence, become also your possession. And when the world will endeavour to tear you away from the Christ, saying: "He is just an ordinary man", reply: "No. He is the Son of God, He is the Star born of Jacob, He is the Sceptre that arises in Israel, He is the Ruler". Let nothing deter you. That is Faith. [4]It's your turn, Andrew.» 324.4

«That is Faith. I am a poor fisherman of the lake of Galilee, and when fishing in the silent nights, in the light of the stars, I had silent conversations with myself. I used to say: "When will He come? Will I still be alive? Many years are still to pass, according to the prophecy". For man, whose life is short, even a few dozen years are as long as centuries... I used to ask myself: "How will He come? Where? From whom?". And my dull human mind made me dream of royal splendour, of royal abodes, processions, clangour, power and unbearable majesty... And I would say: "Who will be able to look at this great King?". I thought that He would be more terrifying, in His manifestation, than Jehovah Himself on Mount Sinai. And I used to say: "The Hebrews saw the mountain lighten, but they were not burned to ashes, because the Eternal Father was beyond the clouds. But here He will look at us with mortal eyes and we shall die...". I was a disciple of the Baptist. And when we were not fishing I used to go to him with other companions. It was a day of this month... The banks of the Jordan were crowded with people who shivered when hearing the words of the Baptist. I had noticed a young handsome man come calmly towards us along a path. His garments were plain,

---

* **reply**, taken from: *Numbers 24:17-19.*

* **prophecy**, in: *Daniel 9:22-27.*

His countenance kind. He seemed to be asking for love and to be giving love. His blue eyes rested for a moment on me, and I felt something that I have never felt again. I felt as if my soul were being caressed, as if I were being lightly touched by the wings of angels. For a moment I felt that I was so far away from the earth, so different, that I said: "I shall die now! This is God calling my soul". But I did not die. I was fascinated contemplating the young unknown man, whose blue eyes were now staring at the Baptist. And the Baptist turned round, ran to Him and bowed. They spoke to each other. And as John's voice was as loud as thunder, their mysterious words reached me, who was listening, tense as I was in the keen desire to know who the unknown young man was. My soul felt that He was different from everybody. They were saying: "I should be baptised by You...". "Never mind just now. It is necessary to fulfil all justice"... John had already said: "Someone will come and I am not fit to undo the straps of His sandals". He had already said: "There is among you, in Israel, One Whom you, do not know. His winnowing-fan is already in His hand and He will clear His threshing-floor and He will burn the chaff in a fire that will never go out". I had in front of me a young man of the common people, whose countenance was mild and humble, and yet I felt that He was the One, Whose sandal-straps not even the Holy One in Israel, the last Prophet, the Precursor was fit to undo. I felt that He was the One, Whom we did not know. But I was not afraid. On the contrary, when John, after the enrapturing thunder of God and after the unimaginable brightness of the Light in the shape of a dove of peace, said: "Here is the Lamb of God", I cried: "I believe!" with the voice of my soul, rejoicing because I had foreseen the King Messiah in the young man who looked so mild and humble. Because of this faith I am His servant. Be so yourselves, and you will have peace. *
324.5 [5]Matthew, it is your turn now to narrate the other glories of the Lord.»

«I cannot use the same serene words of Andrew. He was a just man, I was a sinner. Therefore my word has not the joyful note of happiness, but it has the confident peace of a psalm. I was a sinner. A great sinner. I was living in complete error. I had hardened

* **I am His servant**. The recalling of the apostle Andrew is completed with the explanation given by Jesus in 49.9.

in it and I felt no discomfort. If at times the Pharisees or the head of the synagogue lashed me with their insults and reproaches, reminding me of God, the inexorable Judge, I was terrified for a moment... then I would relax thinking foolishly: "In any case I am as good as damned. Let me have a good time, therefore, as long as I can". And I sank deeper and deeper into sin. Two years ago an Unknown man came to Capernaum in springtime. He was unknown also to me. He was in fact unknown to everybody, because He was at the beginning of His mission. Only a few men knew who He really was: those whom you see here, and few more. I was greatly surprised at His demeanour, which was more chaste than a virgin's. That was the first thing that amazed me. I saw that He was austere and yet He was always willing to listen to the children who went to Him as bees fly to flowers. Their innocent games and ingenious words were His only relaxation. Then His power amazed me. He worked miracles. I said: "He is an exorciser, a holy man". I felt that I was so disgraceful as compared to Him, that I shunned Him. He was looking for me. Or that was what I thought. Every time He passed near my bench He would look at me with His kind but rather sad eyes. And every time I felt my torpid conscience start and it never fell back to the same level of torpor. One day, as people exalted His words, I felt like listening to Him. And hiding behind the corner of a house I heard Him speak to a little group of men. He spoke informally, on charity, which is like an indulgence with regards to our sins... As from that evening, I, the greedy hard-hearted man, wanted my many sins to be forgiven by God. I did things secretly... But He knew that it was I, because He knows everything. Once I heard Him explain just chapter 52 of Isaiah: He said that the lewd and those whose hearts are not circumcised will not enter His Kingdom, the heavenly Jerusalem, and He promised that that Celestial City, the beauty of which He described so convincingly that I felt nostalgia for it, would belong to those who went to Him. And then... Oh! On that day His look was not a sad one, but a commanding one. He broke my heart, He stripped my soul, He cauterised this poor soul of mine, He took it in His hands and tortured it with His exacting love... and I had a new soul. Repentance and desire led me towards Him. He did not wait for me to say: "Have mercy, my Lord!". He said to me: "Follow Me!".

The Mild One had defeated Satan in the sinner's heart. May this tell you, if anyone among you is worried because of his sins, that He is the good Saviour and that you must not shun Him, on the contrary, the more one is a sinner, the more one must go to Him
324.6 with humility and repentance, in order to be forgiven. [6]James of Zebedee, will you speak now?»

«I do not really know what to say. You have spoken and said what I would have said. Because that is the truth and it cannot be changed. I was with Andrew at the Jordan as well, but I only noticed Him when He was pointed out by the Baptist. But I believed at once, and when He left, after His bright manifestation, I was like one who after being on a sunny mountain top, is imprisoned in a dark jail. I was longing to find the Sun again. The world was dark, after the Light of God had appeared to me, and then had disappeared. I was alone among men. I had satisfied my appetite, but I was hungry. While sleeping I was awake with my better part, and money, business, affections, everything had been left far behind my great desire for Him and nothing allured me. Like a child who has lost his mother I moaned: "Come back, Lamb of the Lord! Most High Lord, as You sent Raphael to guide Tobias, * send Your angel to lead me to the way of the Lord, that I may find Him...!". And yet, when He appeared on the path coming from the desert, after we had been waiting for Him in vain for weeks, and we had been looking for Him anxiously, which vain efforts made us feel more sorely the loss of our John who had been arrested for the first time, I did not recognise Him at once. And now, my brothers in the Lord, I want to teach you another way to go to Him and recognise Him. Simon of Jonah said that faith and humility are required to know Him. Simon Zealot has confirmed the absolute necessity of Faith to acknowledge in Jesus of Nazareth what He is in Heaven and on the earth, according to what has been said. And Simon Zealot needed a truly great * faith, also on behalf of his incurable body. That is why Simon Zealot says that Faith and Hope are the means to attain the Son of God. James, the brother of the Lord, has mentioned the power of Strength to keep what has been found. The Strength that prevents the snares of the world and of Satan from undermining our

* **Raphael**, is the angel who revealed himself to Tobias in *Tobit 5:4; 12:15*.
* **what has been said**, in: *Exodus 3:14*.

Faith. Andrew has shown the necessity of joining a holy thirst for Justice to Faith, endeavouring to know and maintain the Truth, whatever be the holy mouth announcing it, not out of human pride to be learned, but out of desire to know God. The man who improves his mind in the Truth will find God. Matthew, once a sinner, has pointed out to you another way to attain God: to divest oneself of sensuality out of spirit of imitation, I would say by reflection of God, Who is infinite Purity. The first thing that impressed him, a sinner, was the "chaste demeanour" of the Unknown man who had come to Capernaum, and as if it had the power to revive his dead continence, he refrains first of all from sensual carnality, clearing the way for the coming of God and for the resurrection of the other dead virtues. From continence he passes on to mercy, from mercy to contrition, he then surpasses himself and arrives at union with God. "Follow Me". "I am coming". But his soul had already said: "I am coming", and the Saviour had already said: "Follow Me", when for the first time the Virtue of the Master had drawn the attention of the sinner. Imitate him. Because the experience of other people, even if painful, is a guide to avoid evil and find good for those who are of goodwill. As far as I am concerned, I say that the more man strives to live for the spirit, the more fit he is to recognise the Lord, and an angelic life favours that in the highest degree. Of us disciples of John, he who recognised him, after His absence, was the virgin soul. Better than Andrew, he recognised Him, notwithstanding penance had altered the visage of the Lamb of God. So I say: "Be
chaste to be able to recognise Him". [7]Judas, will you speak now?» 324.7

«Yes, be chaste to be able to recognise Him. But be chaste also to be able to keep Him within you with His Wisdom and His Love, with His whole Self. It is still Isaiah who in chapter 52 says: "Touch nothing unclean,... purify yourselves, you who carry the vessels of the Lord". Really, every soul that becomes His disciple is like a jar full of the Lord, and the body containing the soul is like one who carries the sacred jar to the Lord. God cannot be where there is impurity. Matthew told you how the Lord explained that nothing unclean or separated from God will be in the celestial Jerusalem. Yes. But it is necessary not to be unclean or separated from God, to be able to enter it. Wretched are those people who wait until the last hour to repent. They will

not always have time to do so. Likewise those who now slander Him will have no time to make amends at the moment of His triumph, and therefore will not enjoy its fruit. Those who in the holy humble King hope to see an earthly monarch, and even more those who are afraid to see in Him an earthly monarch, will not be prepared for that hour; deceived and disappointed in their thoughts, which are not the thoughts of God, but poor human thoughts, they will sin even more. The humiliation of being the Man is upon Him. We must remember that. Isaiah says that all our sins mortify the Divine Person under common appearance. When I consider that the Word of God has around Himself, like a filthy crust, all the misery of mankind since it began to exist, I think with deep compassion and understanding of the suffering that His faultless soul must endure. The horror of a healthy man who was covered with the rags and filth of a leper. He is really pierced by our sins, and covered with sores by man's lust. His soul, living among us, must shudder with horror at such contact, as a body trembles with a high temperature. And yet He does not speak. He does not open His mouth to say: "You horrify Me". But He opens it only to say: "Come to Me, that I may take away your sins". He is the Saviour. In His infinite bounty He veiled His unbearable beauty. If He had appeared in all His beauty, as He is in Heaven, He would have reduced us to ashes, as Andrew said. But His beauty has become engaging, like a mild Lamb, in order to approach us and save us. His oppression, His condemnation will last until, consumed by the effort of being the perfect Man among imperfect men, He is raised above the multitude of those He has redeemed, in the triumph of His holy regality. God Who submits to death, to take us to Life! May these thoughts make you love Him above all things. He is the Holy One. I can say so, as I was brought up with Him, together with James. And I say and will say so, ready to give my life to confirm this profession,
324.8 so that men may believe in Him and have eternal Life. [8]John of
Zebedee, it is your turn to speak.»

«How beautiful on the mountains are the feet of the messen- *
ger! Of the Messenger of peace, Who announces happiness and

* **How beautiful...** a quotation from *Isaiah 52:7*. The speeches of the eight apostoles are, almost all of them, based on chapter 52 of the book of the prophet Isaiah.

preaches salvation, Who says to Zion: "Your God is King!". And those feet have been walking untiringly for two years across the mountains in Israel, gathering the sheep of the herd of God, consoling, curing, forgiving, giving peace. His peace. I am really surprised at seeing that the hills and rivers of our Fatherland do not exult and rejoice at the caress of His feet. But what amazes me most is to see that the hearts of men do not exult or rejoice saying: "Praised be the Lord! The Expected One has come! Blessed be He Who comes in the name of the Lord!". He Who bestows graces and blessings, peace and health, and calls us to His Kingdom opening the way for us, above all He Who pours forth love with every action of His, with every word, glance, breath... What is therefore this world as to be blind to the Light that is living among us? Which slabs, thicker than the stone closing the entrance of a sepulchre, has it placed on the sight of its soul not to see this Light? What mountain of sins has it on itself to be so oppressed, separated, blinded, deafened, chained, paralyzed as to stand inert before the Saviour? What is the Saviour? He is Light blended with Love. The mouths of my brothers have praised the Lord, they have recalled His works, and have pointed out the virtues to be put into practice in order to reach His way. I say to you: love. There is no other virtue that is greater or more like His Nature. If you love, you will practise every virtue without difficulty, beginning from chastity. It will be no burden to you to be chaste, because by loving Jesus you will love no one immoderately. You will be humble, because with the eyes of lovers you will see infinite perfections in Him, and thus you will not pride yourselves on your scanty ones. And you will believe. Who does not believe in him whom one loves? You will be contrite with sorrow that saves, because your sorrow will be honest, that is, you will be sorry for the pain you have caused Him, not for the pain deserved by you. And you will be strong. Oh! yes! When one is united to Jesus, one is strong! Strong against everything. You will be full of hope, because you will not doubt the Heart that loves you with His whole Self. And you will be wise. You will be everything. Love Him Who announces true happiness, Who preaches salvation, Who goes across mountains and valleys tirelessly, gathering the herd, on Whose way there is Peace, as there is peace in His Kingdom, which is not of this world, but it is true as God is true. Flee from any direction that is not His. Get rid of all fog. Go to the Light. Do not be like the world, which does not want to see the Light, which does not want to know it. But go to our Father, Who is the Father of lights, Who is infinite Light, go to Him through His Son, Who is the Light of the world, to enjoy God in the embrace of the Paraclete, Who is the brightness of the Lights in one only beatitude of love that concentrates the Three into One. Infinite ocean of Love, without storms, without darkness, do receive us! All of us! Both those who are innocent and those who have repented. All of us! In Your Peace, forever! All of us! Everybody on the earth, that we may love You, God, and our neighbour, as You want. Everybody, in Heaven, that we may still and always love but You and the celestial inhabitants, that we may love also our brothers militant on the earth in expectation of peace, and like angels of love, we may defend them and support them in their struggles and temptations, so that they may be with You in Your Peace, for the eternal glory of our Lord Jesus, the Saviour, the Lover of man, until the limitless limit of sublime annihilation.»

324.9 [9] As usual, John soaring in his flights of love, draws with him souls where there is refined love and mystic silence.

Only after some time the listeners begin to speak. And Philip is the first, addressing Peter: «Is John, the teacher, not speaking?»

«He will always be speaking to you. Leave him now in his peace and let us be alone with him for a little while. Saba, do what I told you, and you as well, O good Berenice...»

324.10 [10] They all go out and only the eight apostles and two disciples are left in the large room. There is grave silence. They all look rather pale, the apostles because they know what is about to happen, and the two disciples because they foresee it.

Peter opens his mouth to speak, but finds only these words: «Let us pray», and he begins the «Our Father». Then, and he is really so pale that he will probably not look like this when he dies, he says, going between the two and laying his hands on their shoulders: «We now have to part, my children. What shall I say to the Lord on your behalf? He will certainly be anxious to hear about your spiritual state.»

Syntyche falls on her knees covering her face with her hands and John imitates her. Peter has them at his feet and he instinctively caresses them biting his lips not to yield to emotion.

John looks up, his face is heart-rending, and says: «You will tell the Master that we are doing His Will...» And Syntyche: «And ask Him to help us to fulfil it until the end...» Tears prevent longer sentences.

«All right. Let us kiss one another goodbye. This hour was to come...» also Peter stops speaking, choked by a lump in his throat.

«Bless us first» begs Syntyche.

«No. Not I. Better one of Jesus' brothers...»

«No. You are the head. We shall bless with our kisses. Bless us all, both us who are leaving, and them, who are staying» says Thaddeus, and he is the first to kneel down.

And Peter, poor Peter, who is flushed both because of the effort to steady his voice, and by the excitement of stretching out his hands to bless the little group prostrated at his feet, repeats
* the Mosaic blessing, in a voice made harsher by weeping, almost the voice of an old man...

He then bends forward, kisses the forehead of the woman, as if she were his sister, lifts up and embraces John, kissing his cheek... and runs bravely out of the room, while the others imitate his gesture with the two who are staying...

The cart is ready outside. Only Philip and Berenice are present, and the servant who is holding the horse. Peter is already on the cart...

«You will tell the master not to worry about those he recommended» says Philip to Peter.

«Tell Mary that I feel the peace of Eucheria since she has become a disciple» says Berenice to the Zealot in a low voice.

«Tell the Master, Mary, everybody, that we love them, and that... Goodbye! Goodbye! Oh! We will never see them again! Goodbye, brothers! Goodbye...»

The two disciples run out into the street... But the cart which left at a trot, has already gone round the corner... Disappeared...

«Syntyche!»

«John!»

«We are alone!»

---

* **the Mosaic blessing**, as in *Numbers 6:22-27*. The formula is also used in chapters 108.6; 363.3; 397.4.

«God is with us!... Come, poor John. The sun is setting, it will do you no good to stay here...»

«The sun has set forever, as far as I am concerned... Only in Heaven it will rise again.»

And they go back to the room where they were before with the others. They lean on a table, weeping without restraint...

324.11 [11] Jesus says:

«And the torture brought about by a man, wanted only by a wicked man, was accomplished, stopping as a river stops in a lake after completing its course. I wish to point out to you how also Judas of Alphaeus, although more nourished with wisdom than the others, explains the passage of Isaiah, dealing with My sufferings as Redeemer, in a human way. And everybody in Israel did the same, as they refused to accept the prophetic reality and they contemplated the prophecies on My sorrows as allegories and symbols. The grave error whereby in the hour of Redemption only very few people were able to still see the Messiah in the Convict. Faith is not only a wreath of flowers. It contains also thorns. And he is holy who believes both in the hours of glory and in those of tragedy, and loves God whether He covers him with flowers or lays him on thorns.»

325. The Eight Apostles Join Jesus in Achzib.

10th November 1945.

325.1 [1] Jesus, Who is so pale, thin and sad that I would say that He must be suffering, is on the highest point of a little mountain, where there is also a village. But Jesus is not in the village, which although on the mountain top, stretches down the south-east slope. Jesus instead is on a little spur, on the highest point, facing north-west; actually more west than north. *

The place is like this:

* **actually more west than north**. The sketch by M.V. follows the text line: *The place is like this:* 1. *Mediterranean Sea;* 2. *Ptolemais;* 3. *Sicaminon;* 4. *Kishon;* 5. *Carmel*; 6. *Achzib*; 7. *Jiphthahel must be here about.* Also the four main points are marked.

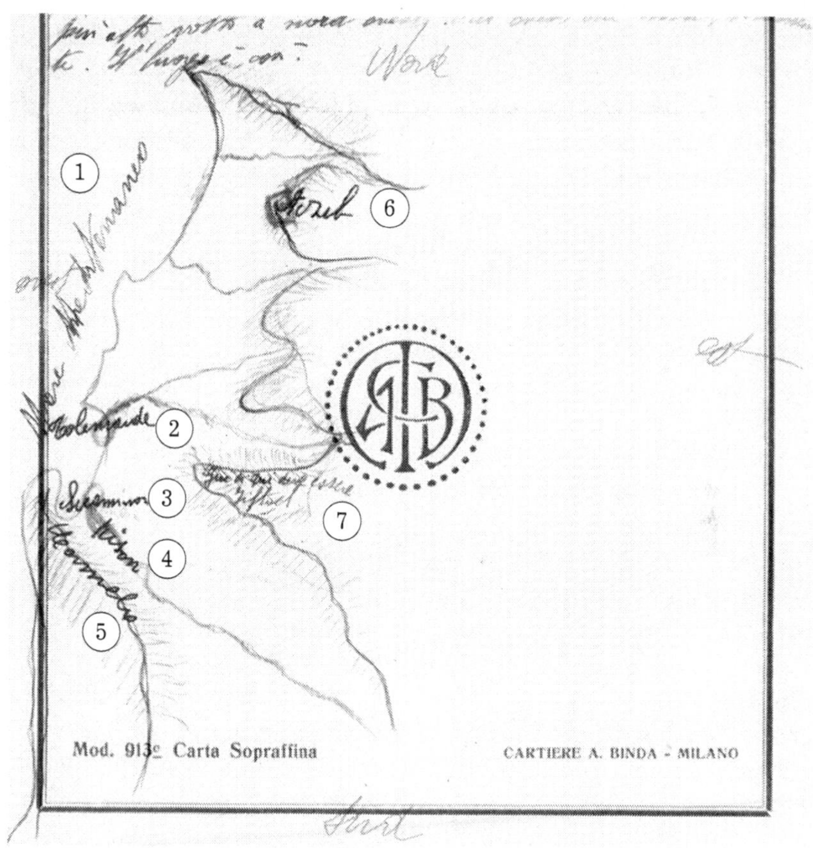

As Jesus is looking in various directions, He can see an undulating chain of mountains the extreme north-west and south-west ends of which jut out into the sea, to the south-west with Mount Carmel, which fades away in the clear day, to the north-west with a sharp cape, similar to the ram of a ship, very much like our Apuanian Mountains particularly in respect of white rocky veins shining in the sunshine. Torrents and streams, all very full of water at this time of the year, descend from this undulated chain of mountains and across the plain along the coast they flow into the sea. The river Kishon, the most important of all of them, flows into the sea near the wide bay of Sicaminon, after forming a sheet of water at the confluence with another little stream near its mouth. The water of the streams glitter like topazes or sapphires in the midday sunshine of a clear day, while the sea looks like a huge sapphire veined with light strings of pearls.

Springtime in the south is already beginning to appear through the new leaves bursting from the open buds, tender shiny leaves, so fresh that I would call them virginal, unaware of dust, of storms, of bites of insects and of the contact of men. And the branches of almond-trees are already tufts of white pinkish foam, so soft and ethereal that they seem to be on the point of flying away from their native branches to sail like little clouds in the serene air. Also the fields in the plain, which is fertile although not large, delimited by the north-west and south-west capes, are verdant with corn, which makes them a pleasant sight, whereas shortly before they were bare.

Jesus is looking. Three roads can be seen from where He stands. One comes from the village and ends where He is: a narrow road suitable only for pedestrians and two other roadways, which descend from the village forking in opposite directions, towards north-west and south-west.

How sick Jesus looks! There are more traces of penance on His face now than when He fasted in the desert. He had then grown pale, but He was still young and vigorous. He is now worn out by complex suffering that crushes both physical and moral strength. His eyes are sad, sweetly and severely sad at the same time. His thin cheeks enhance even more the spirituality of His profile, of His high forehead, long straight nose and lips absolutely devoid of sensuality. An angelical face excluding all materiality. His beard is longer than usual and has grown on His cheeks mixed together with His long hair, which hangs down over His ears, so that of His face only His forehead, eyes, nose and His thin cheek-bones as pale as ivory without the least hint of colour can be seen. His hair is ruffled and dull and as a souvenir of the cave in which He has been, there are little parts of dry leaves and twigs entangled in it. His creased dusty tunic and mantle also bear witness to the wild place in which they were worn without ever being changed.

325.2 [2] Jesus is looking around... The midday sunshine is warming Him and He seems to enjoy it because He avoids the shade of some oak-trees to stand in the sunshine, but although the sun is bright and clear it does not enliven His dusty hair or His tired eyes; neither does it tinge His emaciated face.

It is not the sun that restores or brightens Him up, but it is the sight of His dear apostles who are coming up gesticulating and looking towards the village from the north-west road, the less steep one. His metamorphosis then takes place. His eyes brighten up and His face seems to become less emaciated because of a rosy nuance that spreads over His cheeks and above all because His smile lights it up. He stretches out His arms, which were folded, and exclaims: «My dear ones!». He says so raising His face, casting His eyes around, as if He wanted to communicate His joy to stalks and plants, to the clear sky, to the air, which already smells of springtime. He gathers His mantles around His body so that it may not get caught in the bushes and He runs down along a short cut to meet the apostles who are coming up, but have not yet seen Him. When He is within hearing range He calls them, to stop them going towards the village.

They hear the distant call but perhaps from the spot where they are they cannot see Jesus, Whose dark mantle blends with the darkness of the wood that covers the slope. They look around gesticulating... Jesus calls them again... At last a clearing in the wood shows Him to them, in the sunshine, with His arms stretched out, as if He already wanted to embrace them. Then a loud cry re-echoes along the coast: «The Master!» and they start running up the crags, leaving the road, scratching themselves, stumbling, panting, without feeling the weight of their sacks or the difficulty in climbing... urged as they are by the joy of seeing Him again.

[3] The younger and more agile ones are naturally the first to 325.3
reach Him, that is, Alphaeus' sons, as they proceed with the steady steps of people who live among hills, and John and Andrew, who run as fast as fawns, laughing happily. And they fall at His feet lovingly and reverently, beaming with happiness... Then James of Zebedee arrives and next the ones who are less experienced in races and mountains, Matthew and the Zealot who arrive almost together, and last... Peter.

But he elbows his way through the group in no uncertain manner to reach the Master, Whose legs have been embraced by the first arrivals who are still kissing His mantle or His hands. He grasps John and Andrew who are clinging to Jesus' garments

like oysters to a rock, and panting because of the exertion, he pushes them aside so that he can fall at Jesus' feet saying: «Oh! My Master! I am now back to life, at last! I could not bear it any longer. I have grown old and thin as if I had been seriously ill. Look whether it is true, Master...» and he raises his head to be looked at by Jesus. But in doing so he sees the change in Jesus and he stands up shouting: «Master!? But what have You done? How foolish we are! Just look! Can't you see anything? Jesus has been
325.4 ill!... [4]Master of mine, what happened to you? Tell Your Simon!»

«Nothing, My friend.»

«Nothing? With that face? Then someone has hurt You?»

«No, Simon.»

«It's not possible. You have either been ill or persecuted! I have eyes to see!...»

«So have I. And I see that in fact you have grown old and thin. So, why are you so?» the Lord asks, smiling at Peter who is scanning Him as if he wanted to find out the truth from Jesus' hair, skin, beard...

«But I have suffered! And I do not deny it. Do You think it was pleasant to see so much grief?»

«You have said it! I also suffered for the same reason...»

«Just for that, Jesus?» asks Judas of Alphaeus with so much pity and love.

«Yes, because of that grief, My brother. Because of the grief caused by the necessity to send away...»

«And by the grief of being compelled by...»

«Please!... Be silent! Silence on My injury is dearer to Me than any word uttered to console Me, saying: "I know why You have suffered". In any case, you may all know, that I suffered for *many* reasons, not just for that one. And had Judas not interrupted Me, I would have told you.» Jesus is austere in saying so. They are all subdued.

But Peter is the first to collect himself and he asks: «But where have You been, Master? And what have You done?»

«I was in a grotto... praying... meditating... fortifying My spirit, obtaining strength for you in your mission, and for John and Syntyche in their suffering.»

«But where? Without clothes, without money! How did You manage?» Simon is excited.

«In a grotto I did not need anything.»

«But what about food, fire, a bed, everything... I mean! I was hoping that You would be a guest, like a lost pilgrim, at Jiphthahel, or elsewhere, in a house, I mean. And that gave me some peace. But... eh?! Tell Him whether I was tormented by the thought that He was without clothes, without food, without the possibility of getting any, and above all, without the will of getting it. Ah! Jesus! You should not have done that! And You will *never* do it again! I will not leave You for one hour. I will sew my tunic to Yours, so that I can follow You like a shadow, whether You like it or not. I will part from You only if I die.»

«Or if I die.»

«Oh! not You. You must not die before me. Don't say that. Do You really want to break my heart?»

«No. On the contrary I want to rejoice with you and with everybody in this lovely hour that brings My dearest friends back to Me. See! I am already feeling better because your sincere love nourishes, warms and consoles Me in everything» and He caresses them one by one, while their faces shine with happy smiles, their eyes sparkle with joy and their lips tremble with emotion at those words, and they ask: «Really, Lord?», «Is that so, Master?», «Are we so dear to You?»

«Yes. So dear. [5]Have you any food with you?» 325.5

«Yes. I was sure that You would be exhausted and I got some on the way. I have bread and roast meat, milk, cheese and apples; and a flask of generous wine and some eggs for You. Providing they are not broken...»

«Well, let us sit down here, in this lovely sunshine, and eat. While eating you can tell Me...»

They sit in the sun on a terrace and Peter opens his sack and examines his treasure: «Everything is all right» he exclaims. «Also the honey from Antigonea. Well! Didn't I tell you! On our way back, if they had put us in a barrel and had got a madman to roll it, or if they had put us in a boat without oars, even if the boat leaked, and there was a storm, we would have come back safe and sound... But going there... The more I think of it the more convinced I am that the demon was interfering with us. To prevent us from going with those two poor wretches...»

«Of course! On our way back there was no purpose...» confirms the Zealot.

«Master, did You do penance for us?» asks John, who is so intent in contemplating Jesus that he forgets to eat.

«Yes, John. My thought followed you. I perceived your dangers and your affliction. I helped you as I could...»

«Oh! I felt it! I even told you. Do you remember?»

«Yes. It is true» they all confirm.

«Well, you are now giving back to Me what I gave you.»

«Did You fast, Lord?» asks Andrew.

«Of course He did! Even if He wanted to eat, as He was without money, in a cave, how could you expect Him to get food?» replies Peter.

«All for our sake! How sorry I am!» says James of Alphaeus.

«Oh! no! Do not worry! I did not do it for you only, but for the
325.6 whole world as well. [6]As I did when I began My mission, so I did now. Then, at the end, I was assisted by angels. I am assisted by you now. And believe Me, it is a double joy to Me. Because the ministry of charity is unbreakable by angels. But it is not so easily found among men. You are practising it. And from men, for My sake, you have become angels having chosen to be holy at all costs. You therefore make Me happy, both as God and as Man-God. Because you give Me what comes from God: Charity, and you give Me what pertains to the Redeemer: your elevation to Perfection. That is what comes from you and it is more nourishing than any food. Also then, in the desert, I was nourished with love after fasting. And it restored Me. And what happened then is happening now! We have all suffered. Both you and I. But not in vain. I think, I know that it has helped you more than a full year of teaching. Sorrow, meditation on the harm man can do to his neighbour, the piety, faith, hope, charity you had to practise, all by yourselves, have matured you like children who become men...»

«Oh! yes! I have grown old, I have indeed. I will never again be the same Simon of Jonah as I was when I left. I have understood how sorrowful, how toilsome is our mission, notwithstanding all its beauty...» says Peter with a sigh.

325.7 «Well, we are all together now. [7]Tell Me...»

«Speak, Simon. You can speak better than I can» says Peter to the Zealot.

«No. As a good leader you must speak on behalf of everybody» replies the other.

And Peter begins, stating as a preliminary introduction: «But help me.» He recounts everything in good order until the departure from Antioch. He then begins to speak of their return: «We were all grieved, as You can readily understand. I will never forget the last words of those two...» With the back of his hand Peter wipes two big tears streaming down his cheeks... «They sounded like the last cry of someone drowning... Listen... you had better go on... I cannot... » and he gets up and goes away to control his emotion.

Simon Zealot continues: «None of us spoke for a long while... We could not... We had a lump in our throats, which were aching... And we did not want to weep... because if one of us had begun, it would have been the end... I had taken the reins, because Simon of Jonah, to conceal his sorrowful state, had gone to the end of the cart pretending to search for something in the sacks. We stopped at a little village half way between Antioch and Seleucia. Although moonlight became brighter and brighter as night became darker, we stopped there, because we were not familiar with the roads. And we dozed there, lying on our belongings. None of us would eat... because we could not. We were thinking of those two... At daybreak we crossed the bridge and before the third hour we were at Seleucia. We took the horse and cart back to the hotel-keeper and since he was such a kind man, we asked his advice with regard to the ship. He said: "I will come to the port with you. I know people and they know me". And that is what he did. He found three boats leaving for ports in this area. But on one there were some... queer fellows, who we did not want to be with. Our man told us, as he had heard of them from the owner of the boat. The second one was from Ashkelon and they refused to call at Tyre, unless we paid a sum of money that we could not afford. The third one was a really poor little boat, with a load of timber. A poor boat, with few hands and I think with a great deal of misery. That is why they agreed to call at Tyre, although they were heading for Caesarea, providing we paid for one day's meals and wages for the whole crew. It suited us. Actually both Matthew and I were somewhat worried. There are storms at this time of the year... and You know what happened on our way there. But Simon Peter said: "Nothing will happen". So we went on board. The boat sailed so smoothly and fast that angels seemed to be acting as sails. We reached Tyre in only half of the time which had taken us to get there and when we arrived the owner of the boat was so kind that he agreed to tow our boat until we were near Ptolemais. Peter, Andrew and John had gone into it to handle it... But it was very easy... Nothing like our outward voyage. At Ptolemais we parted. And we were so pleased that before getting into our boat where all our things were, we gave him more money than we had agreed upon. We stopped one day at Ptolemais, and then we came here... But we will never forget what we suffered. Simon of Jonah is right.»

«And are we not right also in saying that the demon interfered with us only on our outward voyage?» some of the apostles ask.

325.8 «You are right. [8]Now listen. Your mission is over. We shall now go towards Jiphthahel, waiting for Philip and Nathanael. And we must do that at once. Then the others will come... In the meantime we shall evangelize here, at the borders of Phoenicia and in Phoenicia itself. But what has recently happened is to be buried in your hearts *forever*. You shall not reply to anybody enquiring about it.»

«Not even to Philip and Nathanael? They know that we came with You...»

«I will speak to them. I have suffered very much, My dear friends, as you have seen yourselves. With My suffering I paid for John's and Syntyche's peace. Do not let My suffering be useless. Do not overburden My shoulders with another weight. I have already so many!... And their weight becomes heavier day by day, hour by hour... Tell Nathanael that I have suffered very much. Tell Philip, and tell them to be good. Tell the other two. If you tell them that you have understood that I have suffered, and that I confirmed it, you are telling them the truth. Nothing else is needed.»

Jesus is speaking wearily... The eight look at Him sorrowfully, and Peter dares to caress His head, standing behind His back. Jesus raises His head and looks at His honest Peter with a sad loving smile.

«Oh! I cannot bear to see You like that! It seems... I feel that the joy of our reunion is over and that only its holiness is left!

Well... Let us go to Achzib. You will change Your clothes, shave Your cheeks and tidy Your hair. You cannot stay like that! I cannot bear to see You like that... You look like one... who has escaped from cruel hands, like one who has been beaten, or is exhausted... You look like Abel* of Bethlehem in Galilee, freed from his enemies...»

«Yes, Peter. But it is the heart of your Master that has been ill-treated... and it will never recover again... On the contrary it will be hurt more and more. Let us go...»

[9] John sighs: «I am sorry... I would have liked to inform Thomas, who is so fond of Your Mother, of the miracle of the song and of the ointment...» 325.9

«You will tell him one day... Not now. One day you will tell everything. You will then be allowed to speak. I Myself will say to you: "Go and tell everything you know". In the meantime see the truth in the miracle. That is: the power of Faith. John and Syntyche calmed the sea and cured the man not by means of words or of the ointment. But through the faith with which they mentioned the Name of Mary and made use of Her ointment. And also because your faith was there as well, and your charity. Charity towards the injured man. Charity towards the Cretan. You saved the life of the former and tried to give faith to the latter. But if it is easy to cure bodies, it is very difficult to cure souls... There is no disease more difficult to wipe out than a spiritual one...» and Jesus gives a deep sigh.

They are within sight of Achzib. Peter goes ahead with Matthew looking for lodgings. The others follow gathered around Jesus. The sun sets fast, while they enter the village...

326. A Stop in Achzib with Six Apostles.

11th November 1945.

[1] «Lord, during the night I was thinking... Why do You want to come so far, and then return to the Phoenician border? Let me go with one of my companions. I will sell Antonius... I regret having to do it... but, we do not need it anymore and it would attract 326.1

* **Abel**, the young protagonist of the episode narrated in 248.5/11.

people's notice. And I will go and meet Philip and Bartholomew. They can only come along *that* road and I shall certainly meet them. And You may rest assured that I will *not* speak. I do not wish to grieve You... You can rest here with the others and it will save us all going all the way to Jiphthahel... and we will save time» says Peter while coming out of the house where they slept. And they look less haggard, as they are wearing clean clothes and their beards and hair have been dressed by skilful hands.

«It is a good idea. I will not stop you. You may go with whichever companion you wish.»

«With Simon, then. Bless us, O Lord.»

Jesus embraces them saying: «With a kiss. Go.»

They watch them descend quickly towards the plain.

«How good Simon of Jonah is! During the past days I have appreciated him as I had never done before» says Judas Thaddeus.

«So did I» says Matthew. «He is never selfish, proud or exacting!»

«He has never taken advantage of the fact that he was our head. On the contrary, he seemed to be the last one, still maintaining his position» adds James of Alphaeus.

«We are not surprised. We have known him for years. He is hot tempered but very kind-hearted. And so honest!» says James of Zebedee.

«My brother is good, even if he is coarse. But since he has been with Jesus, he has become twice as good. My nature is entirely different and sometimes it made him angry, because he knew that I was suffering because of my character. He got angry because he was fond of me. When one understands him, one gets along with him very well» says Andrew.

326.2 [2] «During the past days we have always understood one another and we have always been of one mind» states John.

«That's true! I noticed that myself. During the whole month, even in moments of excitement, we have never been at variance among ourselves... Whereas sometimes... I don't know why...» monologises James of Zebedee.

«Why? But it is easily understood! Because we are righteous in our intentions. We are not perfect; but we are righteous. We therefore accept the good which one proposes and we reject the evil which is pointed out to us as such, whereas previously we had not realized that by ourselves. Why? It is easily said! Because the eight of us are of the same mind: to do things in such a way as to please Jesus. That's all!» exclaims Thaddeus.

«I do not think that the others are of a different mind» says Andrew in a conciliatory tone.

«No. Neither Philip nor Bartholomew, although the latter is rather elderly and *very much* an Israelite... Neither is Thomas although he is inclined to be much more human than spiritual. I would do them wrong, should I accuse them of... Jesus, You are right. Forgive me. But if You knew what it means to me to see You suffer! And because of him! I am Your disciple, like all the rest. But over and above I am Your brother and friend and I have Alphaeus' fiery blood in my veins. Jesus, don't look at me so severely or so sadly. You are the Lamb and I... the lion. And believe me, I find it hard to refrain from tearing with a blow of my paw the network of slander that is enveloping You and from knocking down the shelter in which the true enemy is hiding. I would like to see the real side of his spiritual face, which I call... and perhaps it is calumny; and if I could identify him without the least fear of error, I would mark him in such a way that for the rest of his life he would not dream of hurting You» says Thaddeus passionately, although Jesus had cast a glance at him to stop him, when he began to speak.

James of Zebedee replies to him: «You would have to mark half of the people in Israel!... But Jesus will proceed just the same. During the past days you have seen whether anything can stop Jesus. What shall we do now, Master? Have You spoken here?»

«No. I have not been on these slopes one day yet. I slept in the wood.»

«Why did they not want You?»

«Their hearts rejected the Pilgrim... I was penniless...»

«They are hard-hearted then! What were they afraid of?»

«That I might be a highwayman... But it does not matter. The Father Who is in Heaven made Me meet up with a goat, which was either lost or had run away. Come, I will show her to you. She lives in the thicket with her kid. But she did not run away when she saw Me arrive. On the contrary, she let Me milk her... into My mouth, as if I were her little one, too. And I slept near her, with the little kid almost on My heart. God is good to His Word!»

They go towards the place where they met yesterday, a thorny thicket. In the middle there is an age-old oak tree, surviving I know not how, split as it is, as if the ground had opened breaking apart its robust trunk, all covered with green ivy and bramble bare of leaves at present. The goat is grazing nearby with her little kid and seeing so many men she levels her horns ready to defend herself. But she soon recognises Jesus and calms down. They throw some bread crusts to her and withdraw.

«I slept over there» explains Jesus. «And I would have stayed here, if you had not come. I was hungry. The purpose in fasting was over... And it was not necessary to insist on other things that can no longer be changed...»

Jesus is sad once again.... The six cast sidelong glances at one another, but do not say anything.

«And now? Where are we going?»

«We shall stay here today. Tomorrow we will go down and preach on the road to Ptolemais and then we will go towards the Phoenician border and come back here before the Sabbath.»

And they slowly return to the village.

327. Evangelizing at the Border of Phoenicia. A Sermon on the Common Origin of Peoples and Races.

[No date].

327.1 [1]The road coming from Phoenicia towards Ptolemais is a beautiful road which cuts straight across the plain between the sea and the mountains. Because it is well kept, it is very busy. There are various junctions with secondary roads running from inland towns to towns on the coast, and at the numerous crossroads there is generally a house, a well and a rudimentary forge for quadrupeds that may need shoes.

Jesus, with the six apostles left with Him, covers a good stretch of the road, about two kilometres, seeing the same things all the time. He stops at last near one of those houses with a well and a farriery, at a crossroad near a torrent crossed by a bridge, which although strongly built, is just wide enough to let one cart pass at a time and thus travellers are compelled to stop alternately, because the two opposite currents of traffic cannot pass at the same time. And as far as I can see, that gives the travellers of different races, Phoenicians and true Israelites, the opportunity to join in the same objective: that of cursing Rome, although they hate one another... And yet, without Rome, they would not have that bridge and when the torrent is in flood I do not know how they would be able to cross it. But such is life! An oppressor is always hated, even if he does useful things!

Jesus stops near the bridge, in the sunny corner where the house is; on its side along the torrent there is an ill-smelling smithy shop, where they are forging shoes for a horse and two donkeys that have lost theirs. The horse is harnessed to a Roman wagon in which some soldiers take delight in making faces at the cursing Jews. And they throw a handful of horse manure on an old big-nosed man, the most rancorous of all of them, with a real viperous mouth, someone who I think would willingly bite the Romans to poison them. One can imagine what happens! The old Jew runs away as if he had been infected with leprosy and other Jews join him. The Phoenicians shout ironically: «Do you like the new manna? Eat it, it will give you energy to shout against those who are too good to you, you hypocritical vipers!» The soldiers laugh scornfully... Jesus is silent.

The Roman wagon at last departs and they greet the farrier shouting: «Hail, Titus, may your stay be prosperous!» The man, who is vigorous, elderly, bull-necked, clean shaven with very dark eyes above a sturdy nose and under a wide protruding forehead, which is bald at the temples while his hair is short and frizzly, raises a heavy hammer waving them goodbye and then goes back to the anvil, on which a young man had laid a red-hot iron, while another boy sears the hoof of a little donkey preparing it to be shod.

[2] «Almost all the farriers along the roads are Romans. Soldiers who remained here when they finished their service. And they earn a lot of money... Nothing ever prevents them from curing animals... And a donkey may lose a shoe before sunset on a Sabbath, or at the time of the Dedication...» remarks Matthew. 327.2

«The man who shod Antonius was married to a Jewish woman» says John.

«There are more foolish women than wise ones» states James of Zebedee.

«And to whom do the children belong? To God or to paganism?» asks Andrew.

«They generally belong to the stronger of the two» replies Matthew. «And, unless the woman is an apostate herself, they are Hebrews because men, at least these men, do not interfere. They are not even very... fanatical about their Olympus. I think that now they believe in nothing but the necessity of money. They have all large families.» .

«But they are mean people. They have no faith, no fatherland... they are disliked by everybody...» says Thaddeus.

«No. You are wrong. Rome does not despise them. On the contrary, Rome always helps them. They are more useful now than when they were armed. They penetrate into our country more by corruption of blood than by violence. It is the first generation, eventually, that suffers. Then they spread and... the world forgets...» says Matthew who seems to be well informed.

«Yes, it is the children that suffer. But also the Jewish women, married like that... For themselves and for their children. I feel ·sorry for them. Nobody speaks to them of God any longer. But that will not happen in future. Then there will be no such separations of people and countries, because souls will be united in one Fatherland only: Mine» says Jesus, Who has been silent so far.

«But they will be dead by then!...» exclaims John.

«No. They will be gathered in My Name. No longer Romans or Libyans, Greeks or people from the Black Sea area, Iberians or Gauls, Egyptians or Hebrews, but souls of Christ. And woe betide those who will distinguish souls, whom I equally loved and for whom I equally suffered, according to their nationalities. He who should do that would prove that he has not understood Charity, which is universal.»

The apostles understand the covert reproof and lower their heads without speaking...

327.3 [3]The clangor of iron beaten on the anvil has ceased and the hammer blows on the last hoof of a donkey are deadening. And Jesus takes advantage of the situation to speak loud so that the crowds may hear Him. He seems to be continuing His conversation with the apostles, in actual fact He is speaking to the passers-by and perhaps also to those in the houses, certainly to some women, as women's voices calling one another can be heard in the mild air.

«There is always a relationship among men, even if it does not appear to exist: that is, the origin from One only Creator. If later the children of the Only Father have become separated, the tie of their origin has not changed as the blood of a son who disowns his father's house does not change. In Cain's veins there was Adam's blood also after the crime which compelled him to roam in the wide world. And in the veins of the children born after Eve's grief, weeping over her murdered son, there was the same blood that boiled in the veins of faraway Cain. The same, and for a purer reason, applies to the equality of the children of the Creator. Are they lost, exiled, apostates, guilty, speaking languages different from ours, do they believe in faiths which we loathe, are they corrupted by marrying heathens? Yes? But their souls came from One God, and they are *always* the same, even if they are torn, lost, exiled, corrupt... Even if they are the cause of grief to the God Father, they are still souls created by Him.

[4] The good children of a very good Father must have good feel- 327.4
ings. Good towards the Father, good towards brothers, whatever they may have become, because they are children of the same Father. Good towards the Father by endeavouring to console Him for His grief, taking His children back to Him, as they are the cause of His grief, either because they are sinners or because they are apostates or pagans. Good towards them because they have souls created by the Father, enclosed in guilty, sullied bodies and have become dull through wrong religions, but are always souls of God equal to our own.

Remember, you people of Israel, that there is no one, not even the idolater most remote from God because of his idolatrous religion, not even the most pagan of pagans or the most atheist of man, who is completely devoid of some trace of his origin. Remember, you who have gone wrong in getting detached from our just Religion by descending to mixing sexes, which is con-
* demned by our Religion, that even if you think that everything that was Israel is now dead in you, suffocated by the love for a man of different faith and race, it is not dead. There is something still alive, and that is Israel. And it is your duty to blow the dying

* **condemned**, as in *Genesis 24:1-8*; *Deuteronomy 7:3-4*; *1 King 11:1-13*; *Ezra 9-10*; *Nehemiah 13:23-29*; *Malachi 2:11-12*.

fire, to foster the spark still existing by the will of God, so that it may overwhelm carnal love. That love ends with death, but your souls do not. Remember that. And you, whoever you may be, who see, and at times are horrified at seeing the hybrid marriage of a daughter of Israel with a man of different race and faith, remember that it is your duty and obligation to assist the mislaid sister charitably, so that she may find her way back to the Father. This is the new holy Law, agreeable to the Lord: that the followers of the Redeemer may redeem whoever is to be redeemed, so that God may smile because of the souls that go back to the Father's House and the sacrifice of the Redeemer may not be made unfruitful and mean.

327.5 [5] To leaven dough the housewife takes a little of the dough of the previous week. Oh! only a tiny bit of the whole mass! And she buries it in the dough, and protects it from harmful draughts in the favourable warmth of the house. Do likewise yourselves, you followers of Good, and you, too, who have gone away from the Father and from His Kingdom. Let the former give a tiny part of their yeast to support and reinforce the latter, who will add it to the particle of justice still existing in them. And both of you, protect the new yeast from the hostile draughts of Evil in the warmth of Charity, according to what it is in you: your mistress, or a persistent, although now languishing survivor. Support with the warmth of your homes, with the faith of the same religion what is fermenting in the heart of a mislaid co-religionist, so that she may feel that she is still loved, she is still a daughter of Zion and a sister of yours, and her goodwill may materialise and the Kingdom of Heaven may come to *all* souls.»

327.6 [6] «But who is He?» people ask, and they no longer seem in a hurry to cross the bridge although it is now clear, or to go on their way, if they have already crossed it.

«A rabbi.»

«A rabbi of Israel.»

«Here? At the Phoenician borders? It is the first time that happens!»

«And yet it is so. Aser told me that He is the Holy One, as people call Him.»

«Perhaps He is seeking refuge here because they persecute Him on the other side.»

«They are reptiles indeed!»

«It is a good thing if He stays with us! He will work miracles...»

In the meantime Jesus has gone away along a path in the fields...

328. In Alexandroscene, Meeting with Hermione's Brothers.

12th November 1945.

[1]They reach the road once again after a long tour through 328.1
fields and after crossing the torrent by a little bridge of squeaky boards, fit only for people: a footbridge rather than anything more substantial. And they continue walking along the plain, which becomes narrower and narrower as the hills come closer to the coast, so much so that after another torrent, with the usual essential Roman bridge, the road leaves the plain and becomes mountainous and forks at the bridge: one road, which is not so steep, runs northwards along a valley, the other one, which Jesus takes following the indication of the Roman mile stone: * «Alexandroscene — m.V°», is a real flight of steps in the steep rocky mountain, the sharp ends of which drop into the Mediterranean, while the view of the sea becomes wider and wider as they climb. Only pedestrians and little donkeys can go along that road, or flight of steps, as it should be called. But probably because it is a good short cut, it is very busy and people curiously watch the unusual Galilean group going along it.

«That must be the cape of the storm» says Matthew pointing to the promontory jutting out into the sea.

«Yes, down there is the village of which the fisherman spoke * to us» confirms James of Zebedee.

«I wonder who built this road?»

«Who knows how long it has been here! Phoenician work perhaps...»

«From the top we shall see Alexandroscene beyond which there is the White Cape. You will see a large stretch of sea, My

---

* **«Alexandroscene - m.V°»** that is: "Alexandroscene 5th mile".

* **spoke to us**, during the voyage from Ptolemaide to Tyre, in 318.5.

dear John» says Jesus laying an arm on the shoulders of the apostle. «That will make me happy. But it will soon be dark. Where are we stopping?»

«At Alexandroscene. See? The road is already going down. Down there the plain stretches as far as that town which you can see over there.»

328.2 [2] «It is the town of the woman from Antigonea... How can we satisfy her request?» asks Andrew. *

«You know, Master, she said to us: "Go to Alexandroscene. My brothers have stores there and they are proselytes. Tell them about the Master. We are children of God, too..." and she wept because, as she is a daughter-in-law, she is rather frowned upon... so her brothers never go to see her and she never hears of them...» explains John.

«We will look for her brothers. If they welcome us as pilgrims, we shall be able to satisfy her...»

«But how can we prove that we have seen her?»

«She works for Lazarus. And we are Lazarus' friends» says Jesus.

«That is true. You can speak...»

«Yes. But quicken your pace so that we may find the house. Do you know where it is?»

«Yes, it is near the Fort. They deal very much with the Romans to whom they sell many goods.»

«Very well.»

328.3 [3] They cover the beautiful level road quickly, a real consular road, linked with roads coming from the mainland and it proceeds towards the mainland after the steep flight of steps across the rocky promontory near the coast.

Alexandroscene is more a military than a civil town. It must be of strategic importance, but I do not know why. Enclosed between two promontories it looks like a sentry watching that part of the sea. Now that it is possible to see both capes, many military towers are visible on them, forming a chain with those in the plain and in town, where the imposing Fort dominates near the sea-shore.

They enter the town after crossing another little torrent near

---

* **the woman from Antigonea** is Hermione, met in 323.8.

the gate and they proceed towards the severe mass of the Fort looking around inquisitively and being watched curiously. There are numerous soldiers and they appear to be on good terms with the citizens, which makes the apostles mumble: «These Phoenicians have no sense of honour!»

[4]They reach the stores of Hermione's brothers, while the last customers are coming out laden with all kinds of goods, from pieces of cloth to kitchenware, to hay, corn, oil, foodstuffs. The large entrance hall smells of leather, spices, hay, straw, raw wool and it leads into a yard as wide as a square, with storehouses under the porches. 328.4

A swarthy bearded man goes to meet them: «What do you need? Foodstuffs?»

«Yes... and lodgings, if you do not mind giving hospitality to pilgrims. We come from far and have never been here before. Welcome us in the name of the Lord.»

The man looks carefully at Jesus Who has spoken on behalf of everybody. He scans His face, then says: «Actually we do not give lodgings. But I like You. You are a Galilean, are You not? Better Galileans than Judaeans. Too much mould in the latter. They never forgive us for not having pure blood. It would be much better if their souls were pure. Come, come in here, I will be back at once. I am closing up, it is already dark.» It is in fact twilight and it is even darker in the yard overlooked by the powerful Fort.

They go into a room and, tired as they are, they sit down on seats scattered here and there...

The man comes back with two more brothers, an older and a younger one, and shows them the guests, who stand up greeting, saying: «Here they are. What do you think? They seem to be honest...»

«Yes. You have done the right thing» says the oldest brother to his younger one, and then addressing the guest, or rather, Jesus, Who clearly appears to be the head, he asks: «What are your names?»

«Jesus of Nazareth, James and Judas also of Nazareth, James and John of Bethsaida and Andrew as well, and Matthew of Capernaum.»

«How come you are here? Persecuted?»

«No. We are evangelizing. We have been all over Palestine

more than once, from Galilee to Judaea, from one sea to the other. And we have been beyond the Jordan, as far as Hauran. We have now come here to teach.»

«A rabbi here? It's amazing, isn't it, Philip and Elias?» asks the oldest brother.

«Yes, very. To which caste do you belong?»

«To none. I belong to God. The good people of the world believe in Me. I am poor and I love the poor, but I do not despise rich people, whom I teach to love, to be merciful and to be detached from riches, as I teach the poor to love their poverty trusting in
328.5 God Who does not let anybody perish. [5]Among My rich friends and disciples there is Lazarus of Bethany...»

«Lazarus? A sister of ours is married to one of his servants.»

«I know. That is also one of the reasons why I came. To tell you that she sends you her regards and loves you.»

«Have You seen her?»

«I have not. But these who are with Me were sent to Antigonea by Lazarus.»

«Oh! Tell us! How is Hermione? Is she really happy?»

«Her husband and mother-in-law are very fond of her. Her father-in-law respects her...» says Judas Thaddeus.

«But he does not forgive her her mother's blood. Say so.»

«He is about to forgive her. He praised her very highly. And she has four lovely kind children, who make her happy. You are always in her heart and she asked us to bring you the Divine Master.»

«But... what?... Are You the one who is said to be the Messiah?»

«I am.»

«You really are the... We were told in Jerusalem that You are, that they call You the Word of God? Is that true?»

«Yes, it is.»

«But are You the Word for those over there, or for everybody?»

«For everybody. Can you believe that I am the Word of God?»

«It costs nothing to believe, particularly when one hopes that what one believes in can remove what makes us suffer.»

«That is true, Elias. But do not say that. It is an impure thought, much more impure than mixed blood. Do not rejoice at the hope that what makes you suffer as a man despised by other people may vanish, but rejoice at the hope of conquering the Kingdom of Heaven.»

«You are right. I am half a pagan, Lord...»

«Do not lose heart. I love you also and I have come for you, too.»

328.6 [6] «They must be tired, Elias. You are keeping them here talking. Let us go and have supper and then we will take them to rest. There are no women here... None of the women from Israel wanted us, whereas we wanted one of them... Forgive us, therefore if the house will seem cold and bare.»

«Your kind hearts will warm and adorn it for us.»

«How long are You staying?»

«Not more than one day. I want to go towards Tyre and Sidon and I would like to be at Achzib before the Sabbath.»

«It's not possible, Lord. Sidon is far away!»

«I would like to speak here tomorrow.»

«Our house is like a port. Without going out You will have as many listeners as You wish, all the more so as tomorrow is market day.»

«Let us go, then, and may the Lord reward you for your charity.»

329. At Alexandroscene Market, the Parable of the Vineyard Labourers. The Roman Soldier Aquila.

13th November 1945.

329.1 [1] One half of the yard of the three brothers is in the shade, the other is in the bright sunshine. And it is full of people coming and going, doing their shopping, while outside the main door, in the little square, people are bustling about the noisy market of Alexandroscene, buying donkeys, sheep, lambs, poultry; because it is obvious that people are not so fussy here and thus they take poultry to the market without any fear of contamination. Braying, bleating, cackling of hens and triumphant cock-a-doodle-doos of cockerels mingle with the voices of people in a merry chorus, the notes of which now and again become dramatically high because of some quarrel.

The yard of the brothers is also very busy and people often

wrangle over prices or because a customer has taken what somebody else intended to purchase. Then there is the querulous moaning of beggars in the square, near the main door, wailing over their misfortunes in a singsong as sad as the lamentation of a dying man.

Roman soldiers move imperiously about the square and warehouses. I suppose that they are on duty as I see that they are armed and never alone among the Phoenicians who are all armed.

Jesus also walks up and down the yard with the six apostles, waiting for the right moment to speak. He then goes out into the square, and passing near the beggars He gives them alms. People pause for a moment to look at the Galilean group and ask who the foreigners are. And there are some who tell them, as they have already enquired of the three brothers about their guests.

A murmur follows Jesus' steps as He walks about peacefully caressing the children He meets on His way. There is also someone who sneers and utters unpleasant epithets at the Hebrews, as well as people who honestly wish to hear this «Prophet», this «Rabbi», this «Holy Man», this «Messiah» of Israel, as those are the names by which they refer to Him, according to their faith and their sense of righteousness.

329.2 [2] I hear two mothers say: «But is it true?»

«Daniel told me himself. When in Jerusalem he spoke to people who had seen the miracles of the Holy Man.»

«Yes, I agree! But is this the same man?»

«Oh! Daniel told me that it cannot be but Him, because of what He says.»

«Well... what do you think? Will He grant me the grace, even if I am only a proselyte?»

«I would say so... Try. Perhaps He will not come back here again. Try! He will certainly not hurt you!»

«I am going» says the little woman leaving the vendor of kitchenware with whom she was haggling over some soup-plates. The man, who had heard the conversation of the two women, disappointed and irritated because a good deal had come to nothing, rails at the remaining woman: «Cursed proselyte. Jewish blood. Corrupted woman» etc. etc.

I hear two serious bearded men say: «I would like to hear Him. They say that He is a great Rabbi.»

«A Prophet, you should say. Greater than the Baptist. Elias told me certain things! Wonderful things! And he knows because his sister is married to a servant of a very wealthy man of Israel, and to get news of her he calls on his fellow-servants. That rich man is a great friend of the Rabbi...»

A third man, a Phoenician perhaps, who being close to the two has heard what they said, thrusts forth his thin satyric face between the two and says laughing scornfully: «Lovely holiness! Dressed with wealth! As far as I know a holy man should live in poverty!»

«Hold your cursed tongue, Doro. You, heathen, are not fit to judge these things.»

«Ah! You are fit, particularly you, Samuel. You had better pay me that debt of yours.»

«Here, take it, and don't come near me any more, you faun-faced vampire!»...

I hear an old half-blind man, led by a little girl, ask: «Where is the Messiah?» and the girl says: «Make room for old Mark! Please tell old Mark where the Messiah is!»

The feeble trembling voice of the old man and the girl's argentine and steady one spread in vain over the square, until another man says: «Do you want to go to the Rabbi? He has gone back towards Daniel's house. There He is, standing over there, speaking to the beggars.»

[3] I can hear two Roman soldiers say: «He must be the one whom 329.3
those crooks of the Jews persecute! Only by looking at Him you can see that He is better than they are.»

«That is why He annoys them.»

«Let's go and tell the ensign. That is the instruction.»

«How silly, O Caius! Rome bewares of lambs and puts up with, or rather I would say: caresses tigers.» (Scipio).

«I don't think so, Scipio! Pontius puts people to death quite easily!» (Caius).

«Yes, but he does not close his house to the creeping hyenas who flatter him.» (Scipio).

«Politics, Scipio! Politics!» (Caius).

«Cowardice, Caius, and stupidity. He should make friends with this Man. He would receive help to keep this Asiatic rabble obedient. Pontius serves Rome badly by neglecting this good man and flattering wicked people.» (Scipio).

«Do not criticise our Proconsul. We are soldiers and our superior is as sacred as a god. We have sworn obedience to divine Caesar and the Proconsul is his representative.» (Caius).

«That is alright with regard to our duty towards our sacred and immortal fatherland. But not with regard to one's personal judgment.» (Scipio).

«But obedience is based on judgment. If your judgment is against an order and criticises it, you will not obey wholeheartedly. Rome relies on our blind obedience to defend its conquests.» (Caius).

«You speak like a tribune and you are quite right. But I would point out to you that if Rome is queen, we are not slaves. We are subjects. Rome has no slave citizens, and must not have any. It is slavery to prevent citizens from speaking their minds. I say that it is my opinion that Pontius is wrong in not taking care of this Israelite, call Him Messiah, Holy, Prophet, Rabbi, as you like. And I feel that I can say so because my loyalty to Rome is in no way impaired. Neither is my love. In fact, that is what I would like, because I feel that by teaching people to respect the laws and the Consuls, He cooperates to the welfare of Rome.» (Scipio).

«You are a learned man, Scipio... You will go a long way. You are already well ahead! I am a poor soldier. But look over there. There is a group of people around the Man. Let us go and tell our superiors.» (Caius)...

329.4 [4]In fact near the main door of the three brothers there is a group of people around Jesus, Who is well visible because of His height. Then all of a sudden a shout is heard and the people become excited. Many people rush from the market towards the group while others leave the group and run towards the square and beyond it. Questions... answers...

«What happened?»

«What is the matter?»

«The Man from Israel has cured old Mark!»

«The veil has vanished from his eyes.»

Jesus in the meantime has gone into the yard followed by a train of people. Behind them all, moving with great difficulty there is one of the beggars, a cripple, who is dragging himself along more with his hands than with his feet. But if his legs are crippled and weak, so that without crutches he would not be able to move, his voice is quite strong! He sounds like a siren rending the sunny morning air: «Holy! Holy! Messiah! Rabbi! Have mercy on me!» He is shouting at the top of his voice unrelentingly.

Two or three people turn around: «Spare your breath! Mark is a Jew, you are not.»

«He grants graces to true Israelites, not to the sons of a dog!»

«My mother was Hebrew...»

«And God struck her because of her sin, giving her a monster like you. Away, you son of a she-wolf! Go back to your place, you filthy mud...»

The man leans against the wall, he is down-hearted and frightened by threatening fists...

Jesus stops, turns around, looks at him. He orders: «Man, come here!»

The man looks at Him, looks at those threatening him... and dare not come forward.

Jesus squeezes through the little crowd and goes to him. He takes him by the hand, that is, He lays His hand on the man's shoulder and says: «Be not afraid. Come with Me» and looking at the merciless people He says severely: «God belongs to all men who seek Him and are merciful.»

They take a hint and are now the ones to be left at the rear of the crowd, or rather, they remain where they are.

Jesus turns around again. He sees that they are embarrassed and on the point of going away, and He says to them: «No, you may come forward as well. It will do you good, too, it will straighten and fortify your souls as I am going to straighten and fortify this man, because he has faith. Man, I tell you, be cured of your infirmity.» And He takes His hand off the shoulder of the cripple, after the latter has something like a shock.

The man straightens himself up on his legs now steady, throws away his worn out crutches and shouts: «He has cured me! Praised be the God of my mother!» and he kneels down to kiss the hem of Jesus' mantle.

[5]The tumult of those who wish to see, or have seen and are 329.5
making comments, rises to the highest pitch. In the long entrance hall leading from the square to the yard, the clamour re-

sounds with the resonance of a well and is echoed by the walls of the Fort.

The soldiers think that there is a brawl — which is likely to be the case in places like this one with so many contrasting races and religions — and a squad rushes to the spot; they elbow their way violently through the crowd asking what is the matter.

«A miracle, a miracle! Jonah, the cripple, has been cured. There he is, over there, near the Galilean.»

The soldiers look at one another. They do not speak until the whole crowd has passed by and more people have piled up behind it coming from the warehouses and the square, where only the vendors are left; they are fretting with indignation at the sudden distraction, which has caused the market to be a complete failure that day. Then, when they see one of the three brothers pass by, they ask him: «Philip, do you know what the Rabbi is going to do now?»

«He will be speaking and teaching in my yard!» replies Philip overjoyed.

The soldiers consult with one another: «Shall we stay? Shall we go away?»

«The ensign told us to watch...»

«Whom? The Man? As far as He is concerned we may as well go and amuse ourselves dicing for an amphor of wine of Cyprus» says Scipio, the soldier who had previously defended Jesus talking to his companion.

«I would say that He is the one who needs protection, not the rights of Rome! See Him over there? Amongst all our gods there is not one so mild and yet so manly looking. The mob here are unworthy of Him. And the unworthy are always wicked. Let us stay and protect Him. If necessary we will defend Him and will dust these galley-slaves' jackets» says another one half sarcastically and half admiringly.

«You are right, Pudens. In fact, Actius, go and call Procorus, the ensign who is always dreaming of plots against Rome... and of promotions for himself, as a reward for his keen watching over the health of divine Caesar and of goddess Rome, the mother and mistress of the world, so that he may convince himself that he will not gain any arm-band or crown here.»

329.6 [6] A young soldier runs away and comes back at once saying:

«Procorus is not coming. He is sending triarius Aquila...»

«Very well! Better him than Cecilius Maximus himself. Aquila has served in Africa, in Gaul, and in the wild forests where Varus and his legions were wiped out. He knows Greeks and Britons and he is clever at telling... Oh! Hail! Here is our glorious Aquila! Come, teach us poor wretches how to judge the value of men!»

«Long live Aquila, the master of armies!» they all shout shaking the old soldier whose face, bare arms and calves are marked with scars.

He smiles in a friendly manner and exclaims: «Long live Rome, the mistress of the world! Not me, a poor soldier. What is the matter?»

«We are to watch that tall man, whose hair is as fair as very light copper.»

«Good. But who is He?»

«They say He is the Messiah. His name is Jesus and He comes from Nazareth. You know, He is the one about whom the order was issued...»

«H'm! Maybe... But I think that we are chasing shadows.»

«They say that He wants to proclaim Himself King and supplant Rome. The Sanhedrin, Sadducees., Pharisees and Herodians have denounced Him to Pontius. You know that the Jews have that fixed idea in their heads, and a king pops up now and again...»

«I know, I know... But if they are worried about this one... In any case let us listen to what He says. I think that He is going to speak.»

«I heard from the centurion's soldier that Publius Quintillianus said to him that He is a divine philosopher... The imperial ladies are enthusiastic for Him...» says another young soldier.

«I am sure they are! I would be enthusiastic myself if I were a woman and I would like to have him in my bed...» says another young soldier laughing wholeheartedly.

«Shut up, you wanton fellow! Lust is devouring you!» remarks another one jokingly.

«And not you, Fabius! Anna, Syra, Alba, Mary...»

«Be quiet, Sabinus, He is speaking and I want to listen to Him» orders the triarius. They all become silent.

329.7 [7] Jesus has got onto a case placed against a wall. He can thus be seen by everybody. His kind greeting has spread through the air and is followed by the words: «Children of one only Creator, listen», and in the heedful silence of the crowd He continues.

«The Time of Grace has come not only for Israel, but for everybody in the world. Men of Israel, who are here for various reasons, proselytes, Phoenicians, Gentiles, everybody, listen to the Word of God, understand Justice and become familiar with Charity. If you have Wisdom, Justice and Charity, you have the means of attaining the Kingdom of God, which is not exclusive to the children of Israel, but belongs to all those who from now on ,will love the One True God and will believe in the word of His Word.

329.8 [8] Listen. I have come from very far, but not with the ambition of a usurper or with the violence of a conqueror. I have come to be only the Saviour of your souls. Property, wealth, offices, do not seduce Me. They mean nothing to Me and I do not even look at them. Or rather I look at them to pity them, for I feel sorry for them, because they are chains that hold your souls prisoners, preventing them from coming to the One, Eternal, Universal, Holy, Blessed Lord. I look at them and I approach them as if they were the *greatest* miseries. And I endeavour to rid them of their fascinating but cruel deceit that seduces the sons of man, so that they may use them with justice and holiness, not as cruel weapons that wound and kill men, and first of all the souls of those who do not make a holy use of them.

But I solemnly tell you that it is much easier for Me to cure a deformed body than a perverted soul; it is easier for Me to give light back to blind eyes or health to a dying body, than light to souls and health to diseased spirits. Why? Because man has lost sight of the true purpose of his life and devotes himself to what is transient. Man does not know or does not remember, or although he remembers, he does not want to obey the holy order of the Lord — and I say this also to the Gentiles who are listening to Me — to do Good, which is Good in Rome as in Athens, in Gaul as in Africa, because the moral law exists under every sky, in every religion and in every righteous heart. And religions, from that of God to that of individual morals, say that our better part survives and its destiny in the next life will be according to how it acted on the earth. The aim of man, therefore, is to achieve peace in the next life, not revelry, usury, arrogance, pleasure in this world for a short time, to be paid for with the most dreadful tortures forever and ever. Well, man does not know, or does not remember, or does not want to remember that truth. If he does not know, he is less guilty. If he does not remember, he is somewhat guilty, because the truth is to be kept alight, like a holy torch, in minds and hearts. But if man does not want to remember it, and when it shines he closes his eyes not to see it, as he considers it as hateful as the voice of a pedantic rhetor, then his fault is serious, very serious indeed.

[9] And yet God forgives it, if the soul disowns its wrong doing 329.9
and proposes to pursue, for the rest of its life, man's true purpose, which is the conquest of eternal peace in the Kingdom of the true God. Have you so far followed an evil path? Are you downhearted and are you thinking that it is late to follow the right way? Are you desolate and are you saying: "I knew nothing of all this! And now I am ignorant and I do not know what to do"? No. Do not think that it is the same as with material matters and that it takes a long time and much work to start all over again, but in a holy manner. The bounty of the Eternal True Lord God is such that He will not make you walk back all the way to put you at the junction where, erring, you left the right path for the wrong one. His bounty is such, that from the moment you say: "I *want* to belong to the Truth", that is, to God, because God is Truth, God, through an entirely spiritual miracle, infuses Wisdom into you, whereby from being ignorant you become possessors of the supernatural Science, like those who have possessed it for years.

Wisdom means to want God, to love God, to cultivate one's soul, to tend to the Kingdom of God, repudiating everything that is flesh, world, Satan. Wisdom means obedience to the Law of God, which is the law of Charity, Obedience, Continence, Honesty. Wisdom means to love God with one's whole being and to love our neighbour as ourselves. Those are the two essential elements to be wise in the Wisdom of God. And our neighbours are not only those of our own blood, of our race and religion, but all men, whether rich or poor, wise or ignorant, Hebrews, proselytes, Phoenicians, Greeks, Romans...»

[10] Jesus is interrupted by a threatening howling of some excit- 329.10

ed people. Jesus looks at them and says: «Yes. That is love. I am not a servile master. I speak the truth because that is what I must do to sow in you what is necessary to gain eternal Life. Whether you like it or not, I must tell you, to do My duty as Redeemer. It is for you to do your duty as souls needing Redemption. So we must love our neighbour. *All* our neighbours. And love them with a holy love, not in a questionable communion of interests, whereby a Roman, Phoenician or proselyte are "anathema" or viceversa, as long as there is no sensuality or money involved, whereas if you are anxious to share sensuality or money with them, they are no longer "anathema"...»

The crowd is once again in an uproar, while the Romans, from their place in the hall exclaim: «By Jove! He does speak well!»

Jesus waits for the noise to calm down, then He resumes: «We must love our neighbour as we would like to be loved ourselves. Because we do not like to be ill-treated, harassed, robbed, oppressed, calumniated, insulted. Everybody has the same national or personal feelings. Do not let us do, therefore, the evil which we would not like done to us.

Wisdom means obedience to the ten Commandments of God:

"I am the Lord your God. You shall have no gods except Me. You shall have no idols and shall not worship them.

You shall not utter the Name of God to misuse it. It is the Name of the Lord your God, and God will punish those who use it without any reason, to curse it or to validate a sin.

Remember to sanctify feast days. The Sabbath is sacred to the Lord, Who rested on it after Creation and blessed it and sanctified it.

Honour your father and your mother that you may live peacefully for a long time on the earth and eternally in Heaven.

You shall not kill.

You shall not commit adultery.

You shall not steal.

You shall not bear false witness against your neighbour.

You shall not covet your neighbour's house; you shall not covet his wife, his servant, man or woman, or his ox, or his donkey or anything that belongs to him".

That is Wisdom. He who does that is wise and conquers Life and the Kingdom forever. So, as from today, propose to live according to Wisdom, by preferring it to the poor things of the earth.

11 What are you saying? Speak up. Are you saying that it is 329.11
late? No. Listen to a parable.

A landowner went out at daybreak to hire workers for his vineyard and he made an agreement with them for one denarius a day. He went out again at the third hour and thinking that the workers he had hired were too few and seeing other people idle in the square waiting to be hired, he took them and said to them: "Go to my vineyard and I will give you what I promised the others". And they went. He went out again at the sixth hour and at the ninth and seeing some more workers, he said to them: "Will you work for me? I give my workers one denarius a day". They agreed and went. Finally he went out about the eleventh hour and saw some more standing in the sunshine and he asked them: "Why are you standing here idle? Are you not ashamed of standing here all day without doing anything?". "Because no one hired us for the day. We would have liked to work and earn our living. But no one asked us to go and work". "Well, I am asking you to go to my vineyard. Go and you will have the same pay as the others". He said so because he was a good landowner and felt sorry for the dejection of his neighbour.

In the evening, when the work was finished, the man called his bailiff and said: "Call the workers and pay them their wages, as agreed, beginning with the last arrivals, who are the most needy, as they have not had any food during the day, whereas the others have been fed once and some several times, and who out of gratitude to me, as I felt sorry for them, have worked harder than all the others; I, in fact, have been watching them. Then dismiss them so that they may go and rest, as they deserve, and may enjoy with their families the fruit of their work". And the bailiff did as the landowner ordered, and gave each man one denarius.

When the last ones came, those who had worked from daybreak, they were surprised at receiving one denarius each and they complained to the bailiff who said to them: "That is the order I was given. Go and complain to the landowner, not to me". And they went and said: "You have not been fair! We have worked for twelve hours, first in the dewy moisture, then in the heat of the sun and once again in the dampness of the evening, and you have given us the same wages you gave the lazy workers who worked for one hour only!... Why?". And one of them in particular raised his voice saying that he had been betrayed and exploited undeservedly.

"My friend, in what have I wronged you? What did I agree with you at daybreak? One full day's work and the wages of *one* denarius. Did I not?".

"Yes, that is true. But you have given the same wages to those who have worked much less...".

"Did you agree to that pay because it seemed fair?". "Yes. I agreed because others pay less".

"Were you ill-treated by me?".

"In all conscience ... no".

"I granted you a long rest during the day and I gave you some food, did I not? You had three meals. And food and rest were not agreed upon. Is that right?".

"Yes. They were not agreed upon".

"Why did you accept them, then?".

"Well... You said: 'I prefer to do so, so that you will not get tired going back home'. And we could hardly believe that it was true... Your food was good, and we saved, and...".

"It was a favour that I was doing you gratuitously and that none of you could expect. Is that right?".

"That is true".

"So I did you a good turn. Well, why are you complaining? I should complain of you, because, although you realized that you were dealing with a good master, you worked lazily, whereas those who came after you and had one meal only, and the last arrivals who had none at all, set to work with a will and in a shorter time they did the same work that you did in twelve hours. I would have betrayed you if I had halved your wages to pay them. But that is not the case. So take what is yours and go away. Are you going to come to my house and impose on me to do what suits you? I do what I like and what is fair. Don't be malicious and don't compel me to be unfair. For I am good".

329.12 [12] I solemnly say to all of you who are listening to Me, that the Father God makes the same agreement with all men and promises the same reward to everybody. Those who serve the Lord diligently will be treated by Him with justice, even if they do little work, being close to death. I solemnly tell you that the first will not always be the first in the Kingdom of Heaven, where we shall see that the last are first and the first are last. We shall see there that men who do not come from Israel are holier than many men of Israel... I have come to call everybody, in the name of God. But if many are called, few are chosen, because few want Wisdom. He is not wise who lives according to the world and to flesh, but not according to God. He is neither wise for the earth nor for Heaven. Because on the earth he will make enemies, will receive punishment and will feel remorse. And he will lose Heaven forever.

I repeat: be good to your neighbour, whoever he may be. Be obedient and leave to God the task of punishing those who are unjust in giving orders. Be continent by resisting sensuality, be honest by resisting gold, be coherent by saying anathema to what deserves it, not when it suits you, considering yourselves free to get in touch later with what you previously cursed. Do not do to other people what you would not like done to yourselves, and then...»

[13] «Go away, You boring prophet! You have spoiled our mar- 329.13
ket!... You have taken our customers away!...» shout the vendors, rushing into the yard... And those who had shouted previously in the yard, at the beginning of Jesus' sermon — not only Phoenicians, but also Jews who are in this town for reasons unknown to me — join the vendors insulting, threatening and above all driving away...

They do not like Jesus because He does not advise evil things... He crosses His arms and looks sad, but solemn.

The people, divided into two groups, are quarrelling, defending or offending the Nazarene. Insults, praises, curses, blessings; some shout: «The Pharisees are right. You have sold Yourself to Rome. You are the lover of prostitutes and publicans». Some contradict them: «Be quiet, blasphemous tongues! You have sold yourselves to Rome, you infernal Phoenicians!», «You are demons!», «May hell swallow you!», «Go away!», «Go away, you thieves and usurers who have come to this market!» and so on...

The soldiers intervene saying: «Rather than an instigator, He is a victim!» And with their spears they drive everybody out of the yard and close the door.

Only the three proselyte brothers and the six disciples are left inside with Jesus.

«Why on earth did you make Him speak?» the triarius asks the three brothers.

«So many people speak!» replies Elias.

«Of course. But nothing happens, because they teach what people like. He does not. And He is a bore...» The old soldier stares at Jesus Who has got down off the case and is standing, apparently thinking of something else.

The crowds are still quarrelling outside. In fact more troops come from the barracks led by the centurion himself. They knock at the door and have it opened, while some remain outside to drive away both those who shout: «Long live the King of Israel!» and those who curse Him.

The centurion comes forward and he looks worried. His anger explodes against old Aquila: «Is that how you protect Rome? By letting people acclaim a foreign king in a subject region?»

The old soldier salutes stiffly and replies: «He was teaching respect and obedience and was speaking of a kingdom not of this earth. That is why they hate Him. Because He is good and respectful. There was no reason why I should enjoin silence on a man who was not offending our law.»

The centurion calms down and mumbles: «So it is another sedition of this foul mob... Well. Tell the man to go away *at once*. I do not want trouble here. Carry out my instructions and escort Him out of town as soon as the road is clear. He may go wherever He likes. To hell, if He wants. As long as He gets out of my jurisdiction. Have you understood?»

«Yes, we have, and we will act accordingly.»

The centurion turns around displaying his bright cuirass and causing his purple mantle to flutter, and he goes away without even looking at Jesus.

329.14 [14] The three brothers say to the Master: «We are sorry...»

«It is no fault of yours. And be not afraid. No harm will happen to you. I tell you...»

The three change colour... Philip says: «How are You aware of our fear?»

Jesus smiles kindly, a smile which is like a ray of sunlight on His sad face: «I know what is in hearts and what is in the future.» The soldiers are waiting in the sunshine casting sidelong glances and making comments...

«Can they possibly love us, when they hate even that man who does not oppress them?»

«And who works miracles, you should say...»

«By Hercules! Who was it that came to tell us that there was a suspect to be watched?»

«It was Caius!»

«The zealous man! In the meantime we have missed our rations and I foresee that I am going to miss the kiss of a girl!... Ah!»

«Epicurean! Where is the beautiful girl?»

«I am certainly not going to tell you, my friend!»

«She is behind the potter's, at the Foundations. I know. I saw you there some nights ago...» says another one.

[15]The triarius goes towards Jesus and walks around Him, look- 329.15
ing at Him all the time. He does not know what to say... Jesus smiles to encourage him. The man does not know what to do... But he goes closer. Jesus points to his scars: «All wounds, are they? So, you are a valiant and loyal soldier...»

The praise makes the old soldier blush.

«You have suffered very much for the sake of your Fatherland and of your emperor... Would you not be prepared to suffer something for a greater Fatherland: Heaven? For an eternal Emperor: God?»

The soldier shakes his head and says: «I am a poor pagan. But I may still arrive at the eleventh hour. But who will teach me? You have seen!... They are expelling You. And that is a wound which is sore, not mine!... At least I gave them back to my enemies. But what do You give those who hurt You?»

«Forgiveness, soldier. Forgiveness and love.»

«So, I am right. It is foolish to suspect You. Goodbye, Galilean.»

«Goodbye, Roman.»

[16]Jesus is left alone until the three brothers and the disciples 329.16
come back with some food, which the brothers offer to the soldiers, and the apostles to Jesus. They eat without relish, in the sunshine, whilst the soldiers eat and drink merrily.

Then a soldier goes out to have a look at the silent square. «We can go» he shouts. «They have all gone away. The patrols only are there.»

Jesus stands up submissively, He blesses and comforts the three brothers, with whom He fixes an appointment for Passover at Gethsemane, and He goes out, escorted by the soldiers, and followed by the mortified disciples. They proceed along the empty road until they reach the country.

«Hail, Galilean» says the triarius.

«Goodbye, Aquila. Please, do not ill-treat Daniel, Elias and Philip. I only am the guilty one. Tell the centurion.»

«I will not tell him anything. He has already forgotten all about it and the three brothers supply us with many good things, particularly with the Cyprus wine that the centurion loves more than his own life. Go in peace. Goodbye.»

They part. The soldiers go back to the gate, Jesus and His disciples set out eastwards towards the silent countryside.

330. James and John of Zebedee Become "the Sons of Thunder". Towards Achzib with the Shepherd Anna.

14th November 1945.

330.1 [1]Jesus is walking across a very mountainous region. The mountains are not high, but the road runs up and down hills all the time; and there are many torrents, which flow merrily in the cool fresh season and are as clear as the sky and as fresh as the first leaves that are beginning to grow more and more copiously on the trees. But although the season is so beautiful and cheerful as to comfort one's heart, Jesus' humour does not appear to be much relieved and the apostles look even more worried than He is. They are walking very quietly along the bottom of a valley. Shepherds and flocks are the only visible life. But Jesus does not even seem to see them.

A down-hearted sigh of James of Zebedee and his sudden words, the obvious result of a concerned mind, draw Jesus' attention... James says: «And defeats!... and defeats!... We seem to be cursed»

Jesus lays a hand on his shoulder: «Do you not know that that is the lot of the better ones?»

«Eh! I know since I have been with You! But now and again we would need something different, which we did get in the past, to cheer up hearts and faith...»

[2] «Do you doubt Me, James?» How much grief there is in Jesus' trembling voice. 330.2

«No!...» His "no" is certainly not a very definite one.

«But you do doubt. What, then? Do you no longer love Me as you did before? The fact that you have seen Me expelled, derided, or only neglected near the Phoenician borders, has perhaps weakened your love, has it?» There is deep grief in Jesus' trembling words, although there are no sobs or tears. His very soul is weeping.

«No, my Lord, not that! On the contrary, the more I see You misunderstood, rejected, humiliated, afflicted, the more my love for You increases. And I would willingly offer my life as a sacrifice in order not to see You thus, and to be able to change the hearts of men. You must believe me. Do not crush my heart, which is already so depressed, by doubting that I do not love You. Otherwise... otherwise I will go to extremes. I will go back and I will revenge myself upon those who grieve You, to prove that I love You, to remove Your doubt, and if they catch me and kill me, I will not care in the least. I will be satisfied with giving You a proof of my love.»

«Oh! son of thunder! Whence so much impetuosity? Do you want to be an exterminating thunderbolt?» Jesus smiles at the ardour and intentions of James.

«Oh! At least I see You smile! That is already one result of my intentions. What do you say, John? Shall we carry out my intentions to relieve the Master, Who is depressed because of so many repulses?»

«Oh! yes. Let us go. We will go back and speak to them. And if they still insult Him saying that He is king only by word, or is a laughing-stock king, a penniless or a mad king, we will give them a good thrashing until they realize that the king has an army of faithful men, who are not prepared to stand their mockery. Violence can be useful at times. Let's go, brother!» John replies to him, and angry as he is, he seems to be another man, so different from the ever mild John.

[3] Jesus places Himself between the two, catches them by the 330.3

arms to hold them back and says: «Just listen to them! And what have I been preaching for such a long time? Oh! What a wonderful surprise! Even John, My dove, has become a hawk! Look how ugly, gloomy, perturbed he looks, disfigured by hatred. Oh! shame! And you are surprised because some Phoenicians remain indifferent, some Jews are resentful, some Romans expelled Me, while you are the first who have not understood anything after being with Me for two years, and you have become gall because of the hatred in your hearts, and you cast My doctrine of love and forgiveness out of your hearts and you reject it as if it were a foolish thing, and you welcome violence as a good ally! Oh! Holy Father! This is a defeat indeed! Instead of being hawks sharpening their beaks and claws, would it not be better if you were angels praying the Father to give relief to His Son? When has a storm ever done any good with its thunderbolts and hailstones? Well, in memory of this sin of yours against Charity, in memory of the moment when I saw the animal-man come to light on your faces instead of the man-angel whom I always wish to see in you, I will call you "the sons of thunder".»

Jesus is half serious while speaking to the two excited sons of Zebedee. But His reproach does not last long, because as soon as they repent He clasps them both to His heart, His face shining with love, saying: «Never again do I want to see you like that. And thank you for your love. And thank you for yours, My friends» He says addressing Andrew, Matthew and His two cousins. «Come here, that I may embrace you as well. Do you not know that if I had nothing else but the joy of doing the will of My Father and your love, I would always be happy, even if the whole world smacked Me? I am sad, not about Myself, or about My defeats, as you call them, but because I feel sorry for the souls that reject Life. Good, we are all happy now, are we not, you big babies?
330.4 Come on, then. [4]Go to those shepherds who are milking the sheep and ask them to give you some milk in the name of God. Be not afraid» He says seeing the desolate look of the apostles. «Obey with faith. You will get milk, not a thrashing, even if the man is a Phoenician.»

And the six go off while Jesus waits for them on the road. And the sad Jesus, Whom no one wants, prays in the meantime...

The apostles come back with a little pail of milk, and they say:

«The man asks You to go over there, he wants to speak to You, but he cannot leave his unreliable goats to young shepherds.»

Jesus says: «Well, let us go there and eat their bread.»

And they go to the edge of the ditch where the goats are chewing precariously.

5 «Thank you for the milk you have given Me. What do you want of Me?» 330.5

«You are the Nazarene, are You not? The one who works miracles?»

«I am the one who preaches Eternal Salvation. I am the Way to go to the true God, the Truth that gives itself, the Life that enlivens you. I am not a wizard that works wonders. The miracles that I work are a manifestation of My goodness and of your weakness that needs proofs in order to believe. But what do you want of Me?»

«Well... Were You at Alexandroscene two days ago?»

«Yes, I was. Why?»

«I was there, too, with my kids, and when I realized that there was going to be a quarrel, I went away, because they are in the habit of stirring up trouble to steal what is in the market. They are thieves, all of them: the Phoenicians... and the others. I should not say so because I am the son of a proselyte father and a Syrian mother and a proselyte myself. But it is the truth. Well. Let us go back to my story. I took shelter in a stable with my kids, waiting for my son's cart. And in the evening, when I was leaving the town, I met a woman, who was weeping, with her little daughter in her arms. She had walked eight miles to come to You. Because she lives out in the country. I asked her what was the matter, as she is a proselyte. She had come to sell some goods and do some shopping. She had heard of You and hope had filled her heart. She ran home to get the little girl. But one walks slowly with a load! When she arrived at the warehouse of the brothers, You were no longer there. The brothers said to her: "They expelled Him. But last night He told us that He would go back via the steps of Tyre". As I am a father, too, I said to her: "Well, go there". But she replied to me: "If after what happened He goes back to Galilee by a different road?". I said to her: "Now listen. It is either that road or the one along the border. I am pasturing my flock between Rohob and Lesemdan, on the border road between here and Naphtali. If I see Him I will tell Him, I promise you on my honour". And I have told You.»

330.6 «And may God reward you. I will go to the woman. [6]I must go back to Achzib.»

«Are You going to Achzib? Well, we can go together, if You do not scorn the company of a shepherd.»

«I scorn no one. Why are you going to Achzib?»

«Because my lambs are there. Unless… I have lost them all.»

«Why?»

«Because there is a disease… I do not know whether it was witch-craft or something else. I know that my lovely flock has been taken ill. That is why I brought the goats here, as they are still healthy and I keep them away from the sheep. Two of my sons will look after them here. They are now in town, shopping. But I am going back there, to see them die, my beautiful woolly sheep…» The man sighs… He looks at Jesus and he apologises: «It is foolish to speak to You of these things, considering who You are, and to distress You, as You must be already distressed by the way they treat You. But our sheep are love and money to us, You know?…»

«I understand. But they will recover. Did you get anyone, who is familiar with these things, to see them?»

«Oh! They have all said the same thing: "Kill them and sell the skins. There is nothing else to be done", and they have also threatened me if I take them about… They are afraid of the disease… for their own sheep. So I have to keep them in and they die quicker. They are bad, You know, those of Achzib…»

Jesus says simply: «I know.»

«I say that they have bewitched them…»

«No. Do not believe such nonsense… Will you be leaving at once when your sons arrive?»

330.7 «Yes, I will. They will be here any moment now. [7]Are these Your disciples? Only these?»

«No. I have more.»

«Why do they not come here? Once, I met a group of them near Merom. A shepherd was their head. So they said. A tall strong man, Elias was his name. It was in October, I think. Either before or after the Tabernacles. Has he left You now?»

«None of My disciples have left Me.»

«I was told...»

«What?»

«That You... that the Pharisees... In short, that Your disciples had left You because they were afraid, and that You were...»

«A demon. You may say it. I know. Double merit for you, as you believe just the same.»

«And because of that merit, could You not... but perhaps I am asking for a sacrilege...»

«Tell Me. If it is wicked, I will let you know.»

«Could You not bless my flock, when passing by?» the man says very anxiously...

«I will bless your flock. This one...» and He raises His hand blessing the goats scattered around «... and your flock of sheep. Do you believe that My blessing will save them?»

«As You save men from diseases, so You must be able to save animals. They say that You are the Son of God. Sheep were created by God. So they belong to the Father. I... did not know whether it was respectful to ask You. But if it is possible, please do it, Lord, and I will take large offerings to the Temple. Or rather, I will not! I will give them to You for the poor. It will be better.»

Jesus smiles and is silent. [8]The shepherd's sons arrive and 330.8
shortly afterwards Jesus, the apostles and the old man set out, leaving the young men to look after the goats. They walk fast as they want to reach Kedesh soon and then proceed at once towards the road that from the sea takes to the mainland. It must be the road that forks at the foot of the promontory, the one they took going to Alexandroscene. At least that is what I understand from the conversation of the shepherd with the disciples. Jesus is ahead of them, all alone.

«But shall we not have further trouble?» asks James of Alphaeus.

«Kedesh is not in the jurisdiction of the centurion. It is outside the Phoenician border. And if one does not provoke them, centurions do not interfere with religion.»

«In any case we are not stopping...»

«Will you be able to cover more than thirty miles in one day asks the shepherd.

«Oh! We are perpetual untiring pilgrims!»

They walk on... They reach Kedesh and pass by it without any trouble. They take the straight road. Achzib is indicated on the milestone. The shepherd points it out saying: «We shall be there tomorrow. You will come with me tonight. I know farmers in the valleys, but many of them are within the Phoenician borders... Well... we will cross the frontier. And we will certainly not be found out... Oh! Their vigilance! They had better look out for robbers!...»

The sun sets and daylight is dimmed in the woody valleys. But the shepherd is familiar with the road and proceeds resolutely.

330.9 [9] They reach a little village, just a handful of houses.

«If they give us hospitality here, we shall be with Israelites. We are at the border. If they will not take us in, we will go to another village, a Phoenician one.»

«I am not biased, man.»

They knock at a door.

«Is that you, Anna? With friends? Come in, and may God be with you» says an elderly woman.

They go into a large kitchen, with a gaily blazing fireplace. The members of a large family of all ages are sitting around the table but they kindly make room for the new arrivals.

«This is Jonah. This is his wife, his sons and grandchildren and daughters-in-law. A family of patriarchs faithful to the Lord» says Annas, the shepherd, to Jesus. He then addresses old Jonah: «And this man who is with me is the Rabbi of Israel, Whom you wanted to meet.»

«I bless the Lord that I can give you hospitality as I have room tonight. And I bless the Rabbi Who has come to my house, and I ask Him to bless us.»

Annas explains that Jonah's house is like an inn for pilgrims travelling from the sea to the mainland.

They all sit down in the warm kitchen and the women serve the guests. There is so much respect that it is almost embarrassing. But Jesus overcomes the difficulty by gathering all the children around Him, when the meal is over, and taking an interest in them, and they soon fraternise. And after the children, in the short time between supper and bedtime, also the men in the house become bold and they inform Jesus of what they have learned about the Messiah and ask Him questions. And Jesus explains, confirms, rectifies in a kind peaceful conversation, until both guests and members of the household go to rest, after Jesus has blessed them all.

331. The Bold Faith of the Canaanite Woman. Arrival at Achzib.

15th November 1945.

[1] «Is the Master with you?» the old farmer Jonah asks Judas Thaddeus who is entering the kitchen, where the fire is already blazing to warm the milk and the room, which is rather chilly in the early hours of a beautiful end of January morning, I think, or early February. 331.1

«He must have gone out to pray. He often goes out at dawn, when He knows He can be alone. He will be here shortly. Why are you asking?»

«I have asked also the others, who have gone out looking for Him, because there is a woman in the next room, with my wife. She comes from a village on the other side of the border, and I don't really know how she found out that the Master is here. But she knows and she wants to speak to Him.»

«All right. She will speak to Him. Perhaps she is the woman He is expecting, with her little sick daughter. Her spirit must have brought her here.»

«No. She is alone. There are no children with her. I know her because our villages are close to each other... and the valley belongs to everybody. In any case I do not think that we should be rude to our neighbours, even if they are Phoenicians, if we wish to serve the Lord. I may be wrong, but...»

«Also the Master always says that we must be merciful to everybody.»

«He is merciful, is He not?»

«He is indeed.»

«Anna told me that He was ill-treated even recently. Always ill-treated!... In Judaea, in Galilee, everywhere. Why is Israel so bad to its Messiah? I am referring to the mighty ones in Israel. Because the people love Him.»

«How are you aware of such things?»

«Oh! I live here, far away. But I am a faithful Israelite. It is sufficient to go to the Temple on holy days of obligation to learn all the good and all the evil! But one hears more of evil things than of good ones because good is humble and does not praise itself. Those who receive it should proclaim it. But only few people are grateful after receiving a grace. Man receives assistance and forgets it... Evil instead blows its trumpets loud and has its words heard even by those who do not want to hear them. You, His disciples, are you not aware of how much they run down and accuse the Messiah in the Temple! In their teaching the scribes speak of nothing else. I think they must have made a collection of lessons on how to accuse the Master as well as a collection of facts that they exhibit as plausible charges against Him. And one's conscience must be righteous, firm and free to be able to resist and judge wisely. Is He aware of such manoeuvres?»

«He is aware of everything. And we are more or less aware as well. But He does not worry. He continues His work and disciples and believers in Him are increasing day by day.»

«God grant they may persevere until the end. But man chang-
331.2 es his mind. And weak... [2]Here is the Master coming towards the house with three disciples.»

And the old man goes out, followed by Judas Thaddeus, to pay his respects to Jesus, whose appearance is imposing while He walks towards the house.

«Peace be with you today and always, Jonah.»

«Glory and peace to You, Master, forever.»

«Peace to you, Judas. Have Andrew and John not come back yet?»

«No. I did not hear them go out. I did not hear anybody. I was fast asleep.»

«Come in, Master. Come in, everybody. The air is cool this morning. It must have been very cold in the wood. There is warm milk for everybody over there.»

They are taking their milk and everybody, with the exception of Jesus, dips large slices of bread into it, when Andrew and John arrive with Anna, the shepherd.

«Ah! You are here! We had come back to tell the rest that we had not found You...» exclaims Andrew.

Jesus wishes peace to the three and adds: «Quick. Take your share and let us leave because I want to be at least at the foot of the mountain of Achzib before evening. The Sabbath begins this evening.»

«What about my sheep?», the perplexed question of the shepherd.

Jesus smiles and replies: «They will recover after I bless them.»

«But they are on the eastern side of the mountain! You are going westwards to see that woman…»

«Leave it to God, and He will see to everything.»

[3]The meal is over and the apostles go upstairs to get their trav- 331.3
elling bags and be ready to leave.

«Master… that woman in the next room… are You not listening to her?»

«I have no time, Jonah. I have a long way to go and in any case I have come for the sheep of Israel. Goodbye, Jonah. May God reward you for your charity. I bless you and all your relatives. Let us go…»

But the old man begins to shout at the top of his voice: «Children! Women! The Master is going away! Come, quick!»

As a brood of chicks scattered in a stack-yard rush towards the broody-hen calling them, so women and men — some already busy, some still half asleep — rush from every side, together with half-naked children who are smiling although they have just woken up… They all gather around Jesus, Who is in the middle of the threshing-floor, and the mothers wrap their children in their wide skirts to protect them from the cool air, or they hold them in their arms until a maid-servant brings their clothes and puts them on them.

[4]Also a woman, who is not of the household, comes forth. A 331.4
poor weeping shy woman… She stoops and comes forward almost creeping and when she reaches the group where Jesus is, she begins to shout: «Have mercy on me, O Lord, Son of David! My daughter is tormented very badly by a demon who makes her do shameful things. Have mercy on me because I am suffering so much, as everybody sneers at me because of that, as if my child were guilty of what she does… Have mercy, O Lord, You can do everything. Raise Your voice and Your hand and order the unclean spirit to go out of Palma. She is my only daughter and I am a widow… Oh! don't go away! Mercy!…»

Jesus, in fact, after blessing each member of the household and reproaching the elder ones for telling people of His arrival there — and they justify themselves saying: «We have not said anything, believe us, Lord!» — goes away; He is inexplicably hard towards the poor woman, who is dragging herself along on her knees with her arms stretched out in suppliant attitude, while she says panting: «I saw You yesterday while You were crossing the torrent and I heard them call You: "Master". I followed You, among the bushes, and I heard what these people were saying. I understood who You are... And I came here this morning before daybreak and I remained here, on the threshold, like a little dog, until Sarah got up and made me go in. Have mercy, my Lord, on a mother and a little girl!»

But Jesus is walking fast and turns a deaf ear to her entreaties.

The people of the household say to her: «Resign yourself! He will not listen to you. He said so Himself: He has come for the children of Israel...»

She is desperate but at the same time full of faith, and she stands up saying: «No. I will pray until He listens to me.» And she follows the Master shouting her entreaties, which draw to the doors of the houses in the village all those who are already awake and who, like the people of Jonah's household, begin to follow her to see what happens.

331.5 [5] In the meantime the apostles, seized with astonishment, look at one another and whisper: «Why is He doing that? He has never done it before!...»

And John says: «He cured also those two people at Alexandroscene.»

«But they were proselytes» replies Thaddeus.

«And what about the woman He is going to cure now?»

«She is a proselyte as well» says the shepherd Anna.

«Oh! but how many times has He cured Gentiles or heathens! And what about the Roman girl?...» says Andrew desolately, as he cannot set his mind at rest seeing Jesus' harsh behaviour towards the Cananean woman.

«I will tell you what it is» exclaims James of Zebedee. «The Master is angry. His patience has come to an end before so many attacks of human wickedness. Can't you see how changed He is? He is quite right! From now on He will devote Himself only to those with whom He is familiar. And He is doing the right thing!»

«Good. But in the meantime this woman is following us howling and a train of people are coming behind her. Although He does not want to be noticed, He has found the way to draw even the attention of trees...» grumbles Matthew.

«Let us go and tell Him to send her away... Look at the lovely procession there is behind us! If we arrive at the consular road like this, we shall be in trouble! And she will not leave us unless He drives her away...» says Thaddeus who is very annoyed. He even turns around and says to the woman in a commanding voice: «Be quiet and go away!». And James of Alphaeus is solid for his brother.

But she is not impressed by threats or orders and continues to implore.

«Let us go and tell the Master to send her away, since He does not want to hear her. This cannot go on!» says Matthew, while Andrew whispers: «Poor woman!», and John repeats continuously: «I do not understand... I do not understand... » John is dumbfounded at Jesus' behaviour.

They quicken their pace and reach the Master Who is walking as fast as if He were chased. «Master, please dismiss that woman! It's a scandal! She is shouting after us! She is pointing us out to everybody! The road is getting more and more crowded with people... and many are following her. Tell her to go away.»

«You can tell her yourselves. I have already replied to her.»

«She will not listen to us. Please! You must tell her. And very severely.»

[6] Jesus stops and turns around. The woman takes it as a sign of 331.6
grace, she quickens her step, she raises the already shrill tone of her voice while her face becomes pale with her increased hope.

«Be quiet, woman. And go home. I have already told you. I have come for the sheep of Israel. To cure the ones that are ill and find the ones that are lost. You are not from Israel.»

But the woman is already at His feet and she kisses them, worshipping Him, holding His ankles tight, as if she were a ship-wrecked person who had found a rock of salvation, and she moans: «Lord, help me! You can help me, Lord. Give the order to the demon, since You are holy... Lord, You are the master of everything, of graces and of the world. Everything is subject to You, my Lord. I know. I believe it. Take therefore Your power and use it for my daughter.»

«It is not right to take the bread of the children of the house and throw it to the dogs in the street.»

«I believe in You. And through my faith, from a dog of the street I have become a dog of the house. I told You: I came before daybreak to lie down on the threshold of the house in which You were, and if You had come out there, You would have trampled on me. But You went out from the other side and did not see me. You did not see this poor distressed dog, starving for Your grace, waiting to go in, creeping, where You were, to kiss Your feet, imploring You not to drive it away...»

«It is not right to throw the bread of the children to dogs» repeats Jesus.

«But dogs go into the room where the landlord is eating with his children, and they eat what falls from the table, or the remainders of food, which the family gives them, as they are of no further use. I am not asking You to treat me as a daughter and let me sit at Your table. But give me at least the crumbs...»

331.7 [7]Jesus smiles. Oh! What a transfiguration that joyful smile works on His face!...

The people, the apostles, the woman look at Him with admiration... they realise that something is about to happen.

And Jesus says: «Oh! woman! Great is your faith. And you comfort My spirit by it. Go, therefore, and it will be done to you as you wish. As from this moment, the demon has gone out of your daughter. Go in peace. And as from a stray dog you wanted to be a dog of the house, endeavour in the future to be a daughter sitting at the table of the Father. Goodbye.»

«Oh! Lord! My Lord!... I would like to run away and see my beloved Palma... And I would like to stay with You, and follow You! Blessed! Holy!»

«Go, woman. Go in peace.»

And Jesus resumes His way while the Cananean woman, more agile than a young girl, runs away along the road she came, followed by the crowd anxious to see the miracle...

«But, Master, why did You make her implore You so much, before listening to her?» asks James of Zebedee.

«Through your fault and the fault of all of you. That is not a defeat, James. I was not expelled, derided or cursed here... Let that be a relief to your disheartened spirits. I have already had
today My most delicious food. And I bless God for it. [8]And now 331.8
let us go and see this other woman who believes and can wait with firm faith.»

«And what about my sheep, Lord? In a short while I should take a road, which is different from Yours, to go to my grazing ground...» ask the shepherd Annas once again.

Jesus smiles but does not reply.

It is beautiful to walk now that the sun warms the air and makes the new leaves of woods and the grass of meadows sparkle like emeralds, changing each flower-cup into a setting for the drops of dew shining on the many-coloured wild flowers. And Jesus proceeds smiling. And the apostles, immediately-relieved, follow Him smiling...

They reach the road-junction. The shepherd Anna, who looks mortified, says: «And I should leave You here... Are You really not coming to cure my sheep? I believe, too; and I am a proselyte... Promise, at least, that You will come after the Sabbath!»

«Oh! Annas! Is it possible that you have not yet understood that your sheep were cured when I raised My hand near Lesemdan? You may go, too, to see the miracle and to bless the Lord.»

* I think that Lot's wife, when she was turned into a pillar of salt, was very much like the shepherd, who has remained as he was, a little bent forward, with his face looking up to see Jesus, with one arm half stretched out in mid-air... He looks like a statue. And a label could be placed under it: "The Petitioner". He then comes round and prostrates himself saying: «You are blessed! Holy! Good!... But I promised You a lot of money, and I have only a few drachmae with me... Come to see me after the Sabbath...»

«I will come. Not for the money, but to bless you once again for your simple faith. Goodbye, Annas. Peace be with you.»

And they part...

«And that was not a defeat either, My friends! Neither have
they derided, expelled or cursed Me here... [9]Come on, quick! 331.9

* **Lot's wife**, in *Genesis 19:26*, belonging to the episode of the destruction of Sodom: *Genesis 19:1-29*.

There is a mother who has been waiting for us for days...»

And their march continues, with a short rest to eat some bread and cheese and drink at a spring...

It is midday when they see the road junction appear.

«That is where the steps of Tyre begin, over there» says Matthew. And he cheers up considering that they have covered most of the road.

Leaning on a Roman mile stone there is a woman. At her feet, on a folding-seat there is a little girl about seven or eight years old. The woman is looking in all directions. Towards the steps in the rock. Towards the Ptolemais road. Towards the road on which Jesus is walking, and now and again she bends to caress her child, to protect her head from the sun with a piece of cloth, to cover her feet and hands with a shawl...

«There is the woman! I wonder where she slept these past days?» asks Andrew.

«Perhaps in that house near the cross-road. There are no other houses nearby» replies Matthew.

«Or out in the open» says James of Alphaeus.

«No. Not with the child, surely!» replies his brother.

331.10 [10]Jesus does not speak. But He smiles. All in a row, with in the centre, three on each side, they take up all the road, at this time of the day, when travellers stop to eat, wherever they happen to be at midday. Jesus, tall, handsome, in the centre of the row, smiles and His face is so radiant that all the light of the sun seems to be concentrated on it while rays of light emanate from it.

The woman looks up... They are now about fifty meters apart. Jesus stares at her, which perhaps draws her attention, diverted for a moment by the child's weeping. She looks at Him and in an involuntary gesture of anxiety, she presses her hands against her heart.

Jesus smiles more broadly. And His bright without any expression smile must tell the woman a great deal, as she is no longer anxious, but smiling, as if she were already happy, she bends to pick up her child, and holding her in the folding-seat, with stretched out arms as if she offered her to God, she comes forwards, and when she arrives at Jesus' feet, she kneels down, lifting as much as she can the child in the seat, who looks ecstatically at Jesus' most handsome face.

The woman does not say one word. And what else could she say that is not already deeply expressed in her whole attitude?...

And Jesus says but *one* word, a little, but powerful gladdening word, like God's «Fiat» at the creation of the world: «Yes.» And He lays his hand on the chest of the little girl.

And the child, with the cry of a woodlark freed from a cage, shouts: «Mummy!» and all of a sudden sits up and slides down on to her feet and embraces her mother, who, exhausted as she is, staggers and is on the point of falling back, in a swoon brought about by tiredness, by anxiety that is calming down, by joy that overwhelms the strength of her heart, already weak by so much suffering.

Jesus is ready to hold her. A much stronger support than the
little girl's, who overburdening her mother with her own weight,
is certainly not the best means to support her mother on her
knees. Jesus makes her sit down and instills strength into her...
And He looks at her while silent tears stream down the tired
but happy face of the woman. [11]Then words come to her lips: 331.11
«Thank You, my Lord! Thanks and blessings! My hope has been
crowned... I waited for You so long... But I am happy now...»

The woman, after she comes round, kneels down once again, worshipping, holding the little girl in front of her, while Jesus caresses the child. And she explains: «A bone had been rotting in her back for two years, paralysing her and leading her slowly to death with great pain. We had her visited by doctors at Antioch, Tyre, Sidon and even at Caesarea and Paneas, and we spent so much on doctors and medicines that we were compelled to sell the house we had in town and retire to the one in the country, dismissing the servants of the house and keeping only those who worked in the fields, selling the crops that we used to consume ourselves... But nothing helped her! I saw You. I was aware of what You have done elsewhere. I hoped to receive grace myself... And I did! I will now go back home, without any worries, and thoroughly happy... and I will make my husband happy... It was my James who set hope in my heart by telling me what Your power works in Galilee and Judaea. Oh! Had we not been afraid of not finding You, we would have come with the girl. But You are always traveling around!...»

«And traveling I came to you... But where did you stay these past days?»

«In that house... But at night only the child was in there. There is a good woman who looked after her for me. I remained here all the time, because I was afraid that You might pass by at night.»

Jesus lays a hand on her head: «You are a good mother. That is why God loves you. You can see that He has helped you in every way.»

«Oh! Yes! I could perceive it when I was coming here. I came to town hoping to see You, so I had little money with me and I was alone. Then, following the advice of that man, I came here. I sent word home and I came... and I have never lacked anything: neither bread, nor shelter, nor courage.»

«With that weight on your arms all the time? Could you not get a cart?..» asks James of Alphaeus, who is moved to pity.

«No. She would have suffered too much: it would have been enough to kill her. My Johanna came to Grace in the arms of her mother.»

Jesus caresses both of them on their heads: «You may go now and be always faithful to the Lord. May the Lord and My peace be with you.»

Jesus resumes walking on the road to Ptolemais.

«And that is not a defeat either, My friends. And I was not expelled, derided or cursed here either.»

331.12 [12] Following the straight road they soon reach the forge near the bridge. The Roman farrier is resting in the sunshine, sitting against the wall of his house. He recognises Jesus and greets Him. Jesus returns the greeting and says: «Will you allow Me to stop here and rest a little, while we eat some bread?»

«Of course, Rabbi. My wife wanted to see You... because I told her what she had not heard of Your speech the last time You were here. Esther is Hebrew. But since I am a Roman, I did not dare to tell You. I would have sent her after You...»

«Call her, then.» And Jesus sits on the bench against the wall, while James of Zebedee hands out bread and cheese...

A woman about forty years old comes out, she looks embarrassed and blushes.

«Peace to you, Esther. Have you been anxious to meet Me? Why?»

«Because of what You said... Rabbis despise us, because we are married to Romans... But I have children and I have taken them all to the Temple and the boys have all been circumcised. I told Titus beforehand, when he wanted to marry me... And he is good... And he leaves me completely free with the children. Everything is Hebrew here, customs, rites!... But rabbis and heads of synagogues curse us. You don't... You have compassionate words for us. Oh! Do You know what that means to us? It is like being embraced by our fathers and mothers, who disowned us and cursed us and are severe with us... It is like going back to the homes we left and not feeling like strangers in them... Titus is kind. On our holy days he closes the farriery, with a heavy loss of money, and takes me and the children to the Temple. Because he says that one cannot live without religion. He says that his religion is now his family and his work, as previously it was his duty as a soldier... But I... my Lord... I wanted to speak to You
* about one thing... You said that the followers of the true God must take a little of their holy yeast and put it into the good flour to make it rise holily. I have done that with my husband. I have tried, during the twenty years we have been together, to work his soul, which is good, with the yeast of Israel. But he cannot make up his mind... and he is old... I would like to have him with me in the next life... United by faith as we are now by love... I am not asking for riches, welfare, health. What we have is sufficient, praised be the Lord for it! But that is what I would like... Pray for my husband! That he may belong to the true God...»

«He will. You may be sure of that. You are asking for something holy and it will be granted to you. You have understood the duty of a wife to God and to her husband. I wish all wives did! I solemnly tell you that many of them should imitate you. Continue like that and you will have the joy of having your Titus beside
you, in prayer and in Heaven. [13]Now show Me your children.» 331.13

The woman calls her numerous issue: «Jacob, Judas, Levi, Mary, John, Anne, Eliza, Marcus.» She then goes into the house and comes out again with one who can hardly walk and one of three months, at the most: «And this one is Isaac and this little one is Judith» she says ending the introductions.

* **You said**, in 327.5.

«Plenty!» says James of Zebedee laughing.

And Judas exclaims: «Six boys! And everyone circumcised! And with pure names! Very good!»

The woman is happy and she praises Jacob, Judas and Levi, who help their father «every day except on Sabbaths, when Titus works by himself shoeing horses with shoes made previously» she says. And she praises Mary and Anne «who help their mother.» But she does not forget to praise also the four little ones «as they are good and not naughty. Titus helps me to bring them up, as he was a disciplined soldier» she says casting a loving glance at the man, who, leaning against the door post, with a hand resting on his side, has listened to everything his wife has said, with a hearty smile on his honest face, and who now becomes elated hearing his merits as a soldier being mentioned.

«Very well. The discipline of the army is not disliked by God, when soldiers do their duty humanely. The essential point is to be always morally honest, in every task, in order to be always virtuous. Your past discipline, which you now instil into your children, must prepare you to enter a higher service: the service of God. We must part now. I will just manage to reach Achzib before sunset. Peace to you, Esther, and to your house. May you all belong to the Lord, before long.»

The mother and children kneel down while Jesus raises His hand blessing them. The man, as if he were once again a soldier of Rome in front of his emperor, stands stiffly at attention and salutes in Roman style.

331.14 [14] And they go away... After a few steps Jesus lays a hand on James' shoulder: «And once again, the fourth time today, I would point out to you that that was not a defeat, and We were not expelled, derided, cursed... What do you say about it now?»

«That I am a fool, my Lord» says James of Zebedee impulsively.

«No. You, and all the others, are still and always too human and you have all the alternatives of those who are ruled more by their human nature than by their spirits. When the spirit is sovereign, it is not affected by every breath of wind that cannot always be a scented breeze... It may suffer, but will not change. I always pray that you may reach such sovereignty of spirit. But you must help Me with your efforts... Well! We have come to the end of our journey. During it I have sown what is necessary to prepare the work for you, when *you* will be evangelizing. We can now begin our Sabbath rest with the consciousness that we have done our duty. And we shall wait for the others... Then we shall set out... again... always... until everything is accomplished...»

332. Bartholomew and Philip Join the Master and Learn the Reason for Their Long Separation.

17th November 1945.

[1]Jesus is with the six apostles in a room where there are some very poor beds, placed very close to one another. The free space is barely sufficient to let them go from one end of the room to the other. They eat their very plain food sitting on the beds, because there are no chairs or table in the room. At one point John goes and sits on the windowsill, to be in the sunshine. That is why he is the first to see Peter, Simon, Philip and Bartholomew coming towards the house. He shouts to them and then runs out followed by all the rest. Only Jesus remains inside and He stands up and turns towards the door... 332.1

The new arrivals come in. It is easy to imagine the exuberance of Peter, as it is easy to imagine the deep respect of Simon Zealot. But the attitude of Philip and particularly of Bartholomew is a real surprise. I would say that when they come in they look afraid and worried, and although Jesus opens His arms wide towards them, to exchange the kiss of peace which He has already given Peter and Simon, they fall on their knees, and bend their foreheads to the floor, kissing Jesus' feet, and they remain thus... and Bartholomew's stifled sighs indicate that he is weeping silently on Jesus' feet.

«What is worrying you, Bartholomew? Are you not coming to be embraced by your Master? And you, Philip, why are you so timid? If I did not know that you are two honest people, in whose hearts no wickedness can dwell, I should suspect that you are guilty. But it is not so. Come, therefore! I have been waiting so long to receive your kisses and see the limpid look of your faithful eyes...»

«So have we... Lord...» says Bartholomew raising his face on which tears shine. «We have desired nothing but You, and we have been wondering how we might have displeased You to deserve to be kept away from You for such a long time. And we thought that it was unfair... But now we know... Oh! forgive us, Lord! We ask You to forgive us. I, in particular, because Philip was separated from You because of me. And I have already asked him to forgive me.!... I am the guilty one, I... the old Israelite, who is so reluctant to change, and who has grieved You...»

Jesus bends and forces him to stand up, as He forces Philip and He embraces them together saying: «But of what are you accusing yourself? You have done nothing wrong. Neither has Philip. You are My dear apostles, and today I am very happy to have you here with Me, re-united forever...»

332.2 «No... [2]For a long time we have been unaware of the reason why You rightly distrusted us to the extent of excluding us from the apostolic family. But now we know... and we ask You to forgive us, and I in particular ask You, Jesus, my Master...» And Bartholomew looks at Him full of anxiety, of love and compassion. Old as he is, he seems a father who looks at his afflicted son and scans his face thinned by grief, which he had not noticed, neither had he noticed how that face had thinned and aged... And fresh tears stream down Bartholomew's cheeks. And he exclaims: «But what have they done to You? What have they done to us, to make us all suffer like this? An evil spirit seems to have come among us to upset us, to make us sad, weak, listless, foolish... So stupid that we did not understand that You were suffering...On the contrary we increased Your suffering through our meanness, dullness, respect for public opinion and our old humanity... Yes, the old man has always triumphed in us, and Your perfect vitality has never been able to renew us. That is what disturbs me! Notwithstanding all my love, I have not been able to change, to understand You and follow You... I have followed You only with my body... But You wanted us to follow You with our souls... to understand Your perfection... in order to be able to perpetuate You... Oh! My Master! You will leave us one day, after so many struggles, snares, so much disgust and sorrow, and You will be grieved seeing that we are still unprepared!...» And Bartholomew inclines his head on Jesus' shoulder and weeps desolately, afflicted with the knowledge that he has been a dull disciple.

«Do not lose heart, Nathanael. You see all that like an absurdity that surprises you. But your Jesus knew that you are men... and He does not expect more than you can give. Oh! You will give Me everything. But now you must grow and be perfected... It is slow work. But I can wait. And I rejoice at your perfecting. Because it is a continuous improvement in My Life. Also your tears, also the harmony among those who were with Me, also the kindness that follows the harshness typical of your nature, and comes about after selfishness and spiritual greed, even your present seriousness, everything is a stage of your growing in Me. So, do not worry. Set your mind at rest, for I know. Everything. Your honesty, your good faith, your generosity, your sincere love. Should I doubt My wise Bart and Philip, so sensible and loyal? I would wrong My Father, Who granted Me to have
you among My dearest ones. [3]Now... Let us sit down here, and 332.3
those who have already rested can look after their tired hungry brothers giving them food and relief. In the meantime tell your Master and brothers what they do not know.»

And He sits on His little bed with Philip and Nathanael beside Him, while Peter and Simon sit on the next bed, opposite Jesus, knees to knees.

«Will you speak, Philip? I have already spoken. And you have been more just than I have, all this time...»

«Oh! Bartholomew! Just! I had only understood that if the Master had not taken us with Him, it was not because of inconstancy or animosity towards us... And I endeavoured to set your mind at peace... preventing you from thinking of things, as later you would have repented of your thoughts and would have felt remorse. I had one remorse only... for preventing you from disobeying the Master when you wanted to follow Simon of Jonah who was going to Nazareth to get Marjiam... Later... I saw both your body and soul suffer so much, that I said: "It would have been better if I had let him go! The Master would have forgiven his disobedience and Bartholomew would not be poisoning his soul with such ideas"... But... see? If you had gone, you would never have had the key to the mystery... and perhaps your suspicion of the Master's inconstancy would never have been dispelled. Instead...»

«Yes. Thus... I understood. [4]Master, Simon of Jonah and Si- 332.4

mon Zealot, whom I harassed with questions to find out many things and have confirmation of things I already knew, said only this to me: "The Master has suffered *very much*, so much that He has grown thin and old. And the whole of Israel, and first of all we ourselves, are to be blamed for that. He loves and forgives us. But He does not want to speak of the past. So we advise you not to ask questions and not to say anything...". But I want to say something. I will not ask any question. But I must speak, so that You may know. Because nothing of what is in the soul of Your apostle is to be concealed from You. One day — Simon and the others had already gone away a few days before — Michael of Cana came to me. He is a distant relation, a good friend and an old schoolmate... I am sure that he came in good faith. Because he is fond of me. But he who sent him is not in good faith. He wanted to know why I had remained at home... while the others had left. And he said to me: "So it is true? You parted from them because, as a good Israelite, you could not approve of certain things. And the others, beginning with Jesus of Nazareth, let you go quite willingly, because they know that you would not help them, not even as a silent accomplice. You are doing the right thing! I see that you are still the man of good old days. I thought you had become corrupt by denying Israel. You are doing the right thing for your spirit, your own welfare and for your relatives. Because the Sanhedrin will not forget what is happening, and those who are taking part in it will be persecuted". I said to him: "What are you talking about? I told you that I was instructed to stay at home both because of the season and to send eventual pilgrims to Nazareth or inform them to wait for the Master at Capernaum by the end of Shebat, and you are talking about parting, complicity, persecutions? What do you mean?...". Philip, that is what I said, did I not?»

Philip nods assent.

Bartholomew resumes: «Michael then told me that it was a known fact that You were rebelling against the advice and order of the members of the Sanhedrin by keeping John of Endor and a Greek woman with You... My Lord, I am grieving You, am I not? But I must tell You. I ask You: is it true that they were at Nazareth?»

«Yes, it is.»

«Is it true that they left with You?»

«Yes, it is.»

«Philip: Michael was right! But how did he know?»

«That's no problem! It's those snakes who stopped me and Simon, and goodness knows how many more. The usual vipers» says Peter impulsively.

Jesus instead asks quietly: «Did he not tell you anything else? Be sincere with your Master, to the very end.»

«Nothing else. He wanted to know from me... And I told Michael a lie. I said: "I will be staying at home until Passover". I was afraid he might follow me, or... I don't know... I was afraid I might injure You... Then I understood why You had left me... You realized that I was still too much an Israelite...» Bartholomew begins to weep again... «... and You had doubts about me...»

«No. Absolutely not. It was not necessary for you to be with your companions at that particular moment, whereas you were necessary, and you can see that yourself, at Bethsaida. Each man has his mission; every age has its work...»

«No. Don't put me aside because of work, Lord. Don't worry about that... You are good. But I want to be with You. It is a punishment to be away from You... And I, although silly and incapable... I could have at least comforted You, if I could have done nothing else. I have understood... You sent these ones here away with those two. Don't tell me. I don't want to know. But I feel that it is so, and I say so. Well, in that case, I could and should have been with You. But You did not take me to punish me for being so reluctant to become "new". But I swear it to You, Master, what I suffered has changed me and *never again* will You see the old Nathanael in me.»

«So you can see that our suffering has come to a joyful end for
everybody. [5]And now we shall slowly go to meet Thomas and Ju- 332.5
das, without waiting for them to go to the appointed place. And
we shall set out again with them... There is so much to be done!...
We will set off tomorrow. Quick.»

«And You will be doing the right thing. Because the weather is changing in the north. A calamity for cultivations...» says Philip.

«Yes! The recent hailstorms have destroyed strips of the country. You should see them, Lord! Certain places seem to have been burned out by fire. And the strange thing is that the disaster happened as I said: in strips» says Peter.

«While you were away, we had many hailstorms. One day, about the middle of Tebeth, it looked like a real scourge. I am told that down in the plain they have to sow all over again. It was warmer previously. But since then sunshine is a pleasure. We are going backwards... What strange signs! What will they be?» asks Philip.

«Nothing but the effect of lunations. Do not worry about it. These things should not impress you. In any case we are going towards the plain and it will be pleasant to travel. It will be cold, but not very, and in return it will be dry weather. Come with Me in the meantime. There is lovely sunshine on the terrace. We can rest up there, all together...»

333. Towards Sicaminon with Ten Apostles.

18th November 1945.

333.1 [1] «And now that we have also satisfied the shepherd, what shall we do?» asks Peter, who is alone with Jesus, while the others are in a group a few metres behind them.

«We are going to the road along the coast, towards Sicaminon.»

«Are we?! I thought we were going to Capernaum...»

«It is not necessary, Simon of Jonah. Not necessary. You have had news of your wife and of the boy, and with regard to Judas... it will be easier to go and meet him.»

«Exactly, my Lord. Is he not coming by the inland road, along the river and the lake? It is the shortest and the best sheltered one...»

«But he is not coming that way. Remember that he has to watch over the disciples and they are mostly scattered on the western side in this season, which is also very cold once again.»

«All right. If You say so... I am satisfied with being with You and seeing that You are not so sad. And... I am in no hurry to meet Judas of Simon. I wish we did not meet him!... We have been so well among ourselves!...»

«Simon, Simon! Is that your brotherly charity?»

«Lord... it is my truth» says Peter frankly. And he says so with such impetuosity and expression that Jesus finds it difficult not to laugh. But how can anyone reproach such a frank and loyal man severely?

Jesus prefers to be silent, showing extreme interest in the slopes on their left, while the plain expands on their right. The other nine, in group, are following them talking, and John seems a good shepherd, as he is carrying a lamb on his shoulders, probably a present from Annas, the shepherd.

After a little while Peter asks once again: «Are we not going to Nazareth?»

«We shall certainly go. My Mother will be pleased to hear of the journey of John and Syntyche.»

«And to see You!»

«And to see Me.»

«Will they have left Her at least in peace?»

«We shall find out.»

«But why are they so ruthless? There are so many people like John even in Judaea, and yet... In fact, to spite Rome, they protect them and hide them...»

«You must convince yourself that they do it, not because of John, but because he is a witness for the prosecution against Me.»

«But they will never find him now! You organized everything very well... You sent us all alone... by sea... in a little boat for several miles, and later, on the other side of the frontier, by ship... Oh! all well organized! I really hope that they will be disappointed.»

«They will be.»

«I am anxious to see Judas of Kerioth, to practise a little astrology on him, like a sky swept by winds and full of signs, to see whether...»

«Now, that is enough!»

«You are right. It's a fixed idea I have in here» and he strikes his forehead.

[2] Jesus, to divert his attention, calls all the others and points 333.2
out to them the strange destruction worked by hail and cold that took place when people would presume that the risk was over for that year... Some say one thing, some another, but they are

inclined to consider it a divine punishment for insolent Palestine that will not accept the Lord. And the more learned among them cite similar events, mentioned by ancient stories, while the younger and less educated ones listen with great astonishment and attention.

Jesus shakes His head. «It is the effect of the moon and of remote winds. I have already told you. In the hyperborean countries a phenomenon has taken place and whole regions are suffering from its consequences.»

«But why, then, some fields are beautiful?»

«Hail does that.»

«But could it not be a punishment for the most wicked ones?»

«It could be. But it is not. It would be dreadful if it were...»

«Almost all our Fatherland would become arid and desolate, would it not, Lord?» saysAndrew.

«But in the prophecies it is stated, through symbols, that evil will befall those who do not accept the Messiah. Can the Prophets possibly tell lies?»

«No, Bartholomew. And what was said, will happen. But the Most High is so infinitely good that He wants much more than what is happening at present to punish people. You must be good, too, and not always wish punishment for those whose hearts and minds are hardened. You must wish them conversion, not pun-
333.3 ishment. [3]John, hand the lamb to one of your companions and come and look at the sea from the top of those dunes. I am coming, too.»

In fact they are on a road very close to the sea and it is separated from it only by a large strip of undulating dunes on which some thin palm trees are swaying, or ruffled tamarisks, mastic trees and other sand plants grow.

Jesus goes with John. But who leaves Him? Nobody. And soon they are all up there, in the pleasant beautiful sunshine, facing the clear charming sea...

The town of Ptolemais is very near with its white houses.

«Are we entering it?» asks Judas of Alphaeus.

«It is not necessary. We will stop and eat at the first houses. I want to be at Sicaminon by evening. We may find Isaac there.»

«How much good he is doing, eh? Did You hear Abel, John and Joseph?»

«Yes. But all the disciples are very active. I bless My Father, day and night, for that. You all... My joy, My peace, My security...» and He looks at them with so much love that tears come to the eyes of the ten apostles...

And with such loving look my vision ends.

334. Thomas and Judas Iscariot Meet Up with the Apostolic Group.

19th November 1945.

[1] Although the sun is shining in the clear sky, it is bitter cold in the Kishon valley, swept by an icy wind blowing across the northern hills and destroying the tender plants, which shiver and crumple up, nipped as they are, destined to die with their new verdant foliage. 334.1

«Is this cold going to last long?» asks Matthew wrapping himself in his heavy mantle, through which only a tiny part of his face can be seen, that is, his nose and eyes.

Bartholomew replies in a voice stifled by his large mantle that covers his mouth: «Perhaps until the end of this lunation.»

«In that case we are in for it! But never mind! Fortunately we shall be staying in hospitable houses in Nazareth... And in the meantime it will be over.»

«Yes, Matthew. As far as I am concerned it is already over, now that I see that Jesus is not so depressed. Don't you think that He is more cheerful?» asks Andrew.

«He is. But I... well, it seems impossible to me that He got so run down just because of what we know. Has there really been nothing else, as far as you know?» asks Philip.

«No. Nothing. On the contrary I can tell you that at the Syro-Phoenician border the believers there made Him very happy and He worked those miracles about which we told you» replies James of Alphaeus assuring him.

«He has been very much with Simon of Jonah these last days. And Simon has changed a lot... Of course, you have all changed. I don't know... You seem to be... more austere, I would say» says Philip.

«That is only your impression!... In actual fact we are what

we were. Certainly it was not pleasant to see the Master so depressed for so many reasons, and hear how fierce they are against Him... But we will defend Him. Oh! They will not do Him any
334.2 harm if we are with Him. [2]Last night, after I heard what Hermas was saying, and he is serious and reliable, I said to Him: "You must no longer remain alone. You now have disciples who, as You can see, are active and are doing well, and are continuously increasing. So we will stay with You. I do not mean that You will have to do everything. It is time for You to cheer up, my dear brother. You will stay with us, among us, like Moses on the mountain and we will fight for You, and will be ready, if necessary, to defend You also physically. What happened to John the Baptist must not happen to You". Because, after all, if the disciples of the Baptist had not been reduced to two or three fainthearted ones, he would not have been caught. And we are twelve and I want to persuade some of the most faithful and vigorous disciples to join us or, at least, to be near us. For instance, those who were with John at Machaerus, they are brave and faithful men: John, Matthias and also Joseph. Do you know that he is a promising young man?» says Thaddeus.

«Yes. Isaac is an angel, but his strength is entirely spiritual. Joseph is strong also physically. He is almost our age.»

«And he learns quickly. Did you hear what Hermas said? "If he had studied he would be a rabbi besides being a just man". And Hermas knows what he is talking about.»

«I however... would keep close to us also Stephen and Hermas, and John, the priest because of their knowledge of the Law and of the Temple. Do you know what their presence means for scribes and Pharisees? A check, a restraint... And for people in doubt it means: "Also the best people in Israel are with the Rabbi as His pupils and servants!"» says James of Alphaeus.

«You are right. Let us tell the Master. You heard what He said yesterday: "You must obey, but it is also your duty to open your minds to Me and say what you think is right, so that you may learn how to instruct people in the future. And, if I see that what you say is just, I will accept your ideas"» says the Zealot.

«Perhaps He does that to show that He loves us, seeing that we are all more or less convinced that we are the cause of His suffering» remarks Bartholomew.

«Or He is really tired of having to see to everything and of being the only one who makes decisions and responsibility. Perhaps He also realizes that His perfect holiness is… I would say almost an imperfection, considering what is in front of Him: the world that is not holy. We are not perfect saints. Just not as bad rascals as other people… and therefore more able to reply to those who are just like us» says Simon Zealot.

«And to know them, you should say!» adds Matthew.

«Oh! as far as that is concerned, I am sure that He knows them, too. In fact, He knows them better than we do, because He can read the hearts of people. I am as certain as I am sure that I am alive» says James of Zebedee.

«Well, then, why at times does He behave as He does, exposing Himself to trouble and danger?» asks Andrew desolately.

«Who knows? I cannot tell you» says Thaddeus shrugging his shoulders. And the others agree with him.

[3] John is silent. His brother teases him: «Since you always know 334.3
everything about Jesus — at times you seem to be very close to each other — has He ever told you why He behaves like that?»

«Yes. I asked Him also recently. He always replies: "Because I must. I must act as if the whole world were of ignorant but good people. I teach everybody the same doctrine and thus the children of Truth will be separated from those of Falsehood". He also said to me: "See, John? This is like a first judgement, not a universal or collective one, but a single judgement. According to their action of faith, charity and justice lambs will be separated from kids. And that will also last afterwards, when I shall no longer be here, but there will be My Church, forever and ever, until the end of the world. The first judgement of the mass of human people will take place in the world, where men act freely, before Good and Evil, Truth and Falsehood. As the first judgement took place in the Earthly Paradise, in front of the tree of Good and Evil, infringed by those who disobeyed God. Then at the death of each individual, the judgement already written in the book of human actions by a faultless Mind will be ratified. *The Great, the Terrible Judgement* will be the last one, when the mass of men will be judged again. From Adam to the last man. They will be judged for what they *freely wanted* for themselves on the earth. Now, if I should select by Myself those who deserve the Word of God, His Miracle,

His Love and those who do not — and I could do it by divine right and ability — those who are excluded, even if they were demons, on the day of their individual judgment, would shout loud: 'Your Word is the culprit because He did not want to teach us'. But they will not be able to say that... or rather, they will say so, lying once more. And they will therefore be judged".»

«So to refuse His doctrine is to be a reprobate?» asks Matthew.

«I don't know about that, whether all those who do not believe will be reprobates. If you remember, while speaking to Syntyche He gave us to understand that those who act honestly in life are not reprobates, even if they believe in other religions. But we can ask Him. Israel, which is aware of the Messiah and now believes in Him partly and badly, or rejects Him, will certainly be severely judged.»

334.4 [4] «The Master speaks a lot to you, and you know many things which we don't» remarks his brother James.

«It's your fault and the fault of all of you. I ask Him questions with simplicity. At times I ask Him questions that must make His John appear a big fool to Him. But I do not mind. All I want is to know what He thinks and keep it within me to make it mine. You ought to do the same. But you are always afraid! Of what? Of being ignorant? Of being superficial? Of being blockheads? You should be afraid only of not being yet prepared when He goes away. He always says so... and I always repeat it to myself to be prepared for the separation... But I feel that it will be very sorrowful...»

«Don't make me think of it!» exclaims Andrew. And the others echo his words sighing.

«But when will it happen? He always says: "Soon". But that could be within a month or within years. He is so young and time flies so fast... What is the matter, brother? You have turned very pale...» Thaddeus asks James.

«Nothing! I was thinking...» replies immediately James of Alphaeus with his head lowered.

And Thaddeus bends to see his face... «You have tears in your eyes! What is the matter?...»

«Not more than you have... I was thinking of when we shall be alone.»

5 «Oh! What is the matter with Simon of Jonah who is running ahead shouting like a merganser on a stormy day?» asks James of Zebedee, pointing to Peter who has left Jesus alone and has run away shouting words that the wind prevents his companions from hearing. 334.5

They quicken their pace and see that Peter has taken a little path coming from Sephoris, which is now close at hand (so the apostles say, asking one another whether Jesus has ordered him to go to Sephoris by that short cut). But looking carefully they see that Thomas and Judas are the only two travellers coming from the town towards the main road.

«Look at that! Here? Just here? Oh! What are they doing here? If they were to go anywhere, from Nazareth they were to go to Cana and then to Tiberias...» many remark.

«Perhaps they were coming here looking for disciples. That was their mission» says wise Zealot, who feels suspicion being roused in the hearts of many like an awakened snake.

«Let us quicken our pace. Jesus is alone and He seems to be waiting for us...» advises Matthew.

They go and reach Jesus at the same time as Peter, Judas and Thomas.

Jesus is very pale, so much so that John asks Him: «Are You not feeling well?» Jesus smiles and makes a gesture of denial while He greets the two who have come back after such a long absence.

He embraces Thomas first; he is as prosperous and cheerful as usual, but he becomes serious when he sees the Master so changed and he politely asks: «Have You been ill?»

«No, Tom. I have not. And have you always been well and happy?»

«Yes, I have, Lord. I have always been well and always happy. I missed You, had You been there my heart would have been utterly happy. My father and mother are grateful to You for sending me home for a little while. My father was not very well, so I worked for him. I went to my twin sister's and saw my little nephew and I had him named as you suggested. Then Judas came and he made me go round like a little dove in love, up and down, wherever there were disciples. He had already gone round very much on his own. But he will tell You now, as he worked for ten and deserves to be listened to by You.»

Jesus lets him go and it is now Judas' turn, who has been waiting patiently and now comes forward in a frank, easy, triumphant attitude. Jesus pierces him with His sapphire eyes. But He kisses him and is kissed by him, exactly as He did with Thomas. And the words that follow are full of love: «Was your mother happy to see you, Judas? Is the holy woman well?»

«Yes, Master, and she blesses You for sending her Judas to her. She wanted to send You some gifts. But how could I bring them, since I had to go here and there, across mountains and valleys.
334.6 [6]You need not worry, Master. All the groups of disciples whom I visited are working in a holy manner. The news is spreading out more and more. I wanted to make a personal check on the consequences with the most powerful scribes and Pharisees. I was acquainted with many and I met more now, for Your sake. I approached Sadducees and Herodians... Oh! I can assure You that my dignity was utterly crushed!... But it was for Your sake! I am prepared to do that and more. I received disdainful answers and anathemas. But I was also able to give rise to appreciative understanding in people biased against You. I do not want to be praised by You. It is enough for me that I did my duty and I thank the Eternal Father for helping me all the time. In some cases I had to make use of miracles. And I was sorry, because they deserved thunderbolts, not blessings. But You say that we must love and be patient... I behaved thus to the honour and glory of God and for Your joy. I hope that many obstacles have been removed for good, also because I guaranteed upon my honour that those two, who cast such a gloomy shadow over us, are no longer with You. Later I had a scruple about stating what I did not know for certain. So I decided to check in order to do what might be necessary, as I did not want them to find out that I had lied, which would have made those to be converted suspect me forever. Imagine! I also approached Annas and Caiaphas!... Oh! They wanted to annihilate me with their reproaches... But I was so humble and persuasive, that they ended up by saying to me: "Well, if the situation is really like that... We were told it was different. The rectors of the Sanhedrin, who were in a position to know about it, told us the opposite and...".»

«You are not going to say that Joseph and Nicodemus are liars» interrupts the Zealot, who has controlled himself so far, but can no longer do so, and is livid with his effort.

«Who said so? On the contrary, Joseph saw me when I was coming out of Annas' house and he said to me: "Why are you so upset?". I told him everything, and how, following his advice and Nicodemus', You, Master, had sent away the galley-slave and the Greek woman. Because You have sent them away, have You not?» says Judas staring at Jesus with his jet eyes, which shine to the point of being fluorescent. He seems to want to pierce Jesus with his eyes in order to read what He has done.

Jesus, Who is still in front of him and very close, says calmly: «Please go on, I am very interested in what you are saying. It is an accurate report and can be very useful.»

«Ah! so I was saying that Annas and Caiaphas have changed their minds. That means a lot to us, does it not? And then!... Oh! I will make you laugh, now! Do you know that I was caught in the middle by rabbis who examined me, like a minor who becomes of age? And what an examination! Well. I convinced them and they let me go. Then I became suspicious and I was afraid I had said something that was not true. So I decided to take Thomas and go once again where the disciples were, or where one could presume that John and the Greek woman were sheltered. I went to Lazarus, to Manaen, to Chuza's palace, to Eliza in Bethzur, to Johanna's garden in Bether, to Gethsemane, to Solomon's little house beyond the Jordan, to the Clear Water, to Nicodemus, to Joseph...»

«But had you not seen him?»

«Yes. And he had assured me that he had not seen those two any more. But You know... I wanted to be sure... In short: I inspected every place where I expected him to be... And do not think that I suffered not finding him. You would do me wrong. Every time — and Thomas can confirm this — every time I came out of a place without finding him and without any trace of him, I would say: "Praised be the Lord!", and I said: "O Eternal Father, grant that I may never find him!". I did! It was the desire of
my soul... Esdraelon was the last place... [7]Ah! By the way! Ish- 334.7
mael ben Fabi, who is in his country house at Megiddo, wishes to have You as his guest... But if I were You, I would not go...»

«Why not? I will certainly go. I am anxious to see him, too. In fact, we will go there at once. Instead of going to Sephoris, we will go to Esdraelon, then to Megiddo the day after tomorrow, which is the Sabbath eve, and from there to Ishmael's house.»

«No, Lord! Why? Do You think that he is fond of You?»

«But if you have approached him and changed him in My favour, why do you not want Me to go?»

«I did not approach him... He was in the fields and he recognised me. But I — is that true, Thomas? — I wanted to run away when I saw him. But I could not, because he called me by my name. I can but advise You never to go to any Pharisee, or scribe or the like. It will do You no good. Let us be among ourselves, all alone, with the people, and nothing else. Including Lazarus, Nicodemus and Joseph... It will be a sacrifice... But it is better to make it, to avoid jealousies, hatred... and laying ourselves open to censure... When at table You speak... and they work underhand at Your words. But let us go back to John... I was now going to Sicaminon, although Isaac, whom I met at the border of Samaria, swore to me that he had not seen him since October.»

«And Isaac swore the truth. But what you are advising, concerning contacts with scribes and Pharisees, clashes with what you said before. You defended Me... That is what you did, is it not? You said: "I have demolished many prejudices against You". You said so, did you not?»

«Yes, Master, I did.»

«Well, then, why can I not complete My defence Myself? So we will go to Ishmael. And you will now go back and warn him. Andrew, Simon Zealot and Bartholomew will come with you. We shall go to the peasants and rest with them. As far as Sicaminon is concerned, we have just come from there. And we were eleven. We confirm to you that John is not there. Neither is he at Capernaum or Bethsaida, at Tiberias, Magdala, Nazareth, Korazim, Bethlehem in Galilee, and so forth for all the other places you perhaps wished to call at... to make sure that John is not among disciples or in friendly houses.»

334.8 [8]Jesus speaks calmly, in a natural tone... And yet there must be something in Him that upsets Judas, who changes colour for a moment. Jesus embraces him as if He wanted to kiss him... And while His cheek is against Judas', He whispers to him in a low voice: «You wretch! What have you done with your soul?»

«Master... I...»

«Go away! You stink of hell more than Satan himself! Be quiet!... And repent, if you can.»

Judas... I would have run away at full speed. Not he! He impudently says in a loud voice: «Thank You, Master. But I beg You, before I go, may I speak to You privately for a moment?»

All the others move a good distance away.

«Why, Lord, did You say those words to me? You troubled me...»

«Because it is the truth. He who deals with Satan, smells like Satan.»

«Ah! is it because of necromancy? Oh! You frightened me! That was a joke! Nothing but the joke of a curious child. And it helped me to approach some Sadducees and to lose all desire to meet them again. So You can see that You can absolve me without any worry. They are things of no importance when one has Your power. You were right. Come on, Master! My fault is a very light one!... Great is Your wisdom. But who told You?»

Jesus looks at him severely but does not reply.

«But have You really seen the sin in my heart?» asks Judas somewhat frightened.

«And it disgusted Me. Go away! And say no more.» And He turns His back to him and goes back to the disciples, whom He orders to change direction, after saying goodbye to Bartholomew, Simon and Andrew, who join Judas and go away quickly, while those who have remained walk away slowly, unaware of the truth, which is known to Jesus only.

They are so unaware that they praise Judas for his activity and sagacity. And honest Peter sincerely accuses himself of his heart's rash judgement on his fellow-disciple...

Jesus smiles... a mild, rather tired smile, as if He were abstracted and could just hear the chattering of His companions, who know of events only by what their human nature allows them to know.

335. In the House of the Vile Pharisee Ishmael Ben Fabi, Jesus Cures on the Sabbath.

11th September 1944.

335.1 [1] I see Jesus walk fast along a main road, which the cold wind of a winter morning sweeps and hardens. The fields on both sides of the road are covered with a thin green veil of corn, which has just began to grow and is a promise of future bread, although a promise that is even difficult to imagine. There are drills in the shade, which are still devoid of that blessed green down, and only those in the more sunny places have the light green veil that is so joyous as it announces the oncoming springtime. Fruit-trees are still bare, none of the dark branches have yet put forth buds. Only olive-trees have their everlasting green-grey foliage, which is as sad in the August sunshine as it is in the first light of this winter morning. Also the thick leaves of cacti are green, a mellow green of freshly painted ceramic.

As usual, Jesus is walking two or three steps ahead of His disciples. They are all wrapped in their woolen mantles. At a certain point Jesus stops and turning around He asks the disciples: «Are you familiar with the road?»

«This is the road, but we do not know where the house is, because it is further inland... Perhaps it is over there, where those olive-trees are...»

«No. It must be down there, at the bottom, where those big bare trees are...»

«There should be a road for carts...»

In short: they do not know anything precisely. There are no people to be seen on the road or in the fields. They proceed at random, looking for the road.

They find a little house of poor people, with two or three little fields around it. A little girl is drawing water from a well.

«Peace to you, little girl» says Jesus stopping at the hedge where there is a passage way.

«Peace to You. What do You want?»

«Some information. Where is the house of Ishmael, the Pharisee?»

«You are on the wrong road, Lord. You must go back to the cross-roads and take the road that goes in the direction where the sun sets. But it is a long way, a very long one, because You have to go back to the cross-roads and then walk a good distance. Have You had anything to eat? It is cold and one feels the cold more on an empty stomach. Come in, if You wish. We are poor. But You are not rich either. You can make the best of it. Come.» And in her shrill voice she shouts: «Mother!»

[2] A woman of about thirty-five or forty years old comes to the 335.2
door. Her face is honest but rather sad. She is holding in her arms a half-naked child about three years old.

«Come in. The fire is lit. I will give You bread and milk.»

«I am not alone. I have these friends with Me.»

«Let them all come in and may the blessing of God come with the pilgrims to whom I am giving hospitality.»

They enter a low dark kitchen that is made cheerful by a blazing fire. They sit here and there on rustic chests.

I will have something ready in a moment... It is still early... I have not tidied anything up yet... Excuse me.»

«Are you alone?» It is Jesus who asks.

«I am married and I have seven children. The first two are still at the market in Nain. They have to go because their father is not well. It's a very sad situation... The girls help me. This is the last one. But I have another one just a little older.»

The little one, who is now wearing his little tunic, runs barefooted towards Jesus and looks at Him inquisitively. Jesus smiles at him. They have become friends.

«Who are You?» asks the boy confidently.

«I am Jesus.»

The woman turns around looking at Him attentively. She stops between the fireplace and the table, with a loaf of bread in her hands. She opens her mouth to speak, but does not say anything.

The boy continues: «Where are You going?»

«Along the roads of the world.»

«What for?»

«To bless good children and their homes where people are faithful to the Law.»

[3] The woman makes a gesture. Then she nods to Judas Iscariot 335.3
who is closest to her. He bends towards the woman who asks: «But who is your friend?»

And Judas replies conceitedly (one would think that the Messiah is what He is, thanks to Judas' kindness): «He is the Rabbi of Galilee: Jesus of Nazareth. Don't you know, woman?»

«This is a secluded road and I have so many sorrows!... But... could I speak to Him about them?»

«You can» replies Judas condescendingly. He seems an important person of the world granting an audience.

Jesus is still speaking to the boy who asks Him whether He has any children.

While the girl seen at the well and another older one bring milk and bowls, the woman approaches Jesus. She remains for a moment in suspense, then she stifles a cry: «Jesus: have mercy on my husband!»

Jesus stands up. He dominates her with His height, but looks at her so kindly that she plucks up courage again. «What do you want Me to do?»

«He is very ill. He is swollen like a wineskin and he cannot bend to work. He cannot rest because he chokes and tosses about... And we still have little children...»

«Do you want Me to cure him? But why do you want that of Me?»

«Because You are You. I did not know You, but I heard people speak of You. My good luck has brought You to my house after I looked for You three times at Nain and Cana. My husband was with me twice. He was looking for You, although traveling by cart makes him suffer so much... Even now he has gone with his brother... We were told that the Rabbi, after leaving Tiberias, was going towards Caesarea Philippi. He has gone there waiting for You...»

335.4 «I did not go to Caesarea. [4]I am going to see Ishmael, the Pharisee and then I shall go towards the Jordan...»

«What? You, a good man, are going to Ishmael?»

«Yes, I am. Why?»

«Because... because... Lord, I know that You say that we must not judge, that we must forgive and love one another. I have never seen You before. But I have tried to learn as much as I could about You, and I have prayed the Eternal Father to grant me to hear You at least once. I do not want to do anything which may displease You... But how can one not judge Ishmael and how can one love him? I have nothing in common with him and therefore I have nothing to forgive him. We just shake off the insolent words he says to us when he meets our poverty on his way, with the same patience with which we shake off the dust and mud when he splashes us passing by in his fast coaches. But it is too difficult to love him and not judge him... He is so bad!»

«Is he so bad? To whom?»

«To everybody. He oppresses his servants, he lends on usury and exacts pitilessly. He loves but himself. He is the most cruel man in the countryside. He is not worth it, Lord.»

«I know. You have spoken the truth.»

«And You are going there?»

«He invited Me.»

«Do not trust him, Lord. He did not do it out of love. *He is not capable of loving.* And You... You cannot love him.»

«I love also sinners, woman. I came to save those who are lost...»

«But You will not save him. Oh! Forgive me for judging! You know... Everything You do is good! Forgive my silly tongue and do not punish me.»

«I will not punish you. But do not do it again. Love also wicked people. Not because of their wickedness, but because it is through love that mercy is granted to them, that they may convert. You are good and willing to become even better. You love the Truth and the Truth speaking to you says that He loves you because you are pitiful to guests and pilgrims according to the
* Law and you have brought up your children accordingly. God
will be your reward. [5]I must go to Ishmael who invited Me to 335.5
show Me to many of his friends who want to meet Me. I cannot wait any longer for your husband, who, incidentally, is on his way back home. But tell him to be patient for another little while and to come *immediately* to Ishmael's house. And I ask you to come as well. I will cure him.»

«Oh! Lord!...» the woman is on her knees at Jesus' feet and looks at Him smiling and weeping. She then says: «But this is the Sabbath!...»

---

* **Law**, for strangers in general, in: *Exodus 22:20; 23:9*; *Leviticus 19:10.33-34; 23:22*; *Deuteronomy 10:19; 24:14.17-22; 26:11-13; 27:19.* Jesus remembers in 55.2 that the pilgrim is "protected by the law of God".

«I know. I need it to be the Sabbath to say something to Ishmael concerning it. Everything I do, I do for a definite unerring purpose. You must all be aware of that, including you, My friends, who are afraid and would like Me to follow a behaviour according to human convenience to avoid eventual damage. You are led by love. I know. But you must love in a better way those whom you love. Do not postpone the interests of God to the interests of the person you love. Woman, I must go now, I will wait for you. May peace last forever in this house in which God and His Law are loved, marriage is respected, children are brought up holily, the neighbour is loved and the Truth sought. Goodbye.»

Jesus lays His hand on the heads of the woman and of the two young girls, He then bends to kiss the little ones and goes out.

Winter sunshine now mitigates the very cold air. A boy about fifteen years old is waiting with a rustic ramshackle cart.

«This is all I have. But it will be quicker and more comfortable for You.»

«No, woman. Keep the horse fresh to come to Ishmael's house. Just show Me the shortest road.»

The boy walks at His side and through fields and meadows they go towards an undulating ground, beyond which there is a well cultivated small valley a few acres wide, in the middle of which there is a beautiful large low house, surrounded by a well-kept garden.

«That is the house, Lord» says the boy. «If You no longer need me, I will go back home to help my mother.»

«Go and be always a good son. God is with you.»...

335.6 [6]... Jesus enters Ishmael's magnificent country house. Many servants rush to meet the Guest, Who is certainly expected. Some go and inform the landlord, who comes out to meet Jesus bowing deeply.

«You are welcome to my house, Master!»

«Peace to you, Ishmael Ben Fabi. You wanted to see Me. Here I am. Why did you want Me?»

«To have the honour of having You and to introduce You to my friends. I want them to be Your friends as well. As I want You to be my friend.»

«I am the friend of everybody, Ishmael.»

«I know. But, You know! It is wise to have friends high up. And I and my friends are such. Forgive me for telling You, but You neglect too much those who can help You...»

«And are you one of those? Why?»

«I am. Why? Because I admire You and I want You to be my friend.»

«Friend! But do you know, Ishmael, the meaning I attach to that word? Friend to many people means acquaintance, to some it means accomplice, to some servant. To Me it means: *faithful to the Word of the Father.* Who is not such, cannot be My friend, neither can I be his.»

«I want Your friendship, Master, just because I want to be
faithful. Do You not believe me? [7]Look: there is Eleazar com- 335.7
ing. Ask him how I defended You with the Elders. Hello, Eleazar. Come here, the Rabbi wants to ask you something.»

They exchange greetings with low bows and inquisitive looks.

«Will you repeat, Eleazar, what I said for the Master the last time we met?» says Ishmael. Then he withdraws, leaving his friend with Jesus.

«Oh! A true praise! An impassioned speech! Ishmael spoke so well of You, Master, as of the greatest Prophet who ever came to the people of Israel, that I have longed to hear You ever since. I remember that he said that no one had wiser words than Yours, or greater charm, and that if You can draw Your sword as well as You can speak, there will be no greater king than You in Israel.»

«My Kingdom!... That Kingdom, Eleazar, is not a human one.»

«But the King of Israel!»

«Open your minds to understand the meaning of the arcane words. The Kingdom of the King of kings will come. But not according to human standards. Not with regard to what perishes; but with regard to what is eternal. You do not enter it along a flowery road of triumph or on a carpet made purple by enemy blood; but climbing a steep path of sacrifices and a mild staircase of forgiveness and love. *Our victories over ourselves will give us that Kingdom.* And God grant that most people in Israel may understand Me. But it will not be so. You are thinking of what does not exist. A sceptre will be in My hand, and it will be put there by the people of Israel. A regal eternal sceptre. No king will ever be able to take it off My House. But many people in Israel will not be able to look at it without shuddering with horror, because it will have a dreadful name for them.»

«Do You think that we are not capable of following You?»

«If you wanted, you could. But you do not want to. Why do you not want to? You are elderly now. Your age should make you understand and be just, also for your own sake. Young people... may make mistakes and then repent. But you! Death is always close to elderly people. Eleazar, you are less entangled in the theories of many people of your rank. Open your heart to the Light...»

335.8 [8] Ishmael comes back with five more pompous Pharisees: «Come in» says the landlord. They leave the hall, which is well furnished with seats and carpets, and they enter a room into which amphorae are brought for ablutions. They then pass into the dining room, in which everything has been magnificently arranged.

«Jesus beside me. Between me and Eleazar» orders the landlord. And Jesus, Who had remained at the end of the room, near the rather intimidated and neglected disciples, has to sit at the place of honour.

The banquet begins with numerous dishes of roast meat and fish. Wines and syrups, I think, or at least water sweetened with honey, are served several times.

335.9 [9] Everybody tries to make Jesus speak. A shaky old man asks in a decrepit clucking voice: «Is it true what people say, that You are going to change the Law?»

«I will not change one iota of the Law. On the contrary (and Jesus emphasises His words) I have come to complete it again, as it was given to Moses.»

«Do You mean that it was modified?»

«No, never. It only had the same fate as all sublime things entrusted to man.»

«What do You mean? Explain Yourself.»

«I mean that man, through ancient pride or the ancient incentive of treble lust, wanted to touch up the straightforward word and the result was something that oppresses faithful believers, whilst, with regards to those who touched it up, it is nothing but a pile of sentences... to be left to other people.»

«But, Master! Our rabbis...»

«That is an accusation!»

«Don't disappoint our desire to be of assistance to You!...»

«Hey! They are quite right in saying that You are a rebel!»

«Silence! Jesus is my guest. Let Him speak freely.»

«Our rabbis began their work with the holy purpose of making the application of the Law easier. God Himself began that school when He added detailed explanations to the words of the Ten Commandments. So that man could not find the excuse that he had not understood. The work therefore of those teachers who break into crumbs for the children of God the bread given by God for their souls, is holy work. *But it is holy when it pursues a righteous aim.* Which was not always the case. And least of all it is nowadays. But why do you want Me to speak, when you take offence if I enumerate the faults of the mighty ones?»

«Faults! Have we nothing but faults?»

«I wish you had nothing but merits!»

«But we do not have them. That is what You think and what
Your eyes say. [10]Jesus, one does not make powerful friends by 335.10
criticizing them. You will not reign. You are not acquainted with
that art.»

«I do not ask to reign according to your ideas, neither do I beg for friendship. I want love. Honest holy love. A love that extends from Me to those whom I love and is displayed by making use of what I preach to use: mercy.»

«Since I heard You, I have not lent on usury any more» says one. «And God will reward you for that.»

«God is my witness that I have not thrashed my servants any more, although they deserve to be lashed, after I heard one of Your parables» says another one.

«And what about me? I left over ten bushels of barley in the fields for the poor!» states a third one.

The Pharisees praise themselves excellently.

Ishmael has not spoken. Jesus asks him: «And what about you, Ishmael?»

«Oh! I! I have *always* used mercy. I have but to continue as I behaved in the past.»

«Good for you! If it is really so, you are really the man who feels no remorse.»

«No! I really do not.»

Jesus' sapphire glance pierces him.

335.11 [11] Eleazar says touching His arm: «Master, listen to me. I have a special case to submit to You. I recently bought a property of a poor wretch who ruined himself for a woman. He sold it to me, without telling me that there was an old servant, his nurse, in it. She is now blind and feeble-minded. The vendor does not want her. I... would not like to have her either. But to throw her out. What would You do, Master?»

«What would you do if you were to advise somebody else?»

«I would say: "Keep her. A piece of bread will not be your ruin".»

«Why would you say so?»

«Well!... because I think that is what I would do and what I would like to be done to me...»

«You are very close to Justice, Eleazar. Do as you would advise and the God of Jacob will always be with you.»

«Thank You, Master.»

The others are grumbling among themselves.

«What have you to grumble about?» asks Jesus. «Is what I said not just? And has Eleazar not spoken justly? Ishmael, since you have always been merciful, defend your guests.»

«Master, You are right but... if one always did that!... One would become the victim of other people.»

«Whereas, according to you, it is better if other people become our victims, is that right?»

«I don't mean that. But there are cases...»

«The Law says that we must be merciful.»

«Yes, to a poor brother, to a stranger, a pilgrim, a widow, to an orphan. But this old woman, who turned up in Eleazar's property, is not his sister, a pilgrim, a stranger, an orphan or a widow. She is nothing to him. She is just an old piece of furniture, which does not belong to him, and was forgotten by her true master in the sold property. Eleazar, therefore, could throw her out without any scruple at all. He would not be responsible for the death of the old woman. Her true master would...»

«... and he cannot keep her any longer because he is poor himself and thus he is free from obligations as well. So if the old woman dies of starvation, it is her own fault. Is it not so?»

«It is, Master. It is the destiny of those who... are no longer of any use. Sick, old, unfit people are condemned to misery, to begging. And death is the best thing for them... It has always been like that since the beginning of the world, and it will ever be so...»

[12] «Jesus, have mercy on me!» A moaning voice is heard through 335.12
the closed windows; the room is in fact closed and the chandeliers are lit. Perhaps because it is cold.

«Who is calling Me?»

«A nuisance of a fellow. I will have him driven away. Or a beggar. I will have a piece of bread given to him.»

«Jesus, I am ill. Save me!»

«As I said, it is a pestering fellow. I will punish the servant for letting him in.» And Ishmael stands up.

But Jesus Who is at least twenty years younger than he is and head and shoulders over him, makes him sit down again, laying a hand on his shoulders and ordering: «Stay, Ishmael. I want to see the man who is looking for Me. Let him in.»

A dark-haired man comes in. He must be about forty years old. But he is as swollen as a barrel and as yellow as a lemon, his half open lips are violaceous and he is panting. The woman seen in the first part of the vision is with him. The man comes forward with difficulty because of his disease and because he is afraid. He in fact sees that he is being looked at with such evil eyes!

But Jesus has left His place and has gone towards the unhappy man taking him by the hand and leading him to the middle of the room, in the empty space of the 'U' shaped table, right under the chandelier. «What do you want from Me?»

«Master... I have sought You so much, for such a long time... I want nothing but health... for the sake of my children and of my wife... You can do everything... See in what a state I am...»

«And do you believe that I can cure you?»

«I do believe it!... Every step... every jerk is painful... and yet I have travelled for miles and miles looking for You... and I followed You also by cart, without ever reaching You. Of course I believe!... I am surprised that I have not already been cured, since my hand has been in Yours, because everything in You is holy, O Holy Man of God.»

The poor man is puffing and blowing owing to the effort of

speaking so much. His wife looks at him and at Jesus and weeps.
335.13 [13]Jesus looks at them and smiles. He then turns round and asks: «You, old scribe (He addresses the trembling old man who was the first to speak) tell Me: is it lawful to cure on a Sabbath?»

«It is not lawful to do any work on the Sabbath.»

«Not even to save a man from despair? It is not manual work.»

«The Sabbath is sacred to the Lord.»

«Which deed is more worthy of a sacred day than get a son of God to say to the Father: "I love and praise You because You have cured me"?!»

«He must do so even when he is unhappy.»

«Hananiah, do you know that your most beautiful wood is on fire this very moment and the whole slope of the Hermon is bright in the purple flames?»

The old man jumps as if he had been bitten by an asp: «Master, are You telling the truth or are You joking?»

«I am speaking the truth. I see and I know.»

«Oh! Poor me! My most beautiful wood. Thousands of shekels reduced to ashes! Damn! Cursed be the dogs that set it on fire! May their bowels burn like my wood!» The little old man is in despair.

«It is only a wood, Hananiah, and you are complaining! Why do you not praise the Lord in your misfortune? This man is not losing just wood, which will grow again, but his own life and the bread for his children, and he should praise the Lord, while you do not. Well, scribe, am I allowed to cure him on the Sabbath?»

«Cursed be You, him and the Sabbath! I have more important things to think of...» and pushing Jesus aside, Who had laid a hand on his arm, he rushes out furiously and he can be heard shouting in his clucking voice to have his cart.

«And now?» says Jesus looking around at the others. «Now, will you tell Me? Is it lawful or not?»

No reply. Eleazar lowers his head, after moving his lips, which he sets again, shocked by the cold atmosphere in the hall.

«Well, I will speak» asks Jesus. His countenance is imposing and His voice thundering as usual, when He is about to work a miracle. «I will speak. And I say: man, let it be done to you according to your faith. You are cured. Praise the Eternal God. Go in peace.»

The man remains dumbfounded. Perhaps he thought that he would become as thin as in the past all of a sudden. And he does not think that he is cured. But I wonder what he feels... He shouts with joy and throws himself at Jesus' feet and kisses them.

«Go. You may go! Be always good. Goodbye!»

And the man goes out followed by the woman, who turns around until the last moment to greet Jesus.

14 «But, Master... In my house... On the Sabbath...» 335.14

«You do not approve? I know. That is why I came. You are My friend? No. You are My enemy. You are neither sincere with Me nor with God.»

«Are You offending me now?»

«No. I am speaking the truth. You said that Eleazar is not obliged to keep that old woman because she does not belong to
* him. But you had two orphans who belonged to you. They were the children of two faithful servants of yours, who died working for you, the man with a sickle in his hand, the woman killed by too much work, because she had to serve you both for herself and for her husband, as you exacted from her, in order to keep her. In fact you said: "I made the agreement for the work of two people and if you want to stay here, I want your work and the work of your dead husband". And she gave you that and died with the child she had conceived. Because that woman was a mother. And for her there was not even the compassion one feels for an animal about to give birth to its little one. Where are those two children now?»

«I don't know... They disappeared one day.»

«Do not tell lies now. It is enough to have been cruel. It is not necessary to add falsehood to make your Sabbaths hateful to God, even if they are free from servile work. Where are those children?»

«I do not know. Believe me.»

«I know. I found them one cold, wet, dark November evening. I found them starving and shivering, near a house, like two little dogs looking for a mouthful of bread ... Cursed and expelled by a man with the entrails of a dog, but who was worse than a dog, because a dog would have felt pity for those two little or-

---

* **two orphans**, Mary and Matthew, met in 298.2/6 and in 299.2/8.

phans. But you and that man did not feel any. Their parents were no longer of any use to you, is that right? They were dead. And the dead can only weep, in their graves, hearing their unhappy children's sobs, which other people neglect. But the dead, with their souls, take their tears and the tears of their orphans to God and say: "Lord, take vengeance on our behalf because the world oppresses us when it can no longer exploit us". The two little ones were not yet able to serve you, is that right? Perhaps the girl might have been able to glean... And you drove them away and denied them also the few things, which belonged to their father and mother. They might have died of starvation and cold, like two dogs on a cart-road. They might have lived, becoming one a thief and the other a prostitute. Because starvation leads to sin. But what did it matter to you? A little while ago you were quoting the Law to support your theories. Well, does the Law not say: "You must not be harsh with the widow, or with the orphans, if you are harsh with them and they cry out to Me, I shall hear their cry and My anger will flare and I shall kill you with the sword, your own wives will be widows, your own children orphans"? Does the Law not state that? Well, then, why do you not keep it? And you defend Me against other people? Why, then, do you not defend My doctrine in yourself? You want to be My friend? Why, then, do you do the opposite of what I say? One of you is running at a neck breaking speed, tearing his hair, because of the ruin of
his wood. And he does not tear it because of the ruin of his heart!
335.15 And what are you waiting for to do so? [15]Why do you, whom des-
tiny has placed high up, always want to consider yourselves perfect? And supposing you were perfect in something, why do you not endeavor to be so in everything? Why do you hate Me, because I open your wounds? I am the Doctor of your souls. Can a doctor cure a sore if he does not open it and clean it? Do you not know that many people, and that woman who has just gone out is one of them, deserve the first places in the banquet of God, although they apparently look miserable? External appearance does not count; it is the heart and the soul that matter. God sees you from the height of His throne. And He judges you. How many He sees who are better than you are! So listen. As a rule, always act as follows: When you are invited to a wedding banquet, always choose the last place. Double honour will come to you when

the landlord says to you: "Come forward, my friend". Honour to your merit and your humility. Whereas... It will be a sad moment for a proud man to be shamed and hear the landlord say: "Go down there to the end, because there is someone here more worthy than you are". And do the same in the secret banquet of your souls at the wedding with God. He who humbles himself will be
exalted and he who exalts himself will be humbled. [16]Ishmael, 335.16
do not hate Me for curing you. I do not hate you. I came to cure you. You are more seriously ill than that man. You invited Me to give prestige to yourself and satisfaction to your friends. You often invite people, but you do it out of pride and for pleasure. Do not do that. Do not invite rich people, relatives and friends. Open your house and your heart to the poor, to beggars, cripples, to lame people, orphans and widows. In return they will give you blessings. And God will change them into graces. And at the end... what a happy destiny for all the merciful who will be rewarded by God at the resurrection of the dead! Woe to those who cherish only hopes of profit and later close their hearts to the brothers who can no longer serve them. Woe to them! I will revenge the forlorn.»

«Master... I... I want to please You. I will take those children again.»

«No, you will not.»

«Why?»

«Ishmael?!...»

Ishmael lowers his head. He wants to appear humble. But he is a viper deprived of its poison and does not bite because it knows it has none, but waits for the opportunity to bite...

[17] Eleazar endeavors to restore peace saying: «Blessed are those 335.17
who feast with God, in their souls and in the eternal Kingdom. But, believe me, Master. At times it is life that hinders us. Offices... occupations...»

* At this point Jesus tells the parable of the supper and concludes: «Offices... occupations, you said. It is true. That is why I said to you, at the beginning of this banquet, that My Kingdom is conquered through victories over ourselves, not by means of victories in the battle field. The places at the Great Supper

* **parable**, reported here but it can be read in: *Luke 14:16-24* that M.V. refers to in a typewritten copy.

are for the humble-hearted, who are great through their faithful love, which takes no account of sacrifices and overcomes all difficulties to come to Me. Even one hour is sufficient to change a heart. Providing that heart *wants* to change. And one word is sufficient. I have told you many. And I am looking... A holy tree is springing up in a heart. In the others, there are thorns for Me, and in the thorns there are asps and scorpions. It does not matter. I will proceed in My straight way. Let those who love Me follow Me. I go round calling... Let righteous people come to Me. I go round teaching... Let the seekers of justice approach the Fountain. With regard to the others... the Holy Father will judge. Ishmael, I say goodbye to you. Do not hate Me. Meditate. You will see that I was severe out of love, not out of hatred. Peace to this house and to those who dwell in it, peace to everybody, if you deserve peace.»

336. In Nazareth with Four Apostles. Thomas' Devotion to the Blessed Mother.

20th November 1945.

336.1 [1] Ishmael Ben Fabi. Jesus says: «You will put here the vision that you saw on 11th September 1944.» *

336.2 [2] Jesus is once again with His disciples on the road that from the Esdraelon plain leads to Nazareth. They must have spent the night somewhere, because it is early morning. They walk for some time in silence. Jesus is ahead of them, alone, then He calls Peter and Simon and walks with them, finally they are all in a group until they reach a cross-roads where the Nazareth road joins the road that leads to the north.

Jesus beckons those who are speaking to be quiet and says: «We shall now part. I am going to Nazareth with My brothers, with Peter and Thomas. Under the guidance of Simon Zealot, along the Tabor and caravan road, you will go to Debaret, Tiberias, Magdala, Capernaum, and then towards Meron. You will stop at Jacob's to see whether he has been converted and you will

* **vision**, already reported in the previous chapter.

take My blessing to Judas and Anne. You will stay in those houses where they offer you hospitality more insistently. You will stay one night only in each place, because on the Sabbath evening we will meet on the Saphet road.
[3]I will spend the Sabbath at 336.3
Korazim, in the house of the widow. Call on her and tell her. In this way we will at last give peace to the soul of Judas, who will be convinced that John is not in any of those hospitable places...»

«Master! But I believe it!...»

«But it is always better to make sure, so that you will not blush before Caiaphas and Armas, as I do not blush before you or any other man when I say that John is no longer with us. I am taking Thomas to Nazareth, so that he may rest assured also with regards to that place, as he will be able to see with his own eyes...»

«But, Master... I! What do I care? I am only sorry that that man is no longer with us. He may have been what he was. But since we have known him, he has always been better than many famous Pharisees. It is enough for me to know that he did not deny You and did not grieve You and then... whether he is on the earth or in Abraham's bosom, I do not care. Believe me. If he were in my house... I would not disdain him. I hope that You do not think that in the heart of Your Thomas there is more than a natural curiosity, but no animosity, no spur of a more or less honest investigation, no inclination to voluntary or involuntary or authorized espionage, no desire to be harmful...»

«You are offending me! You are insulting me! You are lying! You have seen that I have always acted in a holy way during this time. So why do you say that? What can you say about me? Speak up!» Judas is furious and wild.

«Be silent. Thomas will reply to Me. To Me only, as I spoke to him. I believe Thomas' words. But *that is what I want*, and that will be done, and none of you are entitled to reprove My behaviour.»

«I am not reproaching You... But his insinuation struck me and...»

«You are twelve. Why did it strike you only, when I spoke to everybody?»

«Because I looked for John.»

Jesus says: «Also other companions of yours did so, and other

disciples will do so, but none will feel offended by Thomas' words. It is not a sin to ask after a fellow disciple in an honest manner. Words like those just uttered do not hurt, when our hearts are full of love and honesty and nothing pricks them or makes them supersensible having already been bitten by remorse. Why do you want to remonstrate thus in the presence of your companions? Do you want to be suspected of sin? Wrath and pride are two bad companions, Judas. They drive one to frenzy, and a frenzied person sees what does not exist, and says what should not be said... just as greed and lust drive people to guilty actions in order to be satisfied... Get rid of such wicked servants... And in the meantime you had better know that during the many days while you were away, there has *always* been very good harmony among us, as well as obedience and respect. We love
336.4 one another, do you understand?... [4]Goodbye, My dear friends. Go and *love* one another. Is that clear to you? Love one another and bear with one another, speak little and act well. Peace be with you.»

He blesses them and while they go to the right, Jesus continues on His way with His cousins, Peter and Thomas.

They proceed in dead silence. Then Peter explodes in a thundering solitary: «Who knows!» as a consequence of I wonder what long meditation. The others look at him...

Jesus immediately wards off possible questions by saying: «Are you two happy to come to Nazareth with Me?» and He lays His arms around the shoulders of Peter and Thomas.

«Can You doubt it?» says Peter in his exuberance.

Thomas, more calmly, with his plump face shining with joy, adds: «Do You not know that to be near Your Mother is such a joy that I cannot find words to explain it to You? Mary is my love. I am not a virgin, and I was not against having a family and I had already set my eyes on some girls, but I was uncertain as to which I should choose as my wife. But now! No... My love is Mary. The love exceeding sense. Sense dies only by thinking of Her! The love that fills the soul with delight. I compare all the good I see in women, also in the dearest ones, such as my mother and my twin sister, to what I see in Your Mother, and I say to myself: "All justice, grace and beauty is in Her. Her loving soul is a bed of heavenly flowers... Her appearance is a poem...". Oh!

in Israel we dare not think of angels and with fearful reverence
* we look at the Cherubim of the Holy of Holies!... How foolish of us! As we do not tremble ten times as much with venerable fear looking at Her! Because I am sure that in the eyes of God She exceeds all angelical beauty...»

Jesus looks at His apostle who loves His Mother so much that he seems to become almost spiritualised, as his feelings for Mary change his good-natured countenance so deeply. «Well, we shall be with Her for a few hours. We shall stay until the day after tomorrow. Then we shall go to Tiberias to see the two children and to get a boat to Capernaum.»

«And what about Bethsaida?»

«We will go there on our way back, Simon, to get Marjiam for the Passover pilgrimage.»...

[5] ... It is the evening of the same day, at Nazareth, in the peace- 336.5
ful little house, where Peter and Thomas are already sleeping. Mother and Son are conversing gently.

«Everything went well, Mother. And they are now in peace. Your prayers helped the pilgrims and are now soothing their grief, like dew on parched flowers.»

«I would like to soothe Yours, Son! How much You must have suffered! Look. Your temples and Your cheeks have become hollow, and a wrinkle furrows Your forehead like the cut of a sword. Who hurt You like that, My darling?»

«The grief of having to grieve, Mother.»

«Just that, My Jesus? Did Your disciples distress You?»

«No, Mother. They have been as good as saints.»

«Those who were with You... But I mean: everyone...»

«You see that I brought Thomas here to reward him, and I would have liked to bring also those who did not come here the last time. But I had to send them elsewhere, ahead...»

«And Judas of Kerioth?»

«Judas is with them.»

Mary embraces Her Son, and lays Her head on His shoulder, weeping.

«Why are You weeping, Mother?» asks Jesus caressing Her hair.

---

* **the Cherubim**, that Solomon had put into the most inner and holiest part of the Temple, are described in: *1 King 6:23-28*.

Mary is silent and weeps: Only after a third question, She whispers: «Because I am terrified... I would like him to leave You... It is a sin, is it not, to wish that? But I am so much afraid of him, for You...»

«Things would change only if he disappeared dying... But why should he die?»

«I am not so bad as to wish that... He has a mother as well! And a soul... A soul, which may still be saved. But... oh! Son! Would death perhaps not be a good thing for him?»

Jesus sighs and whispers: «Death would be a good thing for many people...» He then asks in a loud voice: «Have You heard of old Johanna? What about her fields?...» *

«I went to see her with Mary of Alphaeus and Salome of Simon after the hailstorms. But as her corn had been sown late, it had not yet come up and so it suffered no damage. Mary went back to see her three days ago. She says the fields are like carpets. The nicest fields in the district. Rachel is well and the old woman is happy. Mary of Alphaeus is also happy now that Simon is all in Your favour. You will certainly see him tomorrow. He comes here every day. He had just gone away today when You arrived. You know? No one noticed anything. They would have spoken if they had noticed that they were here. But if You are not really tired, tell Me all about their journey...»

And Jesus tells His Mother everything, except His suffering in the cave at Jiphthahel.

337. The Sabbath in Korazim. The Parable on Hearts that Reject to Be Shaped. Miracle on a Crippled Woman.

21st November 1945.

337.1 [1] Jesus is in the synagogue in Korazim which is slowly becoming crowded with people. The elders of the town must have insisted that Jesus should speak there on this Sabbath. I gather that by their arguing and by Jesus' replies.

«We are not more arrogant than Judaeans or the people of the Decapolis» they say «and yet You go there several times.»

---

* **old Johanna**, encountered in 309.1/4 with her niece **Rachel**, remembered a few lines down and in 338.3.

«I do the same here. I have taught you both with words and works, and with silence and action.»

«But if we are duller than others, You should insist all the more...»

«All right.»

«Of course it is all right! We allow You to use our synagogue as a place where You can teach, because we think that it is right to do so. Accept, therefore, our invitation and speak.»

[2]Jesus opens His arms, beckoning the people present to be silent, and He begins His speech giving a slow emphatic recitation in the tone of a psalm: «"Araunah replied to David: 'Let the lord my king take and offer as he likes. Here are the oxen for the holocaust, the threshing-sled and the oxen's yoke for the wood; Araunah, O king, gives all this to the king'. And he added: 'May the Lord your God accept your offering'. But the king replied and said: 'It shall not be done as you wish. No. I will pay you in money, as I will not offer the Lord my God holocausts that cost me nothing'".» 337.2

Jesus lowers His eyes, because He was speaking with His face turned towards the ceiling, and He stares at the head of the synagogue and the four elders who were with him and asks: «Have you understood the meaning?»

* «That is the second book of the Kings, when the holy king bought the threshing floor of Araunah... But we do not understand why You recited it. There is no pestilence here and no sacrifice to be offered. You are not a king... We mean: not yet.»

«I solemnly tell you that your minds are slow in understanding symbols and your faith is uncertain. If it were certain, you would see that I am already King, as I said, and if your understanding were quick, you would realise that there is a plague here that is more serious than the one that worried David. You are afflicted by the plague of unbelief, which causes you to perish.»

«Well! If we are dull and incredulous, give us intelligence and faith and explain to us what You meant.»

«I say: I do not offer forced holocausts to God, those which are offered for mean interests. I do not agree to speak, if that is granted only to Him Who has come to speak. It is My right

* **the second book of the Kings**. In the *Neo-Vulgate* the quotation corresponds to *2 Samuel 24:22-24*; *1 Chronicles 21:23-24*.

and I assert it. Out in the sun or within closed walls, upon the mountains or down in valleys, on the seaside or sitting on the banks of the Jordan, everywhere it is My right and My duty to teach and to buy through My work the only holocausts that are pleasing to God: converted hearts made faithful by My Word. Here, you people of Korazim, have granted the Word to speak, not out of respect and faith, but because there is in your hearts a voice that torments you like a woodworm gnawing at a piece of wood: "This chilly punishment is due to the harshness of our hearts". And you want to make amends, for your purses not for your souls. Oh! Pagan obstinate Korazim! But not everyone in Korazim is such, and I will speak to those who are not such, by means of a parable.

337.3 [3] Listen. A silly rich man took a lump of material as fair as the finest honey to a craftsman and told him to make an ornate amphora with it.

"This material is not good to work" said the craftsman to the rich man. "See? It is soft and resilient. How can I carve it and shape it?"

"What? It is not good? It is a valuable resin and a friend of mine has a small amphora made with it and his wine acquires an exquisite taste in it. I paid for it as dear as gold to have a larger amphora and thus mortify my friend, who boasts of his. Make it at once. Or I will tell everyone that you are a poor craftsman".

"But your friend's amphora must be of clear alabaster".

"No. It is made with this material".

"It is perhaps made of fine amber".

"No. It is the same matter as this".

"Let us suppose that it is made of this matter, but it must have been made solid and hard by age or by mixing it with other solidifying ingredients. Ask him, then come and let me know how it was done".

"No. He sold me this himself and he assured me that it is to be used as it is".

"In that case he cheated you to punish you for envying his beautiful amphora".

"Watch what you say! Do the work or I will take your shop from you to punish you, in any case everything you possess is not worth what I paid for this wonderful resin".

The desolate craftsman began to work. He kneaded... But the paste stuck to his hands. He tried to solidify part of it with mastic and powders... But the resin lost its golden transparency. He put it close to his blast-furnace hoping that the heat would harden it, but clasping his brow he had to take it away, because it liquified. He had frozen snow brought from Mount Hermon and he immersed the resin into it... It hardened and was beautiful. But he could not mould it. "I will carve it with a chisel" he said. But at the first stroke with the chisel the resin broke into pieces.

The desperate craftsman decided to make a last try, although he was already convinced that it was impossible to work on the material. He gathered all the pieces together and liquified them in the heat of the furnace, he then froze them, but not too much, with snow and he tried to work with chisel and broad knife on the softish mass. It molded! But as soon as he removed chisel and broad knife it resumed its previous shape, just like dough rising in the kneading trough.

The man gave up. And to avoid being retaliated to and ruined by the rich man, during the night he loaded wife, children, furnishings and working tools on a cart and fled beyond the border, after leaving in the middle of his workshop, now completely empty, the fair mass of resin with a note on top of it with the words: "It cannot be worked".

[4] I have been sent to shape hearts according to Truth and Sal- 337.4
vation. I have had in My hands hearts made of iron, lead, tin, alabaster, marble, silver, gold, jasper, gem. Hearts that were hard, wild, too tender, inconstant, hearts hardened by sorrows, precious hearts, hearts of all kinds. I worked at every one of them. And I molded many according to the desire of Him Who sent Me. Some hurt Me while I was working at them, some preferred to break into pieces rather than be completed. But they will always have a recollection of Me, even if it may be a hateful one.

It is not possible to work on you. Nothing is of any avail with you: warm love, patience in teaching you, severe reproaches, chisel work. As soon as I move My hands away from you, you become again what you were. There is only one thing you should do to change: to abandon yourselves entirely to Me. But you do not do that. And you never will do it. The desolate Workman leaves you to your destiny. But, as it is fair, He does not abandon every-

one in the same way. In His desolation He can still choose those
337.5 who deserve His love and He comforts and blesses them. [5]Woman, come here!» He says pointing to a woman who is near a wall and is so bent that she looks like a question mark.

The people look to where Jesus is pointing, but they cannot see the woman, neither can she see Jesus and His hand from her position. Several people say to her: «Go, Martha! He is calling you.» And the poor woman plods along with her walking stick, with her head just reaching to the top of it.

She is now before Jesus Who says to her: «I will give you a souvenir of My passing here and a reward for your silent humble faith. Be cured of your infirmity» He shouts finally, laying His hands on her shoulders.

And the woman stands up at once, as straight as a palm-tree, and raising her arms she cries: «Hosanna! He has cured me! He has seen His faithful servant and has helped her. Praise be to the Savior and King of Israel! Hosanna to the Son of David!»

The crowd sing their hosannas with the woman, who is now on her knees at Jesus' feet, kissing the hem of His tunic, while He says to her: «Go in peace and persevere in your Faith.»

337.6 [6]The head of the synagogue, who obviously still resents the words spoken by Jesus before the parable, wants to repay reproaches with poison and shouts angrily, while the crowds open to let the cured woman pass: «There are six days to work, six days to ask and to give. So come during those six days, both to ask and to give. Come and be cured during those days without infringing the Sabbath, you sinners and misbelievers, corrupted and corrupters of the Law!» and he tries to push everybody out of the synagogue, as if he were driving profanation out of the place of prayer.

But Jesus, Who sees that he is being helped by the four elders seen previously and by others scattered amongst the crowd, who appear to be the most scandalized and... tormented by Jesus' crime, with His arms folded on His chest, looks at him in an imposing severe attitude and shouts: «Hypocrites! Which of you on this day has not untied his ox or his donkey from the manger and taken it out for watering? And who has not taken a sheaf of grass to his sheep and milked their full udders? If you have six days to do so, why have you done it also today, just for a little milk, or for fear that your ox or your donkey might die of thirst and you might lose it? And should I not have freed this woman from her chains after Satan had held her bound for eighteen years, only because this is the Sabbath? Go. I was able to relieve her from a misfortune that she did not want. But I will never be able to relieve you from yours, because you want them, O enemies of Wisdom and Truth!»

The good people, among the many malicious ones in Korazim, approve and agree, while the others, livid with rage, run away, deserting the livid synagogue-leader.

Jesus also leaves him and goes out of the synagogue, surrounded by good people who go with Him as far as the countryside: where He blesses them for the last time. He then takes the main road with His cousins, Peter and Thomas...

338. Going to Saphet. The Apostles, Except Judas, Pleased with the Good Deeds They Performed. The Parable of the Good Farmer.

22nd November 1945.

[1] The road to Saphet leaves the plain of Korazim and climbs a 338.1
remarkable mountain range thickly covered with trees. A stream flows down the mountains towards the lake of Tiberias.

The pilgrims are waiting at a bridge for those who were sent to Merom. And they do not have to wait long. The others in fact walking fast arrive punctually at the meeting and meet the Master and their companions with great joy and inform them of their journey, which was blessed also with some miracles, worked in turn by «all the apostles». But Judas of Kerioth rectifies: «With the exception of me, as I was not able to do anything.» His mortification in admitting it is painful.

«We told you that it was due to the fact that we were dealing with a great sinner» replies James of Zebedee. And he explains. «You know, Master? It was Jacob and he was very ill. That is why he invokes You, because he is afraid of death and of God's Judgment. But he is more avaricious than ever, now that he foresees a real disaster for his crops, which have been completely ruined by frost. He lost all his seed-corn and he cannot sow any more because he is ill and his maid-servant is not fit to plough the field, because she is worn out by fatigue and starvation, as he economizes also on flour for bread, seized as he is with fear that he may be left without any food one day. We ploughed a large extension of ground for him and perhaps we sinned, because we worked all day on Friday, also after sunset until it was dark, and even then with torches and bonfires. Philip, John and Andrew know how to do it, so do I. We worked hard... Simon, Matthew and Bartholomew followed us removing the corn that had come up and had been ruined, and Judas went in Your name to ask Judas and Anne for a little seed, promising that we would call on them today. He got it and it was chosen seed. So we said: "We will sow it tomorrow". That is why we are a little late because we started at the beginning of sunset. May the Eternal Father forgive us considering the reason why we sinned. Judas, in the meantime, remained near Jacob's bed to convert him. He can speak better than we can. At least that is what Bartholomew and the Zealot said spontaneously. But Jacob turned a deaf ear to all his arguments. He wanted to be cured, because his disease costs him money and he insulted the servant calling her a sluggard. Since he said: "I will be converted if I recover", Judas imposed his hands on him to calm him down. But Jacob remained as ill as before. Judas was discouraged and told us. We tried before going to bed. But we did not obtain a miracle. Now Judas maintains that it is because he has lost Your favour, as he displeased You and is now downhearted. But we say that it is because we had in front of us an obstinate sinner, who pretends to get everything he wants and lays down terms and gives orders to God. Who is right?»

338.2 «You seven. You have spoken the truth. [2]What about Judas and Anne? And their fields?»

«Only slightly ruined. But they have means... and everything has already been repaired. And they are good people! Here. They have sent You this offering and this food. They hope to see You some time. It is Jacob's frame of mind that is sad. I would have liked to cure his soul, rather than his body...» says Andrew.

«And what about the other places?»

«Oh! On the way to Deberet, near the village, we cured a man — actually Matthew did — who suffered from bouts of fever. He was just coming back from a doctor who had given up

on him. We stopped at his house and he did not have a temperature from sunset till dawn and he said that he was feeling well and strong. Then at Tiberias Andrew cured a boatman, who had broken his shoulder falling on the bridge. He imposed his hands and the shoulder was cured. You can imagine the man! He insisted on taking us free of charge to Magdala and Capernaum and then to Bethsaida and he remained there, because several disciples are there: Timoneus of Aera, Philip of Arbela, Ermasteus
* and Marcus of Josiah, one of those who were freed from the demon near Gamala. Also Joseph, the boatman, wants to become a disciple... The children, at Johanna's, are very well. They do not seem to be the same. They were playing in the garden with Johanna and Chuza...»

«I saw them. I was there, too. Go on.»

«At Magdala Bartholomew converted an evil heart and cured a wicked body. How well he spoke! He explained that disorderliness of the spirit engenders disorder in the body and that every concession to dishonesty degenerates into a loss of peace, of health and finally of the soul. When he saw that the man was repentant and convinced, he imposed his hands and the man was cured. They wanted to keep us at Magdala. But we obeyed Your instructions and the following morning we went on our way to Capernaum. There were five people there who wanted to be cured by You. And they were about to go away, as they were discouraged. We cured them. We did not see anybody, because we left at once by boat for Bethsaida, to avoid questions by Eli, Uriah and companions.
[3]At Bethsaida! But, Andrew, will you tell 338.3
your brother...» concludes James of Zebedee who has spoken all the time.

«Oh! Master! Oh! Simon! If You saw Marjiam! You would not recognize him!...»

«Goodness gracious! He has not become a girl?» exclaims and asks Peter.

«On the contrary! A fine young man; he is tall and thin, as he has grown so much... He is wonderful! We could hardly recognize him. He is as tall as your wife and as me...»

«Oh! well! Neither you, nor Porphirea nor I are palm-trees!

* **one of those who were freed**, in 186.7.

At the most we could be compared to thorn-bushes...» says Peter, who, however, is overjoyed at the news that his adoptive son has grown up.

«Yes, brother. But at the recent feast of the Dedication he was still a stunted boy who hardly reached up to our shoulders. Now he really is a young man with regards to height, voice and seriousness. He has behaved like those plants that stagnate for years then all of a sudden they become surprisingly luxuriant. Your wife has been very busy lengthening his garments and making new ones. And she makes them with wide hems and flounces at the waist, because she rightly foresees that Marjiam will grow more. And he is growing even more in wisdom. Nathanael in his wise humility did not tell You that for almost two months Bartholomew was the master of the youngest and most heroic of Your disciples, who gets up before daybreak to pasture the sheep, split wood, draw water, light the fire, sweep the floors, do the shopping, out of love for his putative mother, and then in the afternoon, until late at night, he studies and writes like a little doctor. Just imagine! He gathers all the children of Bethsaida together, and on the Sabbath he gives them short evangelical lessons. Thus the little ones, who are excluded from the synagogue, otherwise they should disturb the service, have their day of prayer, just like grown up people. And mothers tell me that it is beautiful to hear him speak and that children love and obey him with respect and are becoming very good. What a disciple he will be!»

«Well, well! I... am moved... My Marjiam! Even at Nazareth, eh! his heroism... for that little girl. Rachel, was it not?» Peter stops in time, blushing for fear he might have said too much.

Fortunately Jesus comes to his rescue and Judas is engrossed in thought and inattentive. Or he pretends he is. Jesus says: «Yes, Rachel. You are right. She is cured. And the fields will yield a good crop of corn. James and I have been there. The sacrifice of a young child can do so much.»

«At Bethsaida James worked a miracle for a poor cripple and Matthew, in the street near Jacob's house, cured a boy. And today, in the square of that village near the bridge, Philip cured a man with diseased eyes and John a boy who was possessed.»

338.4 [4] «You have all done well. Very well. We shall now go to that village on the slopes and will stop in one of the houses to sleep.»

«And You, my dear Master, what have You done? How is Mary? And the other Mary?» asks John.

«They are well and they send you their regards. They are preparing garments and all that is necessary for the springtime pilgrimage. And they are longing to make it in order to be with us.»

«Also Susanna, Johanna and our mother are just as anxious» says John.

Bartholomew says: «Also my wife and daughters want to come this year, after so many years, to Jerusalem. She says that it will never be as beautiful as this year... I don't know why she says so. But she maintains that she feels it in her heart.»

«In that case also mine will come. She has not told me ... But what Anne does, Mary does, too» says Philip.

«And Lazarus' sisters? You have seen them...» asks Simon Zealot.

«They comply with the Master's instructions and with necessities, but they suffer... Lazarus looks very poorly, doesn't he, Judas? He has to lie down most of the time. But they are anxiously awaiting the Master» says Thomas.

«It will soon be Passover and we shall go to Lazarus' house.»

«But what have You done at Nazareth and at Korazim?»

«At Nazareth I greeted relatives and friends and the relatives of the two disciples. At Korazim I spoke in the synagogue and I cured a woman. We stayed at the house of the widow, whose mother died. It was a grief and a relief at the same time, because of their scanty resources and of the working time that the widow lost to take care for the invalid; she is now spinning for other people. But she is no longer in despair. What is indispensable for her is now secured and she is thus happy. Every morning Joseph goes to work with a carpenter near the Well of Jacob to learn the trade.»

[5] «Have those of Korazim become any better?» asks Matthew. 338.5

«No, Matthew. They are becoming worse and worse» Jesus admits frankly. «And they ill-treated us. The mighty ones did, of course. Not the simple people.»

«It is a very awkward place. Don't go there any more» says Philip.

«It would grieve the disciple Elias, the widow and the woman I cured today, and all the other good people.»

«Yes. But they are so few that... I would not worry any more about that place. You said it Yourself: "It is unworkable"» says Thomas.

«Resin is one thing and hearts are a different thing. Something will remain, like seed buried under very hard clods of earth. It will take a long time to spring up, but it will at last come up. The same applies to Korazim. What I have sowed will begin to grow one day. One must not give up the first time one is defeated.

338.6 [6] Listen to this parable. It could be called: "The parable of the good farmer".

A rich man owned a beautiful large vineyard, in which there were various kinds of fig-trees. The vineyard was cultivated by a servant, an expert vine-dresser and pruner of fruit-trees, who did his work with love for his master and for the trees. Every year, at the right season, the rich man used to go to his vineyard several times to see his grapes and figs ripen and to taste them, picking the fruit with his own hands. One day he went towards a fig-tree of a very good quality, the only one of that quality in the vineyard. But also on that day, as in the previous two years, he found that it was all leaves without any fruit. So he called the vine-dresser and said: "For three years I have come looking for fruit on this fig-tree and I have found nothing but leaves. It is obvious that the tree has finished yielding fruit. So cut it down. It is useless to have it here taking up room and wasting your time without any profit. Cut it down, burn it, clean the ground of its roots and put another young tree in its place. In a few years' time it will yield fruit". The vine-dresser, who was patient and loving, replied: "You are right. But leave it to me for another year. I will not cut it down. On the contrary, I will dig the ground with greater care, I will manure it and trim it. It may yield fruit again. If after this last try it does not bear fruit, I will comply with your desire and cut it down".

Korazim is the tree that does not bear fruit. I am the Good Farmer. You are the impatient rich man. Leave it to the Good Farmer.»

338.7 [7] «Very well. But the parable is not finished. Did the fig-tree bear fruit the following year?» asks the Zealot.

«It did not and it was cut down. But the farmer was justified for cutting down a tree which looked young and flourishing, be-

cause he had done *all* his duty. I also wish to be justified for cutting off some people with an axe and removing them from My vineyard, in which there are unfruitful and poisonous plants, nests of snakes, sap-suckers, parasites or poisons that spoil or injure their fellow disciples, or they penetrate creeping with their wicked roots to proliferate, without being called into My vineyard, where they rebel to being grafted, as they entered only to spy, to denigrate and to make My field sterile. I will cut them off after trying everything to convert them. For the time being, instead of an axe, I make use of shears and of the pruner's knife and I thin out branches and engraft... Oh! it will be hard work. Both, for Me Who does it and for those who undergo the treatment. But it is to be done. So that in Heaven they may say: "He has accomplished everything, but the more He pruned, grafted, hoed and manured them, shedding perspiration, tears and blood while working, the more sterile and wicked they have become...
[8]There is the village. Go ahead, all of you and look for lodgings. 338.8
You, Judas of Kerioth, stay with Me.»

They remain alone and in the twilight they proceed close to each other, in dead silence.

At last Jesus says, as if He were speaking to Himself: «And yet, even if we lose God's favour by infringing His Law, we can always become what we were by renouncing sin...»

Judas does not reply.

Jesus resumes: «And if one understands that it is not possible to have the power of God, because God is not there where Satan is, one can easily remedy by preferring what God grants to what our pride desires.»

Judas is silent.

They have by now reached the first house of the village and Jesus, still speaking to Himself, says: «And to think that I did severe penance that he might mend his ways and go back to his Father...»

Judas starts, raises his head, looks at Him... but does not say anything.

Jesus also looks at him... and then He asks: «Judas, to whom am I speaking?»

«To me, Master. It is because of You that I no longer have power. You took it away from me to increase it in John, Simon,

James, in everybody, except me. You do not love me, that's what it is! And I will end up by not loving You and by cursing the hour when I did love You and I ruined myself in the eyes of the world for a cowardly king, who is overwhelmed even by the populace. I was not expecting this from You!»

«Neither I from you. But I have never deceived you. And I have never forced you. So why do you remain with Me?»

«Because I love You. I cannot part from You. You attract me and You disgust me. I desire You as much as I desire air to breathe and... You frighten me. Ah! I am cursed! I am damned! Why do you not drive the demon out of me, since You can?» Judas' face is livid and upset, he looks like a madman full of hatred and fear... He reminds me, although faintly, of the satanic mask of Judas on Good Friday.

And Jesus' face reminds me of the scourged Nazarene, Who sitting on an upturned tub in the courtyard of the Praetorium looks at His sneerers with all His loving pity. He says, and a sob already appears to be in His voice: «Because there is no repentance in you, but only hatred against God, as if He were guilty of your sin.»

Judas utters a horrible curse between his teeth...

338.9 [9] «Master, we have found lodgings. There is room for five in one place, for three in another, for two in a third place and then two places can accommodate one each. We could not find anything better» say the disciples.

«All right. I will go with Judas of Kerioth» says Jesus.

«No. I prefer to be alone. I am upset. You would not be able to rest...»

«As you wish... I will go with Bartholomew. You can do as you like. In the meantime let us go where there is more room, so that we may all have supper together.»

339. Towards Meiron. A Sinful Night of Judas Iscariot.

23rd November 1945.

339.1 [1] A beautiful springtime dawn makes the sky rosy and the hills a pleasant sight. The disciples rejoice at the sight while gathering at the entrance of the village waiting for the latecomers.

«It is the first day that it is not cold, after the hailstorms» says Matthew rubbing his hands.

«It was about time! This is the new moon of the month of Adar!»* exclaims Andrew.

«Very well! If we had to go up on the mountains with the cold weather of the past days!...» comments Philip.

«But where are we going?» asks Andrew.

«I wonder... From here we can go either to Saphet or to Meiron. And then?» replies James of Zebedee and he turns round to ask the sons of Alphaeus: «Do you know where we are going?»

«Jesus told us that He wants to go to the north. That is all» says Judas of Alphaeus laconically.

«Again? At the next moon we must begin our Passover pilgrimage...» says Peter not very enthusiastically.

«We have plenty of time» remarks Thaddeus.

«Yes. But no time to rest at Bethsaida...»

«We shall certainly go there to get the women and Marjiam» replies Philip to Peter.

«What I ask of you is not to look bored or indifferent or the
like. [2]Jesus is most depressed... Yesterday evening He was weep- 339.2
ing. I found Him weeping while we were preparing supper. He was not praying out on the terrace, as we thought. He was weeping» says John.

«Why? Did you ask Him?» they all ask.

«Yes, I did. But all He said was: "Love Me, John".»

«Perhaps... it's because of the people of Korazim.»

The Zealot, who has just arrived, says: «The Master is coming here with Bartholomew. Let us go and meet Him.»

And they set out but they continue their conversation: «Or it is because of Judas. They remained alone last night...» says Matthew.

«That's right! And Judas had previously stated that he was upset and wanted to be alone» remarks Philip.

«He did not want to stay even with the Master! Whereas I would have been so glad to be with Him!» says John with a sigh.

«And I!» says everybody.

«I do not like that man... He is either ill, or bewitched, or

* **Adar**: february-march.

mad, or possessed... There is something wrong with him» says Thaddeus resolutely.

«And yet, believe me, on our way back here he was a model disciple. He always defended the Master and the interests of the Master, as none of us ever did. I saw him and heard him myself! And I hope you do not doubt my word» states Thomas.

«Do you think that we do not believe you? No, Thomas! And we are pleased to hear that Judas is better than we are. But you can see it yourself. He is strange, is he not?» asks Andrew.

«Oh! He certainly is. Perhaps innermost problems worry him... Or probably because he did not work any miracle. He is rather proud. Oh! for a good purpose! But he is keen on doing things and he likes to be praised for them...»

«H'm! It may be! But the Master is sad. Look at Him over there: He does not look like the man we have always known. But, long live the Lord! If I find out who is making the Master suffer... Well! That's all! I know what I will do to him» says Peter.

339.3 [3] Jesus, Who is talking intently to Nathanael, sees them and quickens His pace smiling. «Peace to you. Are you all here?»

«Judas of Simon is missing... I thought he was with You, because at the house, where he slept, they told me that they found his room empty and tidied up...» explains Andrew.

Jesus frowns for a moment and becomes engrossed in thought, lowering His head. He then says: «It does not matter. Let us go just the same. Tell the people in the last houses that we are going to Meiron and to Giscala. If Judas should look for us ask them to direct him there. Let us go.»

They all feel that the atmosphere is stormy and they obey without uttering a single word.

Jesus continues His conversation with Bartholomew and is a few steps ahead of the others. I can hear famous names being mentioned by them during their conversation: Hillel, Jael, Barak and glorious events of Israel, which they recollect, commenting and admiring the great doctors, while Bartholomew regrets the past...

«Oh! if Wise Hillel were still alive! He was good and strong. He would not have been upset. He would have judged You by himself, independently of others!»

«Do not worry, Bartholomew! And bless the Most High

Who has received him in His peace. The spirit of the Wise Man thus did not become aware of the excitement of so much hatred against Me...»

«My Lord! Not only hatred!...»

«More hatred than love, My friend. And it will always be so.»

«Do not be sad. We will defend You...»

«It is not death that grieves Me... It is the sight of men's sins...»

«Death!... No!... Don't speak of death. They will not go to that extent... because they are afraid...»

«Hatred will be stronger than fear. Bartholomew, when I am dead and when I am far away, in Holy Heaven, say to men: "He suffered more because of your hatred, than because of His death"...»

«Master! Don't say that! No one will hate You so much as to cause You to die. You can always prevent it. You are powerful...»

[4] Jesus smiles sadly, I would say wearily, while with measured 339.4
steps He climbs the mountainous road leading to Meiron, and the more the road climbs, the wider becomes the beautiful view of the lake of Tiberias, visible through an opening in a gorge on nearby arch-shaped hills, which, however, obstruct the sight of lake Merom while the view extends beyond the lake of Tiberias, on the tableland beyond the Jordan, as far as the remote indented mountains of Hauran, Trachonitis and Perea.

But Jesus points to north-north-east saying: "After Passover we will have to go there, to Philip's tetrarchy. And we shall just have enough time to do so, as we shall have to be in Jerusalem once again for Pentecost.»

«Would it not be more convenient to go there now? We could go beyond the Jordan, towards its sources... and then come back through the Decapolis...»

Jesus passes His hand across His brow, with the tired gesture of one whose mind is clouded, and He whispers: «I do not know, I do not know yet!... Bartholomew!...» How much depression, sorrow, entreaty there is in His voice!...

Bartholomew bends a little, as if he were hurt by Jesus' strange unusual tone, and he says with loving anxiety: «Master, what is the matter with You? What do You want from old Nathanael?»

«Nothing, Bartholomai... Your prayer... That I may clearly see

339.5 what is to be done... [5]But they are calling us, Bartholomai... Let us stop here...» And they stop near a group of trees.

The others appear round a bend of the path; they are in a group: «Master, Judas is running after us at a neck breaking speed...»

«Let us wait for him.»

And in fact Judas soon appears, running... «Master... I am late... I overslept and... »

«Where, if I did not find you in the house?» asks Andrew who is amazed.

Judas remains dumbfounded for a moment, but he is quick in collecting himself and he says: «Oh! I am sorry that my penance has become known to everybody! I was in the wood, all night, praying and doing penance... At dawn I was overcome by sleep. I am weak... But the Most High Lord will pity His poor servant. Is that right, Master? I woke up late and I was aching all over.»

«In fact you look rather worn out» remarks James of Zebedee.

Judas laughs: «Of course! But my soul is delighted. Prayer does one good. Penance makes one's heart joyful. And it grants humility and generosity. Master, forgive Your foolish Judas...» and he kneels at Jesus' feet.

«Yes. Stand up and let us go.»

«Give me peace with a kiss of Yours. It will be a sign that You have forgiven the bad mood I was in yesterday. I did not want You, that is true. But it was because I wanted to pray...»

«We could have prayed together...»

Judas laughs and says: «No, You could not have prayed with me last night, or be where I was...»

«Oh! That's nice! Why not? He has always been with us and He taught us to pray!» exclaims Peter who is utterly amazed.

They all laugh. But Jesus does not laugh. He stares at Judas who has kissed Him and is now looking at Him with eyes glaring with biting malice, as if he wanted to defy Him. He dares to repeat: «Is it not true that You could not have been with me last night?»

«No, I could not. Neither will I ever be able to share the embraces of My soul with the Father, with a third party, nothing but blood and flesh, like you, and in the places where you go. I love solitude peopled with angels, to forget that man is the stench of flesh corrupted by sensuality, by gold, by the world and by Satan.»

Judas no longer laughs, not even with his eyes. He replies
seriously: «You are right. Your spirit has seen the truth. [6]So 339.6
where are we going?»

«To venerate the tombs of the great rabbis and heroes of Israel.»

«What? Gamaliel does not love You. And the others hate You» many of the apostles say.

«It does not matter. I bow to the tombs of the just awaiting Redemption. I am going to say to their bones: "He Who inspired your souls will soon be in the Kingdom of Heaven, ready to descend from there on the last Day, to make you live again and forever in Paradise".»

They proceed until they find the village of Meiron. A lovely village, well kept, full of light and sunshine, situated among fertile hills and mountains.

«Let us stop. In the afternoon we will leave for Giscala. The great sepulchers are scattered along these slopes, awaiting the
* glorious resurrection.»

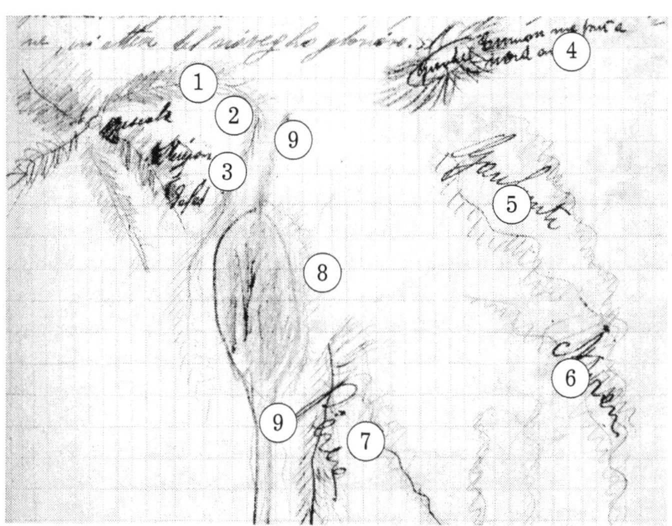

* **glorious resurrection**: the drawing shows, to the North-West the cities of: 1. *Giscala*; 2. *Meiron*; 3. *Safed* or *Sefet*; to the North-East: 4. *the Great Hermon, but more to the North*; to the East: 5. *Trachonitis*; 6. *Hauran*; to the South: 7. *Perea*. In the middle: 8. *the lake of Tiberias* and 9. *the Jordan* are sketched.

340. Judas Iscariot Asks for Forgiveness. At Hillel's Sepulchre at Giscala, a Clash with a Group of Hostile Rabbis.

24th November 1945.

340.1 [1]From the village of Meiron Jesus and His apostles take a mountainous road that runs north-west through woods and pastures rising all the time. They have perhaps already venerated some sepulchers, because I can hear them speak about them.

The Iscariot is now ahead with Jesus. At Meiron they must have received and given alms and Judas is now giving an account of what he received and what he gave. He concludes saying: «And here is my offer. I swore last night I would give You it for the poor and as a penance. It is not much. I have not much money with me. But I convinced my mother to send me some frequently through many friends. In the past, when I came away from home, I had a good deal of money. But this time, as I had to travel across mountains by myself or with Thomas only, I took only what was sufficient for our journey. I prefer to do that. The only thing is... sometimes I will have to ask You for permission to leave You and go and see my friends. I have already arranged everything... Master, shall I continue to keep the money? Do You still trust me?»

«Judas you are saying everything by yourself. And I do not
340.2 know why you do that. [2]You must know that nothing has changed as far as I am concerned... because I hope that you will change and become once again the disciple you were in the past, and that you will become a just man for whose conversion I pray and suffer.»

«You are right, Master. But with Your help I will certainly become so. In any case... they are minor imperfections. Things of no importance. In fact, they help us to understand our fellowmen and cure them.»

«Your morals, Judas, are strange indeed! And I should say more than that. I have never heard of any doctor falling voluntarily ill in order to be able to say: "Now I know how to cure people affected by this disease". So am I an incapable man?»

«Who says that, Master?»

«You do. As I do not commit sins, I cannot cure sinners.»

«You are You. But we are not You, and we need experience to learn...»

«That is your old idea, the very same idea of twenty months ago. The only difference is that you then thought that I should commit sin to be able to redeem. I am really surprised that you have not tried to correct this... fault of Mine, according to your way of judging, and to gift Me with this.... ability to understand sinners.»

«You are joking, Master. And I am glad. I felt sorry for You. You were so sad. And it is double joy to me that I have made You joke. But I never thought of claiming to be Your master. In any case, as You can see Yourself, I have corrected my way of thinking as I now say that this experience is necessary only to us. To us, poor men. You are the Son of God, are You not? Your wisdom, therefore, needs no experience to be what it is.»

«Well, you had better know that innocence is also wisdom a much greater wisdom than the low dangerous knowledge of sinners. When the holy ignorance of evil should limit our ability to guide ourselves and other people, the angelical ministry which is always present in pure hearts, makes up for that. And you may rest assured that the angels, who are most pure, can tell Good from Evil and they can lead the pure souls, whom they guard, on the just path and to just deeds. Sin does not increase wisdom. It is not light. It is not a guide. Never. It is corruption, it is derangement of mind, it is chaos. Thus, he who commits it, tastes its flavor but at the same time loses the ability to savor many other spiritual things and no longer has an angel of God, a spirit of order and love, to guide him, instead he has an angel of Satan to lead him into greater and greater disorder, because of the unappeasable hatred that devours those diabolical spirits.»

[3] «Listen, Master. And if one wanted to attain angelical guid- 340.3
ance again? Is repentance sufficient or does the poison of sin last even after one has repented and has been forgiven?... You know? For instance, one who has taken to drinking, even if he swears that he will not get drunk again, and is really determined in swearing so, always feels the stimulus to drink. And one suffers...»

«One certainly suffers. That is why one should never become

the slave of evil. But to suffer is not to sin. It is expiation. And as a repentant drunkard commits no sin but gains merits if he resists the stimulus heroically and does not drink any more, so he who has sinned and repents and resists all stimuli, gains merit and will not lack supernatural help to resist. It is not a sin to be tempted. On the contrary it is a battle that brings victory. And believe Me, in God there is only the desire to forgive and help who has done wrong but has later repented...»

Judas is silent for a little while... Then he takes Jesus' hand and kisses it remaining bent over it: «Last night I exceeded the limit. I insulted You, Master. I told You that I would end up by hating You... How much I blasphemed! Can I ever be forgiven?»

«The greatest sin is to despair of God's mercy... Judas, I said: * "Every sin against the Son of man will be forgiven". The Son of Man has come to forgive, to save, to cure, to lead souls to Heaven.
340.4 Why do you want to lose Heaven? [4]Judas! Look at Me! Wash your soul in the love emanating from My eyes...»

«Do I not disgust You?»

«Yes, you do... But love is stronger than disgust. Judas, poor leper, the greatest leper in Israel, come and invoke health from Him Who can give it to you...»

«Give me it, Master.»

«No. Not that way. There is no true repentance or firm will in you. There is only a faint effort of surviving love for me and for your past vocation. There is a hint of repentance, but it is entirely human. That is not entirely bad. On the contrary, it is the first step towards Good. Cultivate it, increase it, graft it into the supernatural, change it into real love for Me, make it a real return to what you were when you came to Me, at least that! Make it not a temporary, emotional inactive throb of sentimentalism, but a true active feeling attracting you to Good. Judas, I will wait. I can wait. I will pray. I will take the place of your disgusted angel, while waiting. My pity, patience and love are perfect and therefore: greater than the pity, patience and love of angels, and I can remain beside you, in the disgusting stench of what is fermenting in your heart, in order to help you...»

340.5 [5]Judas is moved, he is really moved, he is not simulating. With

* **I said**, in 269.8.

trembling lips and voice made shaky by his emotion, looking pale, he asks: «Do You really know what I have done?»

«I know everything, Judas. Do you want Me to tell you or shall I spare you this humiliation?»

«I... cannot believe it...»

«Well let us go over the past few days and tell the incredulous apostle the truth. This morning you lied several times. With regard to the money and to where you spent the night. Last night you tried to suffocate in lust your feelings, your hatred, your remorse. You...»

«That's enough! That's enough! For pity's sake, say no more! Or I will run away from Your presence!»

«On the contrary, you ought to cling to My knees and ask to be forgiven.»

«Yes, forgive me, Master! Forgive me! Help me! It's stronger than I am. Everything is stronger than I am.»

«Except the love you ought to have for Jesus... But come here, that I may help you to resist temptation and relieve you of it.»And He takes Judas in His arms shedding silent tears on his dark-haired head.

[6]The others, who are a few yards behind, have wisely stopped 340.6
and comment:

«See?! Perhaps Judas is really in trouble.»

«And this morning he has spoken to the Master about it.»

«What a fool! I would have done so straight away.»

«It is probably something painful.»

«Oh! It is certainly not bad behavior of his mother! She is a holy woman! What can be so painful?»

«Perhaps business not doing well...»

«No! He spends and helps people generously.»

«Well! It's his business! The important thing is that he is in agreement with the Master, and that seems to be the case. They have been talking for some time and peacefully. They are now embracing each other... Very well.»

«Yes, because he is very capable and has many acquaintances. It is a good thing that he is of goodwill and in agreement with us and above all with the Master.»

«Jesus at Hebron said that the tombs of the just are places where miracles are worked, or something like that... There are many of them here. Perhaps those of Meiron worked a miracle for Judas' perturbation.»

«Oh! if so, he will become entirely holy now at Hillel's sepulchre. Is it not at Giscala?»

«Yes, Bartholomew.»

«And yet last year we did not come this way...»

«No wonder! We came from the other side!»

Jesus turns around and calls them. They run towards Him joyfully.

«Come. The town is close at hand. We must cross it to arrive at Hillel's tomb. Let us proceed in one group» says Jesus without any further information, while the eleven apostles cast inquisitive side glances at Him and Judas. The latter's face looks pacified and humble, and Jesus' is certainly not radiant. He is solemn but grave.

340.7 [7] They enter Giscala, a beautiful large well-kept town. There must be a flourishing rabbinical centre because I see many groups of doctors with disciples listening to their lessons. The apostles passing through and the Master especially draw the attention of many people and a great deal of them follow the group. Some sneer, some call Judas of Kerioth. But he is walking beside the Master and does not even turn around.

They go out of town towards the house in the neighborhoods of which is Hillel's sepulcher.

«How impudent of You!»

«He is imprudent and impudent!»

«He is provoking us.»

«Desecrator!»

«Tell Him, Uzziel.»

«I will not be contaminated. Saul, you are only a pupil, you can tell Him.»

«No. Let us tell Judas. Call him.»

The young man, whose name is Saul, a thin pale fellow with very large eyes and mouth, approaches Judas and says to him: «Come. The rabbis want you.»

«I will not come. I am staying where I am. Leave me alone.»

The young man goes back to his masters and tells them.

In the meantime Jesus, in the middle of His apostles, is praying reverently near Hillel's whitewashed sepulcher.

The rabbis approach the group slowly, like silent snakes, and watch, and two elderly bearded ones pull the tunic of Judas, who, since they gathered to pray, is no longer protected by his companions.

«Well, what do you want?» he asks in a low but resentful voice.

«Is one not even allowed to pray?»

«Just one word. Then we will leave you in peace.»

Simon Zealot and Thaddeus turn round and tell the noisy disturbers to be quiet.

Judas moves a few steps aside and asks: «What do you want.»

I do not hear what the older man whispers in Judas' ear. But I distinctly see the gesture of Judas who steps aside resolutely saying: «No. Leave me in peace, poisoned souls. I don't know you, I don't want to have anything more to do with you.»

The rabbinical group burst into a scornful laugh and threaten: «Watch what you do, you silly boy!»

«You had better watch. Go away! You can go and tell the others. *All* the others. Have you understood? You can apply to anybody you like, but not to me, you devils» and he leaves them. He has spoken so loudly that the apostles turn around dumbfounded. Jesus does not. Not even after the scornful laugh and threat: «We will see you again, Judas of Simon! We will meet again!» that resounds in the silence of the place.

Judas goes back to his place, he moves aside Andrew who had gone close to Jesus, and as if he wished to be defended and protected, he takes the hem of Jesus' mantle in his hands.

[8]The angry men then rage against Jesus. They come forth 340.8
threatening and shouting: «What are You doing here, You, anathema of Israel? Go away? Don't make the bones of the Just man, whom You are not worthy to approach, stir in the grave. We will tell Gamaliel and will have You punished.»

Jesus turns around and looks at them, one at a time.

«Why are You looking at us like that, You demoniac?»

«To become better acquainted with your faces and your hearts. Because not only My apostle will see you again. I will, as well. And I want to know you well so that I can recognize you at once.»

«Well: have You seen us? Go away. If Gamaliel were here, he

would not allow You to be here.»

«I was here last year with him...»

«That is not true, You liar!»

«Ask him, and since he is an honest man, he will tell that I was here with him. I love and venerate Hillel, I respect and honor Gamaliel. They are two men through whose justice and wisdom the origin of man is revealed, as they remind us that man was made in the likeness of God.»

«We don't, do we?» interrupt the energumens.

«It is dimmed in you by interests and hatred.»

«Listen to Him! That is how He speaks and offends in the house of other people. Go away from here, corrupter of the best people in Israel! Or we will have to pick up stones. Rome is not here to protect You, You intriguer with the heathen enemy...»

«Why do you hate Me? Why do you persecute Me? What wrong have I done you? Some of you have benefited from Me; everybody has been respected by Me. So why are you so cruel against Me?» Jesus is humble, meek, afflicted and loving. He implores them to love Him.

They take it as a sign of weakness and fear and they become more furious. The first stone flies skimming James of Zebedee, who quickly makes the gesture of reacting by throwing it against the assailers, while all the others gather around Jesus. But they are twelve against about one hundred. Another stone strikes Jesus' hand while He is telling His disciples not to react. The back of His hand is injured and bleeds. It seems to be already wounded by the nail...

340.9 [9] Jesus then stops praying. He straightens up imposingly, looks at them and crushes them with a glare. But another stone strikes the temple of James of Alphaeus and it begins to bleed.

Jesus is now compelled to paralyse their action by means of His power to defend His apostles, who obeying Him, receive the volley of stones without reacting. And when the cowards are overwhelmed by Jesus' will and by His *frightful* imposing attitude, He says: «I am going. But you must know that Hillel would have cursed you for what you are doing. I am going away. But remember that not even the Red Sea prevented the Israelites from *

* **But remember**, as narrated in: *Exodus 14:15-31.*

going on the way pointed out to them by God. Everything flattened out and became a level road for the passing God. The same applies to Me. As Egyptians, Philistines, Amorites, Canaanites and other peoples could not stop the triumphal march of Israel, so you, who are worse than they were, will not be able to stop * My march and mission: Israel. Remember what they sang at the well of the water given by God: "Rise, O well, that was sunk by the princes and dug by the leaders of the people, with the giver of the Law, with their staves". I am that Well! It was dug by Heaven in response to the prayers and the justice of the true princes and leaders of the holy People, which you are not. No. You are not. The Messiah would never have come for you, because you do not deserve Him. In fact His coming is your ruin. Because the Most High is aware of *all* the thoughts of men and has *always* been aware of them, even before Cain, from whom you descend, existed, and before Abel, whom I resemble, before Noah, My symbol, and before Moses who first used My symbol, before Balaam who * prophesied the Star, before Isaiah and all the prophets. And God knows your hearts and is struck with horror at them. He has always been horrified at them as He has always rejoiced at the just for whose sake it was just to send Me and who really drew Me from the depths of Heaven, that I might bring Living Water for the thirst of men. I am the Source of eternal Life. But you do not wish to drink at it. And you will die.»

And He walks slowly through the paralysed rabbis and their pupils and goes on His way, slowly, solemnly, in the amazed silence of men and things.

341. The Wounded Hand of Jesus. The Deaf-Mute Cured Near the Phoenician Border.

25th November 1945.

[1] I do not know where the pilgrims spent the night. I know that 341.1
it is morning once again, that they are on their way, still across mountainous places, that Jesus' hand is bandaged, and so is the forehead of James of Alphaeus, while Andrew is limping badly

* **what they sang**, in: *Numbers 21:17-18.*
* **prophesied**, in: *Numbers 24:15-19.*

and James of Zebedee is without his bag, which his brother John is carrying.

Twice Jesus has asked: «Can you manage to walk, Andrew?»

«Yes, Master. I walk badly because of the bandage. But it is not very painful.» And the second time he adds: «And what about Your hand, Master?»

«A hand is not a leg. It is resting and it is not very sore.»

«H'm! Swollen as it is and with the wound into the bone, I can hardly believe that it is not very sore... Oil is good for it. But perhaps we should have got some of that ointment of Your Mother's from...»

«From My Mother. You are right» says Jesus quickly on hearing what is about to escape the lips of Peter, who blushes with embarrassment and looks desolately at Jesus. The Master smiles at him and lays His injured hand on Peter's shoulder to draw him to Himself.

«It will hurt if You hold it this way.»

«No, Simon. You love Me and your love is a very wholesome oil.»

«Oh! In that case You should already be cured! We have all suffered seeing You ill-treated like that, and there are some of us who wept.» And Peter looks at John and Andrew...

«Oil and water are good medicines, but tears of love and pity are more powerful than anything. See? I am much more cheerful today than yesterday. Because today I know how obedient you are and how much you love Me. Everyone.» And Jesus looks at them with His normally sad mild eyes, which this morning are shining, although faintly, with joy.

341.2 [2] «But what hyenas they are! Never seen so much hatred!» says Judas of Alphaeus. «They must have been all Judaeans.»

«No, brother. Regions have nothing to do with it. Hatred is the same everywhere. Remember that I was driven out of Nazareth months ago and they wanted to pelt Me with stones. Do you not remember?» says Jesus calmly, which comforts the Judaean apostles for Thaddeus' words.

They are in fact so consoled that the Iscariot says: «But I will tell them that! Oh! I will indeed! We were not doing anything wrong. We did not react and He spoke of nothing but love from the very beginning. And they threw stones at us, as if we were snakes. I will tell them.»

«And who are you going to tell, if they are all against us.?»

«I know who I will tell. In the meantime, I will tell Hermas and Stephen as soon as I see them. And Gamaliel will know at once. But at Passover I know who I will tell. I will say: "It is not fair to do that. Your fury is against the law. You are guilty, not He".»

«It would be better· if you did not approach those men!... I think that you are guilty in their eyes, as well» advises Philip wisely. «That's true. It is better if I never get in touch with them again. Yes. It is better. But I will tell Stephen. He is good and has no poison...»

«Never mind, Judas. You would not change anything for the better. I have forgiven them. Let us forget about it» says Jesus calmly and convincingly.

[3] Twice, crossing two little streams both Andrew and the two 341.3
Jameses dampen the bandages on their bruises. Jesus does not. He proceeds peacefully as if He felt no pain.

But His hand must be really sore, if He has to ask Andrew to break His bread, when they stop to eat; and if He has to beg Matthew to tie His sandal, when the sandal laces come undone... Above all if, when going down a steep short cut, He bumps into a tree trunk, because His foot has slipped, and He cannot help moaning, while His bandage becomes stained once again with blood. In fact they stop at the first house of the village, where they arrive at sunset, to ask for some water and oil to treat His hand, which, once the bandage has been removed, looks all swollen with a large bluish bruise on the back and the red wound in the middle.

While waiting for the landlady to come with what they have asked for, they all bend to look at the wound and they make their comments. But John moves away to one side to hide his tears.

Jesus calls him: «Come here. It is nothing serious. Do not weep.»

«I know. If I had it, I would not weep. But You have it. And You are not telling us how painful is this dear hand, which has never harmed anybody» replies John, to whom Jesus has abandoned His wounded hand; and John gently caresses the fingertips, the wrist, all around the bruise and then gently turns it over to kiss the palm and rest his cheek in the hollow of the hand saying: «It is hot!... How painful it must be!» and loving tears drop on it.

The woman brings water and oil and John with a piece of linen cleans the blood that stains the hand, gently pouring some lukewarm water on the wound, which he then dresses with oil and binds up with clean strips of cloth and finally kisses the bandage. Jesus lays His other hand on John's lowered head.

341.4 [4] The woman asks him: «Is He your brother?»

«No. He is my Master. Our Master.»

«Where have you come from?» she asks the others.

«From the Sea of Galilee.»

«So far! Why?»

«To preach Salvation.»

«It is almost evening. Stop in my house. It's a poor house. But we are honest. I can give you some milk as soon as my sons come back with the sheep. My husband will be pleased to welcome you.»

«Thank you, woman. We will stay here if the Master wishes so.» The woman goes away to do her housework while the apostles ask Jesus what to do.

«Yes. It is a good idea. Tomorrow we will go to Kedesh and then towards Paneas. I have been thinking, Bartholomew. It is better to do as you suggested. You gave Me a good piece of advice. I hope I will thus be able to find other disciples and send them ahead of Me to Capernaum. I know that some must have already been to Kedesh, and the three shepherds from Lebanon are among them.»

The woman comes back and asks: «Well?»

«Yes, good woman. We are staying here for the night.»

«And for supper. Oh! accept my invitation. It is no burden to me. And after all we have been taught to be merciful by some men who are the disciples of that Jesus of Galilee, who is called the Messiah and works so many miracles and preaches the Kingdom of God. But He has never been here. Perhaps because we are at the Syro-Phoenician border. But His disciples came. And that is already a lot! Here in the village, we all want to go to Judaea at Passover, to see if we can find this Jesus. Because we have some sick people and His disciples cured some of them but not everyone. Among the latter there is the young son of a brother of my brother-in-law's wife.»

«What is the matter with him?» asks Jesus smiling.

«He is... He does not speak and he does not hear. Perhaps a
demon entered the womb of his mother to make her suffer and
drive her to despair. But he is good, not like a possessed. The
disciples said that Jesus of Nazareth is needed for him, because
there must be something missing, and only that Jesus... [5]Oh! 341.5
here are my sons and my husband! Melkiah, I have welcomed
these pilgrims in the name of the Lord and I was telling them
about Levi... Sarah, go and milk the sheep and you, Samuel, go
down into the grotto and bring some oil and wine and get also
some apples in the attic. Hurry up, Sarah, we will prepare the
beds upstairs.»

«Do not tire yourself, woman. Any place will suit us. Could I see the man of whom you were speaking?»

«Yes... But... Oh! Lord! Are You perhaps the Nazarene?»

«I am.»

The woman drops on her knees shouting: «Melkiah, Sarah, Samuel! Come and worship the Messiah! What a day! And I have Him in my house! And I have been speaking to Him! And I brought Him water to cleanse His wound... Oh!..» she is choking with emotion. She then runs to the basin and sees that it is empty: «Why have you thrown that water out? It was holy water! Oh! Melkiah! The Messiah is here with us.»

«Yes, but be good, woman and do not tell anybody. Go and get the deaf-mute and bring him here...» says Jesus smiling...

[6]... And Melkiah is soon back with the deaf-mute, his relatives 341.6
and at least half of the people in the village... The mother of the
poor fellow worships Jesus and implores Him.

«Yes, it will be done as you wish» and He takes the deaf-mute by the hand and draws him away from the crowd, who are pressing together and whom the apostles are busy pushing back, to protect Jesus' wounded hand. Jesus draws the deaf-mute close to Himself, puts His forefingers into his ears, touches his lips with His tongue: then raising His eyes to the sky, which is growing dark, He breathes on the face of the man and shouts in a loud voice: «Be opened!» and lets him go.

The young man looks at Him for a moment while the crowds

whisper. The change in the countenance of the deaf-mute is surprising: from listless and sad it becomes amazed and smiling. He touches his ears with his hands, presses them, takes his hands away... He persuades himself that he can really hear, he opens his mouth saying: «Mother! I can hear! Oh! Lord, I adore You!»

The crowd is seized by the usual enthusiasm, also because they ask one another: «How can he be able to speak if he never heard a word since he was born? A miracle in the miracle! He loosened his tongue and opened his ears and at the same time He taught him to speak. Long live Jesus of Nazareth! Hosanna to the Holy Messiah!»

And they press against Jesus Who raises His wounded hand to bless them, while some, urged by the woman of the house, wet their faces and limbs with the remaining drops of water left in the basin.

Jesus sees them and shouts: «Because of your faith you are all cured. Go home. Be good and honest. Believe in the word of the Gospel. And keep to yourselves what you know, until it is time to announce it in the squares and throughout the whole world. May My peace be with you.»

And He goes into the large kitchen where the fire is blazing and the light of two lamps flickers.

342. At Kedesh. The Signs of the Times. The Prophecy of Habakkuk.

26th November 1945.

342.1 [1]The town of Kedesh is built on a little mountain, at a short distance from a long chain of mountains on its eastern side, stretching from north to south. A parallel chain of hills stretches also from north to south on its western side. The two parallel lines, however, bend inwords at their central part forming a rough "X". In the narrowest part, a little closer to the eastern chain, there is the mountain on the slopes of which Kedesh is built. The town stretches from the top down to the almost flat slopes and dominates a fresh green valley, which is very narrow to the east and wider to the west.

It is a beautiful walled town with lovely houses and a magnif-

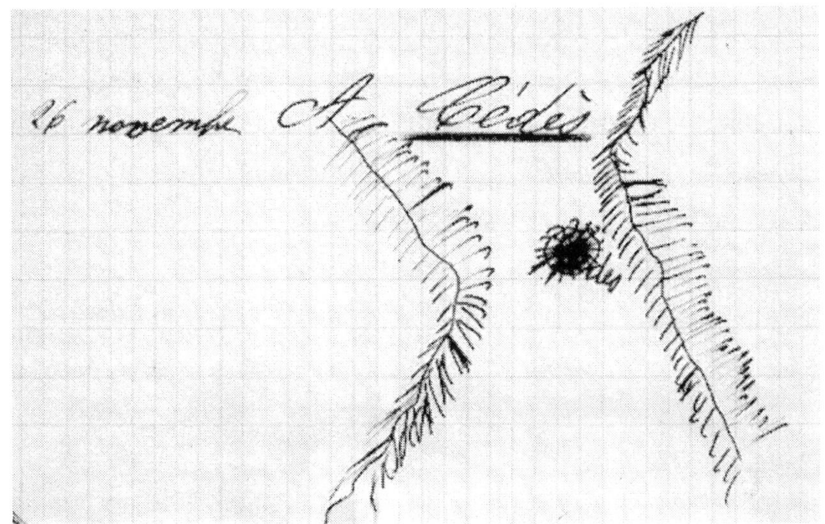

icent synagogue; there is also an imposing fountain with many jets that pour abundance of cool water into a basin, from which little streams flow to feed other fountains or, probably, to water gardens. I do not know.

Jesus enters the town on a market day. His hand is no longer bandaged, but there is still a dark scab and a large bruise on the back of it. James of Alphaeus also has a small dark reddish scab on his temple and a large bruise around it. Andrew and James of Zebedee, who were not so badly injured, show no sign of the past incident and they walk fast, looking around, and particularly at their sides and behind them, as the apostles have formed little groups around the Master. I am under the impression that they have stopped for two or three days at the place that I described yesterday or in its neighborhood, perhaps to rest or to keep at a good distance from rabbis, in the event the latter should turn their steps towards the main towns, hoping to catch them at fault and injure them again. At least that is what I gather from their conversation.

«But this is a city of refuge!» says Andrew.

«And would you expect them to respect the refuge and holiness of any place! How simple you are, brother!» Peter replies to him.

Jesus is walking between the two Judases. James and John

are ahead of Him, and behind them there is the other James with Philip and Matthew. Peter, Andrew and Thomas are behind the Master. Simon Zealot and Bartholomew are the last two.

342.2 [2] Everything goes well until they enter a beautiful square, the one with the fountain and the synagogue, where many people are discussing business. The market, instead, is further down, to the south-west of the town, where two roads join: the main road from the south and the road along which Jesus came, from the west; the two roads meet at a right angle and form one road only that enters through the gate and widens into a rectangular square, where there are donkeys, mats, vendors, buyers and the usual clamor...

But when they reach the most beautiful square — the heart of the town, I think, not so much because it is equidistant from the perimeter of the walls, but because the spiritual and commercial life of Kedesh thrives here, as appears also from its high dominating position above most of the town, which is suitable to be defended like a citadel — trouble begins. Like snarling dogs awaiting to attack a defenseless puppy, or rather, like blood-hounds on the watch for game that they smell in the wind, a large number of Pharisees and Sadducees are leaning against the wide portal, ornate with sculptures and decorations, of the synagogue. Mingled with them, to poison them completely, there is a handful of the rabbis we saw at Giscala, and among them there is Uzziel. They immediately point out Jesus and the apostles to one another.

«Alas! Lord! They are here as well!» exclaims John, who is obviously frightened, turning round to speak to Jesus.

«Be not afraid. Go on fearlessly. But if any of you do not feel like facing those rogues, let them go back to the inn. I definitely want to speak here, in this Levitical city of refuge.»

They all protest: «Can You believe that we would leave You alone?! Let them kill us all, if they want. We will share Your lot.»

342.3 [3] Jesus passes before the enemy group and stops near the wall of a garden where a pear-tree is shedding its white blossoms. The dark wall and the white cloud outline the Christ Who has His twelve apostles before Him.

Jesus begins to speak: «Come and listen to the Gospel, all of you who are gathered here, because the conquest of the Kingdom of Heaven is more important than trade and money...» His beautiful loud voice fills the square and makes people turn towards Him.

«Oh! That is the Galilean Rabbi!» says one. «Come, let us go and listen to Him. Perhaps He will work a miracle.»

And another adds: I saw Him work one at Bethginna. How well He speaks! Nothing like those predatory hawks and astute snakes.»

Jesus is soon surrounded by a crowd. And He continues to speak to the attentive listeners.

«From the heart of this Levitical town I do not wish to remind you of the Law. I know that it is present in your hearts, as in few towns in Israel, as it is proved by the order I have noticed here, by the honesty I found in your merchants from whom I bought food for Myself and My little flock, and by this synagogue, which is as ornate as is suitable to the place where God is worshipped. But in each of you there is also a place where God is honored, a place where the most holy yearnings are, where the sweetest words of hope resound with the most ardent prayers that your hope may become true. Your souls. The holy unique place that speaks of God and to God, while waiting for the Promise to be accomplished. And the Promise is accomplished. Israel has its Messiah, Who brings you the news and the certainty that the time of Grace has come, that Redemption is close at hand, that the Savior is
among you, and the invincible Kingdom has begun. [4]How many 342.4
times have you heard Habakkuk! And the more meditative ones among you whispered: "I also can say: 'How long, O Lord, am I to cry for help, while You will not listen?'". Israel has been wailing thus for ages. But the Savior has now come. The great robbery, the endless trouble, disorder and injustice brought about by Satan are about to collapse, because the envoy of God is on the point of restoring man to his dignity of son of God and coheir of the Kingdom of God. Let us look at Habakkuk's prophecy with fresh eyes and we will see that it bears witness to Me, and it already speaks the language of the Gospel, which I bring to the children of Israel. But now it is I who must wail: "Sentence was passed, but opposition is triumphing". And I moan so sorrowfully. Not so much for My own sake, as I am above human judgment, as for those who are in opposition and thus condemn themselves,

and for those who are misled by opposers. Are you surprised at what I am saying? Among you there are merchants from other parts of Israel. They can confirm that I am not lying. I do not lie by leading a life that is the opposite of what I teach, by not doing what people expect the Savior to do, neither do I lie by stating that human opposition sets itself up against the judgment of God, Who sent Me, and against the judgment of humble sincere crowds who have heard Me and judged Me for what I am.»

Some of the people in the crowd whisper: «That is true! It is true indeed! We belong to the people and we want Him and we know that He is holy. But they (and they point to the Pharisees and their companions) are hostile to Him.»

Jesus continues: «And because of that opposition the Law is torn to pieces, and will be torn more and more, until it will be abolished, in order to do a supreme wrong, which, however, will not last long. And blessed are those who during the short fearful pause, when opposition will appear to have triumphed over Me, have continued to believe in Jesus of Nazareth, in the Son of God, in the Son of man, predicted by the Prophets. I could fulfill the judgment of God to the very end, by saving all the children of Israel. But I will not be able because the impious will triumph against themselves, *against their own better part*, and as they trample on My rights and oppress My believers, so they will trample on the rights of their souls, which need Me to be saved and which are presented to Satan in order to deny them to Me.»

342.5 [5] The Pharisees begin to murmur. But a stately old man has just approached the place where Jesus is, and now, in a pause of His speech, he says: «Please. Come into the synagogue and teach us there. No one is more entitled to do so than You are. I am Matthias, the head of the synagogue. Come, and may the Word of God be in my house as it is on Your lips.»

«Thank you, O just man of Israel. May peace be always with you.»

And Jesus, through the crowd that opens to let Him pass and then closes like a wake following Him, crosses the square again and enters the synagogue, after passing before the snarling Pharisees. But they enter the synagogue as well, elbowing their way overbearingly. But the people look unfavorably on them saying: «Where are you from? Go and wait for the Rabbi in your own synagogues. This is our house and we do not want strangers here.» And the rabbis, Sadducees and Pharisees must put up with the situation and remain quietly near the entrance to avoid being thrown out by the citizens of Kedesh.

Jesus is near the head of the synagogue and other people of the synagogue; I do not know whether they are his sons or assistants. He resumes speaking: «Habakkuk says: — and how lovingly he invites you to meditate! — "Cast your eyes over the nations, look, and be amazed and astounded, for something has happened in your own days, that no man will believe when he is told of it". Even nowadays we have physical enemies in Israel. But let us leave out the little detail of the prophecy and consider only the great prediction contained in it. Because prophecies always have a spiritual meaning, even when they appear to have a material reference. So the event that has taken place — and is such that no one will accept it unless one is convinced of the infinite goodness of the True God — is that He has sent His Word to save and redeem the World. God Who parts from God to save the guilty creature. And I have been sent for that. And none of the powers in the world will be able to hold back the impetus of My Triumph over kings and tyrants, over sin and stupidity. I will win because I am the Triumpher.»

[6] A scornful laugh is heard together with a shout from the end 342.6
of the synagogue. People protest and the head of the synagogue, whose eyes are closed, as he is so engrossed in listening to Jesus, stands up and commands silence, threatening to have the disturbers expelled.

«Let them speak. Invite them to expound their objections» says Jesus in a loud voice.

«Oh! good! Very well! Let us come near You. We want to ask You some questions» shout the contradictors ironically.

«Come. People of Kedesh, let them pass.»

And the crowd, casting hostile glances and making faces at them — with a few reviling epithets as well — let them pass.

«What do you want to know?» Jesus asks severely.

«So You say that You are the Messiah? Are You really sure?»

Jesus, standing with folded arms, looks at the man who has spoken with such overwhelming authority, that his irony immediately vanishes and he becomes silent.

But another one resumes speaking: «You cannot expect us to believe You on Your word. Anyone can lie, even in good faith. One needs proof to believe. So prove to us that You really are what You say.»

«Israel is full of My proof» replies Jesus sharply.

«Oh! those!... Trifles that any holy man can work. They have already been done and will be done again by the just in Israel!» says a Pharisee.

Another one adds: «Neither is it certain that You do them through holiness and the help of God! In fact they say, and it is really credible, that You are helped by Satan. We want other proof. Of a superior level. That Satan cannot give.»

«Of course! A victory over death...» says another one.

«You have already had it.»

«They were cases of catalepsy. Show us a decomposed body that revives and is recomposed, for instance. So that we may be sure that God is with You. God: the Only One Who can give life back to mud that is becoming dust again.»

«No one ever asked the Prophets for that in order to believe them.»

A Sadducee shouts: «You are greater than a Prophet. You are the Son of God, at least so You say!... Ah! Ah! So why do You not act as God? Come on! Give us a sign!»

«Yes! A sign from Heaven proving that You are the Son of God, we will then worship You» shouts a Pharisee.

«Certainly! You are right, Simon! We do not want to commit Aaron's sin again. We will not worship an idol, the golden calf. * But we could worship the Lamb of God! Are You not it? Providing Heaven proves that You are» says the one named Uzziel and who was at Giscala, laughing sarcastically.

Another one shouts: «Let me speak, for I am Sadoc, the golden scribe. Listen to me, Christ. You have been preceded by too many false Christs. We have had enough frauds. We want a sign that You really are Christ. And if God is with You, He cannot deny You that. And we will believe in You and help You. Otherwise You know what is due to You, according to the Commandment of * God.»

---

* **sin**, the one narrated in: *Exodus 32:1-6*.

* **Commandment**, in *Leviticus 24:16*.

Jesus raises His injured hand and shows it to His interlocutor. «Do you see this sign? You did it. You have pointed out a further sign. And when you see it incised in the flesh of the Lamb, you will rejoice. Look at it! Can you see it? You will also see it in Heaven, when you appear to give an account of your way of living. *Because I will be your Judge*, and I will be there with My glorified Body, with the signs of My ministry and of yours, of My love and of your hatred. And you will see it, too, Uzziel, and you, Simon, and Caiaphas and Annas will see it, and many more, on that Last Day, the day of wrath, the dreadful day, and you will then prefer to be in the abyss, because the sign on My injured hand will torture you more than the fire of Hell.»

«Oh! those are blasphemous words! You will be in Heaven with Your body?! Blasphemer! You will be judge in the place of God?! Anathema on You! You are insulting the Pontiff! You deserve to be stoned» shout in chorus Pharisees, Sadducees and doctors.

[7] The head of the synagogue stands up again: he looks patri- 342.7
archal and stately in his old age, like a Moses, and he shouts: «Kedesh is a city of refuge and a Levitical city. Respect it...»

«That's an old story! It doesn't count anymore!»

«Oh! Blasphemous tongues! You are sinners, not He, and I will defend Him. He is not saying anything wrong. He is explaining the Prophets and has brought us the Good Promise, and you are interrupting, provoking and offending Him. I will not allow that. He is under the protection of old Matthias of the stock of Levi by father and of Aaron by mother. Go out and let Him instruct my old age and the youth of my sons.» And he lays his old wrinkled hand on Jesus' forearm, in a gesture of protection.

«Let Him give us a real sign and we will be convinced and go away» the hostile group shouted.

«Do not be upset, Matthias. I will speak» says Jesus calming the head of the synagogue. And addressing the Pharisees, Sadducees and doctors, He says: «In the evening you scan the sky, and if it is red at sunset, you state, according to an old saying: "The weather will be fine tomorrow, because sunset has reddened the sky". Likewise at dawn, when the heavy foggy damp air prevents the sun from shining as brightly as gold, you say: "There will be a storm before the day is over". So you can tell the future of the day by the changing signs of the sky and by the even more inconstant signs of winds. And you cannot tell the signs of times? That does no credit to your minds and your science, and brings utter dishonor on your souls and your alleged wisdom. You belong to a wicked adulterous generation, born in Israel of a marriage of one who fornicated with Evil. You are their heirs and you increase your wickedness and adultery by repeating the sin of the fathers of that error. Well, listen, Matthias, and you, citizens of Kedesh and whoever is present here either as a believer or as an enemy, listen! This is the prophecy that I make, of My own, in the place of the one of Habakkuk, which I wanted to explain to you: this wicked and adulterous generation, which is asking for a sign, will be given no other sign but the sign of Jonah... Let * us go. Peace be with everyone of goodwill.» And through a side door that opens on a quiet street among gardens and houses, Jesus goes away with His disciples.

342.8 [8] But the people of Kedesh do not give in. Some follow Him, and when they see Him enter a small inn in the eastern suburbs of the town, they inform the head of the synagogue and their fellow citizens. And Jesus is still eating when the sunny yard of the inn becomes crowded with people and the old head of the synagogue and other elders of Kedesh go to the door of the room in which Jesus is, and the old man, bowing, implores: «Master, the desire to hear Your word is still in our hearts. The prophecy by Habakkuk * was so beautiful, as You were explaining it! Are those who love You and believe in Your Truth to be left without the knowledge of You, only because there are some people who hate You?»

«No, father. It would not be fair to punish the good because of the wicked. Well, listen...» (and Jesus stops eating and goes to the door to speak to those who have thronged in the peaceful yard).

«The words of your head of the synagogue echo those of Habakkuk. On his own behalf and yours, he confesses and professes that I am the Truth. Habakkuk confesses and professes: "You have been since the beginning and You are with us and we shall not die". And so it will be. He who believes in Me will not perish.

---

* **of Jonah**, already in 269.10.

* **prophecy**, its explanation started with the quotations of *Habakkuk 1:2.3.5*, followed, after the interruption by the Pharisees, with the quotations of *Habakkuk 1:12-13; 2:3.4.6.9.12.18; 3:2-5.*

The Prophet describes Me as the One Whom God has appointed to judge, as the One Whom God made strong in order to punish, as the One Whose eyes are too pure to rest on wickedness and Who cannot bear iniquity. But while it is true that sin disgusts Me, you can see that, as I am the Savior, I open My arms to those who have repented of their sins. I thus turn My eyes towards culprits and I invite the impious to repent...

[9]People of the Levitical city of Kedesh, the city sanctified by 342.9
the proclamation of charity towards those who are guilty of crimes — and every man is guilty towards God, his soul and his neighbour — come to Me, the Refuge of sinners. Here, in My love, not even the anathema of God would strike you, because My imploring glance would change the anathema of God into blessings of forgiveness for you.

Listen! Write this promise in your hearts as Habakkuk wrote his certain prophecy on a roll. It is written there: "If it comes slowly, wait, because He Who is to come, will come without fail". Now: He Who was to come, has come: it is I.

"He who is incredulous, has not a righteous soul" says the Prophet and his word condemns those who provoked and insulted Me. I do not condemn them. But the Prophet, who foresaw Me and believed in Me, condemns them. As he describes Me, the Triumpher, so he describes a proud man saying that he is not honorable, as he opened his soul to greed and insatiability, as hell is greedy and insatiable. And he threatens: "Trouble is coming to the man who amasses goods that are not his and loads himself with thick mud". Evil deeds against the Son of man are that mud, and the desire to deprive Him of His holiness so that it may not dim one's own, is greed.

The Prophet says: "Trouble is coming to the man who grossly exploits others for the sake of his house, to fix his nest on high and so evade the hand of misfortune". He who does that disgraces himself and kills his own soul. "Trouble is coming to the man who builds a town with blood and founds a city on crime". Really too many in Israel build the castles of their covetousness on tears and blood and are awaiting the last blood to make a richer mixture. But what can a fortress do against the arrows of God? And what can a handful of men do against the justice of the whole world shouting for horror at the unequalled crime?

Oh! How well Habakkuk says! “What is the use of a carved image?”. And the false holiness of Israel is nothing but an idolatrous statue. The Lord only is in His holy Temple and to Him only the earth will bow and tremble with adoration and fear, while the promised sign will be given a first time and a second time and the true Temple in which God rests will ascend gloriously to say in Heaven: “It has been accomplished!”, as He will have whispered it to the earth to cleanse it through His announcement.

“Fiat!” said the Most High. And the world was created. “Fiat” the Redeemer will say, and the world will be redeemed. I will give the world the means to be redeemed. And those will be redeemed who want to be so.

342.10 [10] Now stand up! Let us say the prayer of the Prophet, but as it is right to say it in this time of grace:

“I heard, O Lord, Your announcement and I rejoiced”. It is no longer the time of fright, O believers in the Messiah.

“Lord, Your work is in the middle of the course of years, make it live, notwithstanding the snares of enemies. In the middle of the course of years You will manifest it”. Yes. When the time is completed the work will be accomplished.

“His mercy will shine, notwithstanding His wrath” because His wrath will strike only those who have cast nets or laid snares or shot arrows at the Lamb Savior.

“From the Light God will come to the world”. I am the Light that came to bring you God. My splendor will inundate the earth springing in torrents “where the pointed horns” will have torn to pieces the Flesh of the Victim, the last victory “of Death and of Satan, who will be beaten and will flee before the Living Holy One”.

Glory to the Lord! Glory to the Creator of the world! Glory to the Giver of the sun and stars! To the Maker of the mountains. To the Creator of the seas. Glory, infinite Glory to the Good Lord, Who wanted the Christ to save His people and redeem man.

Join Me, sing with Me, because Mercy has come to the world and the time of Peace is close at hand. He Who stretches out His hands to you exhorts you to believe and live in the Lord because Israel will be shortly judged with justice.

Peace to you who are present here, to your families and to your homes.»

Jesus makes a wide gesture blessing them and is about to withdraw.

But the head of the synagogue begs Him: «Stay a little longer.»

«I cannot, father.»

«At least send us Your apostles.»

«You will have them without fail. Goodbye. Go in peace.»

[11] They are alone... 342.11

«I would like to know who sent them our way. They look like necromancers...» says Peter.

The Iscariot turns pale and comes forward. He kneels at Jesus' feet. «Master, I am the culprit. I spoke in that village... to one of them, whose guest I was...»

«What? Was that your penance? You are...»

«Be silent, Simon of Jonah! Your brother is accusing himself sincerely. Respect him because of his humiliation. Do not worry, Judas. I forgive you. *You know* that I forgive. But be wiser the next time... And now let us go. We will walk as long as it is moonlight. We must cross the river before dawn. Let us go. The wood begins over there. Both the good and the wicked will lose trace of us. Tomorrow we will be on the way to Paneas.»

343. The Yeast of the Pharisees. Who Really is the "Son of Man"? Peter's Primacy.

27th November 1945.

[1] The Jordan runs across a plain before flowing into lake 343.1
Merom. It is a beautiful plain where cereals grow more and more vigorously day by day and fruit-trees blossom. The hills beyond which Kedesh lies are now behind the pilgrims, who are walking fast at daybreak. They appear to be very cold, as they cast keen glances at the rising sun and they look for it, as soon as its rays shine on meadows and caress leaves. They must have slept out in the open, or at the most in a stack-yard, because their garments are creased and show particles of straw and dry leaves, which they remove as they see them in the light, that is becoming clearer and clearer.

The river is detected through its gurgling, which sounds loud in the silent morning in the country, and by the sight of a thick line of trees, the new leaves of which are quivering in the light morning breeze. But it cannot be seen as yet, sunken as it is in the flat plain, although it is swollen by many torrents flowing into it from the eastern hills. When they can see its blue water sparkle through the new greenery on its banks, they are almost on its bank.

«Shall we walk along the bank as far as the bridge, or shall we cross the river here?» they ask Jesus, Who was alone, pensive, and has now stopped waiting for them.

«See if there is a boat to cross over. It is better to cross here...»

«Yes, at the bridge, which is just on the road to Caesarea Pane-as we might come across someone who has been sent to follow our footsteps» remarks Bartholomew frowning, while he looks at Judas.

«No. Don't look back at me. I did not know that we were coming here, and I have not said anything. It was easy to understand that from Saphet Jesus would go to the sepulchers of the rabbis and to Kedesh. But, I would never have thought that He wanted to go as far as Philip's capital. So they know nothing about it. So we shall not find them through my fault or through their own decision. Unless Beelzebub himself leads them» says calmly and humbly the Iscariot.

«Very well. Because with certain people... We must be sharp-sighted and speak very carefully, without letting them have any clue of our plans. We must watch everything. Otherwise our evangelization will become a perpetual flight» replies Bartholomew.

John and Andrew come back. They say: «We found two boats. They will take us to the other side for a drachma each boat. Let us go down the embankment.»

And they cross to the other side in the two little boats, in two trips. There is a fertile plain also on this side, fertile but not *
thickly populated. Only the local farmers live there.

343.2 [2]«H'm! What shall we do for bread? I am hungry. And there are no Philistine ears of corn here... Grass and leaves, leaves and flowers. I am neither a little sheep nor a bee» grumbles Peter to

* **fertile plain**. The sketch by M.V. represents the area: 1. *Hills* (to the West); 2. *Caesarea Paneas* or *Philippi* (to the North East); 3. *Rather high mounts* (to the East); 4. *Hills* (to the South); 5. *Place of the crossing* (in the centre, along the river).

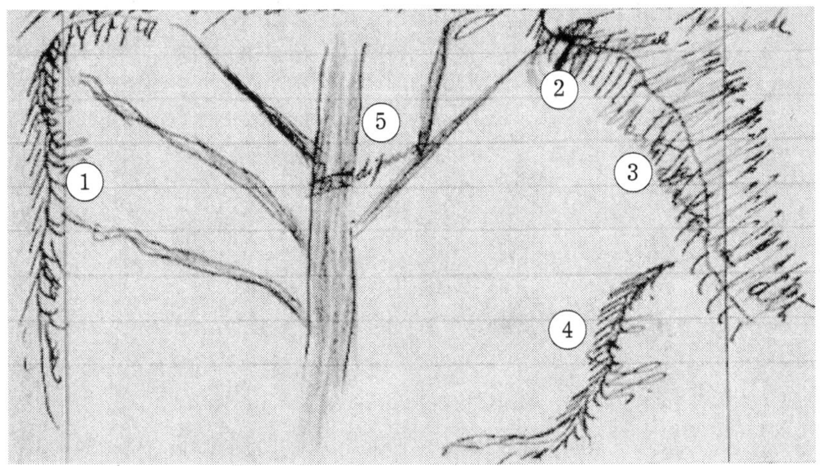

his companions who smile at his remark.

Judas Thaddeus turns around — he was a little ahead — and he says: «We will buy some bread in the next village.»

«Providing they don't make us flee» concludes James of Zebedee.

«You, who say that we have to watch everything, be careful lest you pick up the yeast of the Pharisees and Sadducees. I think that is what you are doing, without considering the wrong you are doing. Be careful, very careful!» says Jesus.

The apostles look at one another and whisper: «What is He saying? The bread was given to us by the woman of the deaf-mute and by the inn-keeper at Kedesh. I still have it here. It is the only bread we have. And we do not know whether we will be able to find any more to satisfy our hunger. So why does He say that we buy bread of Sadducees and Pharisees with their yeast? Perhaps He does not want us to buy any in the villages here...»

Jesus, Who once again was ahead of them all alone, turns around. «Why are you afraid to be left without bread? Even if all the people here were Sadducees and Pharisees, you would not be without bread because I told you not to buy any. I am not speaking of the yeast which is in bread. So you can buy bread anywhere you like to satisfy your hunger. And if nobody would sell you any, you would not be left without bread just the same. Do you not remember the five loaves with which five thousand people appeased their hunger? Do you not remember that you collected twelve baskets full of the scraps remaining? I could do for you, who are twelve and have one loaf, what I did for five thousand people with five loaves. Do you not understand to which yeast I am referring? To the yeast that rises in the hearts of Pharisees, Sadducees and doctors against Me. It is hatred. It is heresy. You are now going towards hatred, as if part of the Pharisaical yeast had entered your hearts. Not even your enemy is to be hated. Not even a very small inlet is to be opened to anything that is not God. After the first element, others opposed to God would enter. Sometimes one perishes or is defeated because one wants to fight enemies with equal weapons. And once you have been defeated, you could by contact absorb their doctrine. Be charitable and reserved. You are not yet in a position to oppose such doctrines, without being infected. Because you have some of their elements as well. And hatred is one of them. I would also warn you that they may change method in order to entice you and take you away from Me, by being extremely polite, showing that they are repentant and anxious to make peace. You must not avoid them but when they try to imbue you with their doctrines, you must reject them. That is the yeast to which I was referring. Animosity, which is against love, and false doctrines. I say to you: be prudent.»

343.3 [3] «That sign which the Pharisees asked for yesterday, was it "yeast", Master?» asks Thomas.

«It was yeast and poison.»

«You did the right thing in not giving it to them.»

«But I will give it to them one day.»

«When?» they ask curiously.

«One day...»

«And what sign is it? Are You not telling even us, Your apostles? So that we may recognize it at once» asks Peter who is anxious to know.

«You should not need a sign.»

«Oh! It is not to be able to believe in You! We have not many ideas as the people have. All we want is to love You» says James of Zebedee passionately.

343.4 [4] «But the people you approach in a simple friendly way, more than I do, without making them feel uneasy, as I may do, who do they say that I am? And who do they say the Son of Man is?»

«Some say that You are Jesus, that is the Christ, and they are the best. Some say that You are a Prophet, some only a Rabbi, others, and You know, say that You are mad and possessed.»

«But some call You by the same name that You use and they say: "Son of man".»

«And some say that that is not possible, because the Son of man is a different thing. But that is not always a denial. Because in actual fact they acknowledge that You are more than the Son of man: You are the Son of God. Others instead say that You are not even the Son of man, but a poor man agitated by Satan or deranged by madness. You can thus see that there are many different opinions» says Bartholomew.

«What is the Son of man, therefore, according to the people?»

«He is a man in whom there are all the most beautiful virtues of men, a man gifted with all the requisites of intelligence, wisdom, grace, which we think were in Adam, to which some add the gift of not having to die. You know that there is already a rumor that John the Baptist is not dead. They say that he was only carried elsewhere by angels and that Herod, and above all Herodias, to prevent people from saying that they had been defeated by God, killed a servant, had him beheaded and then showed his mutilated body saying it was the corpse of the Baptist. People say so many things! So many think that the Son of man is either Jeremiah, or Elijah, or one of the Prophets, or the Baptist, who was gifted with grace and wisdom and said that he was the Precursor of the Christ. Christ: the Anointed of God. The Son of man: a great man, born of man. Some cannot admit, or do not want to admit, that God has sent His Son to the earth. You said so yesterday: "Only those will believe who are convinced of the infinite goodness of God". Israel believes more in God's severity than in His goodness...» says Bartholomew again.

«Yes. They feel so undeserving that they consider it impossible that God has been so good as to send His Word to save them. The degraded state of their souls is a hindrance to their believing that» confirms the Zealot. And he adds: «You say that You are the Son of God and of man. In fact in You there is all grace and wisdom as man. And I really think that he who was born of Adam in the state of grace, would have been like You in beauty and intelligence and all virtues. The power of God shines in You. But who can believe that among those who consider themselves gods and judge God by their standards in their infinite pride? Cruel, hateful, greedy, impure as they are, they cannot possibly think that God has gone to such an extreme of kindness as to give Himself to redeem them, His love to save them, His generosity to be at their mercy, His purity to sacrifice His life among men. Since they are so inflexible and captious in looking for faults and punishing them, they cannot believe that.»

343.5 [5] «And who do you say that I am? Tell Me your own personal opinion without taking into account My words or the words of other people. If you were compelled to judge Me, who would you say that I am?»

«You are the Christ, the Son of the Living God» exclaims Peter, kneeling down with his arms stretched upwards, towards Jesus, Who looks at him with His face bright with love and Who bends to raise and embrace him, saying:

«Simon, son of Jonah, you are a happy man! Because it was not the flesh and blood that revealed this to you, but My Father in Heaven. Since the first day you came with Me, you have been asking yourself that question, and because you are simple and honest, you have been able to understand and accept the reply that came to you from Heaven. You did not see supernatural manifestations as your brother, John and James did. You did not know My holiness as son, workman, citizen, as My brothers Judas and James did. You did not receive any miracle neither did you see Me work any; I showed no sign of power to you as I did with Philip, Nathanael, Simon Cananean, Thomas and Judas, who saw them. You were not subdued by My will, as Levi the publican was. And yet you exclaimed: "He is the Christ!". You believed since the first moment you saw Me, and your faith was never shaken. That is why I called you Cephas. And that is why on you, Peter, I will build My Church and the gates of Hell shall not prevail against it. I will give you the keys of the Kingdom of Heaven. Whatever you bind on earth shall also be bound in Heaven. And whatever you loose on the earth shall also be lost in Heaven, O prudent faithful man, whose heart I have been able to test. And now, from this moment you are the head, to whom obedience and respect are due as to another Myself. And I proclaim him such before all of you.»

343.6 [6] If Jesus had crushed Peter under a hailstorm of reproaches, Peter would not have wept so copiously. He is weeping and is shaken by sobs, with his face on Jesus' chest. His weeping can be compared only to the tears he will shed in his grief for denying Jesus. He now weeps for many good humble feelings... A little of the old Simon — the fisherman of Bethsaida who had laughed incredulously and facetiously at his brother's first announcement saying: «Of course, the Messiah would appear just to you!...» — a good little of the old Simon crumbles under those tears and from his vanishing frail human nature, Peter appears, more and more clearly, the Pontiff of the Church of Christ.

When he raises his shy embarrassed face, he can make only one gesture to say *everything*, to promise *everything*, to strengthen himself *completely* for his new ministry: he throws his arms around Jesus' neck, compelling Him to bend and kiss him, mingling his somewhat bristly grizzled hair and beard with the soft golden hair and beard of Jesus. And he looks at Jesus with his large, loving, imploring and adoring eyes, still shining and red with tears holding the Master's ascetic face, bent over his own, in his rough large stumpy hands, as if it were a vase from which a vital liquid flowed... and he drinks kindness, grace, confidence and strength from Jesus' face, eyes and smile...

[7] They separate at last, and resume their journey towards Cae- 343.7
sarea Philippi, and Jesus says to everybody: «Peter has spoken the truth. Many guess it, you are aware of it. But for the time being, do not say to anybody who the Christ is, in the full truth known to you. Let God speak to the hearts of people, as He speaks to yours. I solemnly tell you that those who add perfect faith and perfect love to My statements or yours, will learn the true meaning of the words "Jesus, the Christ, the Word, the Son of man and of God".»

344. At Caesarea Philippi, Meeting with the Disciples. The Sign of Jonah.

28th November 1945.

[1] The town must have been built recently, like Tiberias and 344.1
Ashkelon. Situated on an inclined plane it culminates in a massive fortress with many towers, flanked with Cyclopean masonry and protected with deep moats into which part of the water of

two little rivers that first come close together forming an angle flows, then part, as one runs out of the town and the other flows through it. Beautiful streets, squares, fountains, and buildings in Roman style leads us to understand that here also servile homage prevailed in Tetrarchs, trampling on all respect for the customs of the Fatherland.

The town is very busy and crowded, probably because it is the junction of important main roads and caravan-tracks for Damascus, Tyre, Saphet and Tiberias, as indicated on mile-stones at each gate. Pedestrians, horsemen, long caravans of donkeys and camels meet in the wide well kept streets, and groups of business men or idlers are standing in the squares, under the porches, near the magnificent buildings, perhaps there are also some Thermae, discussing business or in idle conversation.

344.2 [2] «Do you know where we can find them?» Jesus asks Peter.

«Yes, I do. Those whom I asked told me that the disciples of the Rabbi meet for their meals in the house of some faithful Israelites, near the citadel. And they described the house to me. I cannot go wrong: it is a Jewish house also on the outside, the front has no windows and there is a high main door with spy-hole, on the side of the wall there is a little fountain, the high walls of the garden extend on two sides along two lanes, and there is a roof-terrace with many doves.»

«Very well. Let us go then.»

They cross the whole town as far as the citadel. They arrive at the house they are looking for and knock. The wrinkled face of an old woman appears at the peep-hole.

Jesus moves forward and greets her: «Peace be with you, woman. Have the disciples of the Rabbi come back?»

«No, man. They are at the "Great Spring" with other people who have come from many towns on the other side of the river looking for the Rabbi. They are all waiting for Him. Are You waiting for Him as well?»

«No. I am looking for the disciples.»

«Well, look: see that street which is almost opposite the fountain? Take that one and go up until You arrive in front of a massive wall of rock from which water comes out and flows into a kind of vat and then becomes a little stream. You will find them there. But have You come from far? Do You want to come in and refresh Yourself and wait for them here? If You wish so, I will call my masters. They are good Israelites, You know? And they believe in the Messiah. They are disciples although they have only seen Him once in Jerusalem, in the Temple. But now the disciples of the Messiah have taught them and have worked miracles here because...»

«Very well, good woman. I will come back later with the disciples. Peace to you. You may go back to your housework» says Jesus kindly but firmly to stop the avalanche of words.

[3] They carry on walking and the younger apostles laugh whole- 344.3
heartedly at the performance of the woman and they make Jesus smile as well.

«Master» says John «I thought that she was the "Great Spring". Don't You think so? She poured out continuous waves of words and treated us as vats that become streams because they are full of words...»

«Yes. I hope that the disciples have not worked a miracle on her tongue... We would have to say: you have worked *too big* a miracle» says Thaddeus, who contrary to his habit, laughs heartily.

«There will be fun when we go back and she finds out who the Master is! Who will be able to keep her quiet then?» asks James of Zebedee.

«No, she will be so shocked that she will become dumb» says Matthew, joining in the conversation of the younger ones.

«I will praise the Most High if astonishment paralyses her tongue. It is probably because I have not had any breakfast yet, but the flood of her words certainly made me feel dizzy» says Peter.

«And how she shouted! Is she perhaps deaf?» asks Thomas.
«No. She thought we were deaf» replies the Iscariot.

«Leave the poor old woman alone! She is good and a believer. Her heart is as generous as her tongue» says Jesus half-seriously.

«Oh! Master! In that case the old woman is so generous that she is heroic» says John laughing heartily.

[4] The calcareous rocky wall can now be seen and the gurgle of 344.4
the water falling into the vat is heard.

«There is the stream. Let us follow it... There is the spring... and there... Benjamin! Daniel! Abel! Philip! Ermasteus! We are here! The Master is here!» shouts John to a large group of men gathered round someone who, however, is not visible.

«Be quiet, boy, or you will be like that old hen» suggests Peter.

The disciples have turned around. They have seen: and to see and rush down from the terrace is all one thing. Now that the group has opened out, I can see that people from Kedesh and from the village of the deaf-mute have joined the many disciples, who are all seniors by now. They must have taken more direct routes, because they have preceded the Master.

Their joy is great. Their questions and answers are numerous. Jesus listens and replies patiently until thin Isaac appears smiling, laden with supplies, together with two more people.

«Let us go to the hospitable house, my Lord. And when there You will be able to explain to us what we have not been able to clarify because we do not know it ourselves... These people here, the last arrivals — they have been with us only a few hours — want to know what the sign of Jonah is, the one You promised to give this wicked generation that persecutes You» says Isaac.

«I will explain it to them while going...»

Going! It is not so easy! Like bees attracted by the scent of flowers that has spread in the air, people rush from all directions to join those who are around Jesus.

«They are our friends» explains Isaac. «People who have believed and have been waiting for You...»

«People who have received graces from the disciples and from him in particular» shouts one in the crowd pointing at Isaac.

Isaac blushes and as if he wanted to apologize he says: «But I am a servant. He is the Master. Here is the Master, for Whom you have been waiting. Here is Jesus!»

It was the last straw! The peaceful district of Caesarea, a little out of the way, in the suburb area, becomes busier than a market. And noisier. Hosannas! Acclamations! Entreaties! Everything!

Jesus proceeds very slowly, hemmed in on all sides by so much love. But He smiles and blesses. He proceeds so slowly that some people have time to run away and spread the news, and then come back with friends or relatives, holding their children high up in order to arrive safely close to Jesus, Who caresses and blesses them.

[5]They thus arrive at the house seen previously and knock. The 344.5
same old servant, on hearing all the voices, opens without any hesitation. But... she sees Jesus in the middle of the cheering crowd, and she understands... She drops to the floor moaning: «Have mercy, my Lord. Your servant did not recognize You and did not worship You!»

«No harm, woman. You did not recognize the man, but you believed in Him. That is what is required to be loved by God. Stand up and take Me to your masters.»

The old woman obeys, trembling with respect. But she sees her masters, overwhelmed with respect, leaning against the wall at the end of the rather dark entrance-hall. She points at them: «There they are.»

«Peace to you and to this house. May the Lord bless you for your faith in the Christ and for your charity to his disciples» says Jesus going towards the two old people, who are either husband and wife, or brother and sister.

They worship Him and then take Him to the wide verandah where several tables are laid under a heavy velarium. The view stretches over Caesarea as far as the mountains behind it and on its sides. Doves fly from the terrace to the garden full of trees in blossom.

While an old servant adds more places to the tables, Isaac explains: «Benjamin and Anne welcome not only us, but whoever comes looking for You. They do so in Your Name.»

«May Heaven bless them every time they do so.»

«Oh! We have means, but have no children. At the end of our days, we are adopting the poor of the Lord» says simply the old woman.

And Jesus lays His hand on her grey-haired head saying:
«And that makes you mother more than if you had conceived
seven times and seven times. [6]But now allow Me to explain to 344.6
these people what they wanted to know, so that we can then dis-
miss them and sit down to our meal.»

The terrace is crammed with people and more continue to arrive taking up every possible bit of room. Jesus is surrounded by children who look at Him ecstatically with their large innocent eyes. His back is turned to the table and He smiles at the children even when talking of the important subject. He seems to be reading on their innocent faces the words of the requested truth.

«Listen. The sign of Jonah that I promised to the wicked, and * I promise to you as well, not because you are wicked, on the contrary, that you may reach perfection in believing when you see that it is accomplished, is this.

As Jonah remained in the belly of the sea-monster for three days and then was vomited on the shore to convert and save Nineveh, so it will happen to the Son of man. To calm the billows of a great satanic storm, the mighty ones in Israel will deem it necessary to sacrifice the Innocent. But they will only increase their dangers, because in addition to Satan who will perturb them, they will have God Who will punish them after the crime. They could defeat the storm by believing in Me. But they will not believe, because they see in Me the cause of their perturbation, of their fears, dangers and refutation of their false holiness. But when the hour comes, the insatiable monster, that is, the bowels of the earth, which swallow every man who dies, will open up to give the Light back to the world that denied it.

So as Jonah was a sign of the power and mercy of the Lord for the people of Nineveh, so the Son of man will be the sign for this generation. With the difference that Nineveh was converted whereas Jerusalem will not be converted, because it is full of the wicked generation of which I spoke. So the Queen of the South will rise on Doomsday against the men of this generation and will condemn them. Because she came, in her days, from the end of the world to listen to Solomon's wisdom, whilst this generation, which has Me with them, will not listen to Me and they persecute and drive Me away as if I were a leper and a sinner, and yet I am much greater than Solomon. Also the people of Nineveh will rise on Doomsday against the wicked generation that will not turn to the Lord its God, because they were converted by the preaching of a man.

And I am greater than any man, be it Jonah or any other Prophet. I will therefore give the sign of Jonah to those who ask for a definitely unequivocal sign. I will give *one and one sign* to those who arrogantly refuse to bow to the proof that I have already given them of people rising from death by My command. I

* **promised** in 269.10 and 342.7.

will give all signs. The sign of a decomposed body that becomes alive and wholesome, and the sign of a body that rises by Itself from death because Its Spirit is gifted with almighty power. But they will not be graces. They will not smooth the situation. Neither here, nor in the eternal books. What is written, is written. And proof will pile up like stones for a lapidation. They will pile up against Me, to harm Me, but unsuccessfully. And against them to crush them forever by the sentence of God reserved for the wicked incredulous.

That is the sign of Jonah of which I spoke. Have you any more questions to ask Me?»

«No, Master. We will inform our head of the synagogue, who was very close to the truth when considering the promised sign.»

«Matthias is a just man. [7]And the Truth is revealed to the Just 344.7
as it is revealed to these innocent children who know Who I am, better than anybody else. Before I dismiss you, let Me hear these angels of the earth praise the mercy of God. Come here, children.»

The children who have been quiet with some difficulty so far, run towards Him.

«Tell Me, children without malice, which is My Sign for you?»

«That You are good.»

«That You cured my mother by means of Your Name.»

«That You love everybody.»

«That You are so handsome as no other man can be.»

«That You make bad people become good, as You did with my father.»

Each child announces a loving distinctive feature of Jesus, or recollects sufferings that Jesus has changed into smiles.

But the dearest of them all is a lively little child, about four years old, who climbs up on Jesus' lap and clasps His neck saying: «Your sign is that You love all children, and children love. You. A love as big as this...» and he opens his little plump arms wide, and laughs, and he then embraces Jesus' neck once again, rubbing his childish cheek against Jesus', Who kisses him asking: «But why do you love Me if you have never seen Me before?»

«Because You look like the angel of the Lord.»

«But you have not seen him, My dear little fellow...» says Jesus tempting him and smiling.

The child remains dumbfounded for a moment. He then smiles showing all his little teeth and he says: «But my soul did see him! Mummy says that I have it, and it's here, and God sees it, and my soul has seen God and the angels, and sees them. And my soul knows You, because You are the Lord.»

Jesus kisses his forehead saying: «May this kiss increase in you the light of your intellect» and He puts him down. The child runs to his father, holding a hand on his forehead where it was kissed, and he shouts: «To mummy, to mummy! So that she may kiss here where the Lord kissed, and her voice will come back to her and she will not weep anymore.»

They explain to Jesus that the child's mother suffers from throat trouble and was very anxious to receive a miracle; but the disciples were unable to cure her disease as it was too deep and untouchable.

«The youngest disciple, her little boy, will cure her. Go in peace, man. And have faith... like your son» He says dismissing the child's father.

He then kisses the other children who are anxious to have the same kiss on their foreheads and He dismisses the citizens. Only His disciples, the people from Kedesh and the other places remain with Him.

344.8 [8] While waiting for the meal to be served, Jesus organizes the departure of the following day of *all* the disciples, who will precede Him to Capernaum, where they will join the others who will have gone there from other places. «You will then take with you Salome, the wives and daughters of Nathanael and Philip, Johanna and Susanna, as you proceed towards Nazareth. You will get My Mother there, and the mother of My brothers and you will take them to Bethany, to the house in which Joseph lives in Lazarus' property. We will come through the Decapolis.»

«And what about Marjiam?» asks Peter.

«I said: "you will precede Me to Capernaum". I did not say: "go". But from Capernaum you will be able to inform the women of our arrival, so that they may be ready, when we go towards Jerusalem: via the Decapolis. Marjiam, who is now a young man, will go with the disciples escorting the women...»

«The fact is... that I wanted to take also my wife, poor woman, to Jerusalem. She has always wanted to go, but she never came, because I did not want any trouble. But I would like to make her happy this year. She is so good!»

«Of course, Simon. That is another reason for sending Marjiam with her. We shall travel very slowly and we shall all meet there...»

The old landlord says: «Such a short time with me.»

«Father, I have still so much to do. I want to be in Jerusalem at least eight days before Passover. Remember that the first phase of the moon of Adar is already over...»

«That is true. But I longed so much for You!... I seem to be in the light of Heaven with You here... and that the light will go out as soon as You go away.»

«No, father. I will leave it in your heart. I will leave it also to your wife and to everybody in this hospitable house.»

They sit at the tables and Jesus offers and blesses the food, which a servant passes to the various tables.

345. A Miracle in the Castle of Caesarea Paneas.

29th November 1945.

[1]The meal in the hospitable house is over. And Jesus goes out 345.1
with the Twelve, His disciples and the old landlord. They go back to the Great Spring. But they do not stop there. They continue along the same road, which is uphill all the way, northwards.

The road, although very steep, is comfortable, because it is also manageable to carts and horses. At the end of it, on the top of the mountain there is a massive castle or fortress, whichever it may be and it is amazing because of its strange shape. It seems to consist of two buildings placed at different levels, so that the rear one which is also more warlike looking is a few meters higher than the front one, which it dominates and defends. Between the two buildings there is a high broad wall fortified with square squat towers; but it must be *one* building only because it is surrounded by an ashlar wall, with slanting ashlars at the base to support the weight of the rampart. I cannot see the western side. But the northern and southern sides fall sheer down to the mountain, which is isolated and drops vertically on both sides. I think that the western side is similar.

Old Benjamin, who, like all of us, is proud of his town, explains the importance of the Tetrarch's castle, which besides being a castle is also a fortress for the town, and he points out its beauty, its powerful solidity, its attributes such as cisterns, vats, space, wide view all around, position etc. «Also the Romans say that it is beautiful. And they are good judges!...» concludes the old man. He then adds: «I am familiar with the superintendent. That's why I can go in. I will show you the widest and most beautiful view of Palestine.»

Jesus listens to him kindly. The others smile faintly: they have seen so many views... but the old man is so kind that they do not have the heart to mortify him and they countenance him in his desire to show beautiful things to Jesus.

345.2 [2] They reach the summit. The view is really magnificent even from the emplacement before the main iron gate. But the old man says: «Come... come... It is more beautiful inside. We will go to the top of the highest tower in the citadel... You will see...»

And they enter a dark corridor dug in the wall, which is several meters wide, until they reach a yard where the superintendent is waiting for them with his family.

The two friends greet each other and the old man explains the reason for the visit.

«The Rabbi of Israel?! What a pity that Philip is not here. He was so anxious to see Him, because we heard of His fame. He is very fond of true rabbis, because they are the only ones who defended his rights, and also to spite Antipas who does not like them. Come, come...» The man eyed Jesus very carefully first and then decided to honor Him by giving Him a bow worthy of a king.

They go through another corridor into a second yard where there is another iron postern with access to a third yard, beyond which there is a deep moat and the turreted wall of the citadel. Faces of curious warriors and batmen appear from everywhere. They enter the citadel and then, climbing a narrow staircase, they reach the bastion and then a tower. Only Jesus, the superintendent, Benjamin and the Twelve enter the tower, and they are packed like sardines, so the others cannot go in and they remain on the bastion.

Jesus and those who are with Him enjoy a superb view when they go out on the little terrace at the top of the tower and look over the high stone parapet! Leaning out over the abyss on this western side, the highest part of the castle, they can see the whole of Caesarea stretched out at the foot of the mountain, and they can see it very well because it is not on level ground, but on gentle slopes. Beyond Caesarea there is a fertile plain that extends as far as lake Merom. And it looks like a little green sea, the water of which sparkles like light turquoises, strewn over the green expanse like particles of clear sky. And then there are beautiful hills spread here and there at the borders of the plain, like necklaces of dark emerald streaked with the silver of olive-trees. And airy plumes of trees in blossom, or trees in blossom as compact as huge balls... And looking to the north and the east there is the powerful Lebanon and the Hermon shining in the sun with its pearly snow and the mountains of Ituraea; and one can catch a glimpse of the imposing Jordan valley, enclosed between the hills of the sea of Tiberias and the mountains of Gaulanitis, fading away in the distance like a dream.

«How beautiful! It is very beautiful!» exclaims Jesus admiring the view and He seems to be blessing or to be wishing to embrace these beautiful places by opening His arms wide and smiling joyfully. And He replies to the apostles asking for this or that elucidation, pointing out the places where they have already been, that is to the various regions and the directions in which they lie.

«But I cannot see the Jordan» says Bartholomew.

«You cannot see it, but it is over there, in that expanse between the two chains of mountains. The river is immediately beyond the western one. We will be going down there, because Perea and the Decapolis are still awaiting the Evangelizer.»

[3]But He turns around, as if He were listening to the air, be- 345.3
cause of a long choked wailing that He has heard more than once. He looks at the superintendent as if to ask him what is happening.

«It is one of the women of the castle. A young wife. She is about to have a baby. It will be her first and last one because her husband died at the beginning of the month of Chislev. I do not know whether she will live, because since her husband died, she has been doing nothing but melt into tears. She has worn herself to a shadow. Can You hear her? She has not even got the strength to cry... Of course... A widow at seventeen... And they were very fond of each other. My wife and my mother-in-law keep saying to her: "You will find your Toby in your son". But they are just words...»

They come down from the tower and go round the bastions admiring the place and the view. The superintendent then insists in offering the guests some fruit and drinks and they enter a large room in the front of the castle, to which the servants bring what has been ordered.

The moaning becomes more heart-rending and is closer, and the superintendent apologizes also because the incident keeps his wife away from the Master. But a cry, which is even more painful than the previous moaning, is now heard and hands carrying fruit or cups to mouths are left mid air.

«I am going to see what happened» says the superintendent. And he goes out while the painful noise of cries and weeping is heard more distinctly through the half-open door.

345.4 [4]The superintendent comes back: «The baby died as soon as it was born... What a torture! She is trying to revive it with her failing strength... But it does not breathe any more. It is purple!...» and shaking his head he says: «Poor Dorca!»

«Bring Me the baby.»

«But it is dead, Lord.»

«Bring Me the baby, I said. As it is. And tell the mother to have faith.»

The superintendent runs away. He comes back: «She does not want to give it. She says that she will not give it to anybody. She seems to be mad. She says that we are trying to take it away from her.»

«Take Me to the door of her room, so that she may see Me.»

«But...»

«Never mind! I will be purified later, if necessary...»

They go quickly along a dark corridor as far as a closed room Jesus Himself opens the door and remains on the threshold facing the bed on which a very pale woman is pressing to her heart a little baby giving no sign of life.

«Peace to you, Dorca. Look at Me. Do not weep. I am the Savior. Give Me your baby...»

I do not know what there is in Jesus' voice. I know that the poor wretch, as soon as she sees Him, clasps the new-born baby to her heart in a wild attitude, then she looks at Him and her distressed countenance changes and becomes sorrowful but hopeful at the same time. She hands the baby wrapped in linen swaddling bands to the superintendent's wife... and remains motionless, with her hands stretched out, with her wide eyes full of faith and life, deaf to the entreaties of her mother-in-law, who would like her to lie down on the bed pillows.

[5]Jesus takes the bundle of swaddling clothes containing the 345.5
half-cold child, holds it straight by its armpits, lays His lips on the little half-closed lips of the baby, bending a little because the little head is leaning back. He blows hard down the inert throat... and remains for a moment with His lips pressed against the little mouth... then moves away... and a chirping trembles in the still air... then a louder one...a third one... and finally a real cry from a little quivering head...The baby moves its hands and feet and, in the meantime during its long triumphant cry, its bald head and tiny face begin to color. And its mother asserts: «My son! My love! The offspring of my Toby! On my heart! Come to my heart!... that I may die a happy death...» she murmurs dropping her voice to a whisper, which ends in a kiss and in an understandable reaction of relaxation.

«She is dying!» shout the women.

«No. She is beginning to rest, as she deserves. When she wakes up tell her to call the baby: Jesai Tobias. I will see her at the Temple on the day of her purification. Goodbye. Peace be with you.» He slowly closes the door and turns round to go back to His disciples. But they are all there, deeply moved at what they have seen and looking at Him full of admiration.

They go back together to the yard. They say goodbye to the dumbfounded superintendent who keeps repeating: «How sorry the Tetrarch will be that he was not here!» and they begin to descend towards the town.

Jesus lays His hand on the shoulder of old Benjamin saying: «Thank you for what you have shown to us and for being the occasion for a miracle.»...

346. Jesus Predicts His Death for the First Time. Peter's Disavowal and Jesus' Sharp Reproach.

30th November 1945.

346.1 [1]Jesus must have left the town of Caesarea Philippi at daybreak, because the town is now far behind with its mountains, and Jesus is once again in the plain going towards lake Merom, from where He will go to the lake of Gennesaret. His apostles are with Him together with all the disciples who were at Caesarea. But no one is surprised to see such a numerous caravan on the road, because there are many more caravans of Israelites or proselytes going to Jerusalem from all parts of the Diaspora, as they wish to remain some time in the Holy City to listen to the rabbis and breathe the air of the Temple for a long time.

They proceed quickly but although the sun is already high in the sky, it is not troublesome as springtime sunshine gently warms new leaves of trees in blossom and makes flowers open everywhere. The plain before the lake is like a flowery carpet, and the pilgrims looking at the hills surrounding it see them spotted with white, rosy, pink or almost red blossoms of the various fruit-trees, or on passing near the houses of farmers or forges on the roadside, they enjoy the sight of the first rose-bushes full of flowers in gardens, along hedges or against the walls of houses.

«Johanna's gardens must be all in flower» remarks Simon Zealot.

«Also the garden in Nazareth must look like a basket full of flowers. Mary is the sweet bee that passes from one rose-bush to another, then to the jasmines, which will soon be blooming, to the lilies, which are already in bud, and She will pick a branch of the almond-tree, as She is wont to do, or better, now She may pick a branch of the pear-tree or of the pomegranate, to put it into the amphora in Her little room. When we were young boys, every year we used to ask Her: "Why do You always have a flowery branch there, and You do not put the early roses in it?". And She replied: "Because on those petals I can see an order written, which came to Me from God and I smell the pure scent of celestial air". Do you remember, Judas?» James of Alphaeus asks his brother.

«Yes. I do. And I remember that when I grew up I used to wait anxiously for springtime, so that I could see Mary walking in

Her garden, under Her trees, the blossoms of which were like clouds, or among the bushes of the early roses. I never saw anything more beautiful than the eternal girl passing lightly among Her flowers while doves were flying around Her...»

[2] «Oh! Let us go to Her soon, Lord! That I may see all that as well!» implores Thomas. 346.2

«All we need do is quicken our steps and rest less, at night, to arrive in Nazareth in good time» replies Jesus.

«Will You really take me there, Lord?»

«Yes, Thomas, I will. We shall all go to Bethsaida and then to Capernaum, where we shall part. We shall proceed to Tiberias by boat and then to Nazareth. Thus, with the exception of you Judaeans, we shall all be able to get lighter garments, as winter is now over.»

* «Yes. And we shall go and say to the Dove: "Rise, make haste, my beloved one, and come, for winter is past, the rains are over and gone, the flowers appear on the earth... Rise, my friend, and come, my dove hiding in the clefts of the rock, show me your face, let me hear your voice".»

«Well done, John! You sound like a sweetheart singing a song to his girl!» says Peter.

«I am. I am full of love for Mary. I will never see other women excite my love. Except Mary, Whom I love with my wholeself.»

«I said the same a month ago, didn't I, Lord?» says Thomas.

«I think that we are all full of love for Her. Such a noble celestial love!... As only that Donna can inspire. And our souls love Her soul completely, our minds love and admire Her intelligence, our eyes admire and delight in Her pure grace, which gives joy without any anxiety, as when one looks at a flower... Mary, the Beauty of the earth, and, I think, the Beauty of Heaven...» says Matthew.

«That is true! We all see in Mary what is sweetest in women: the pure girl, and the most sweet mother. And we do not know whether we love Her more for the former or the latter grace...» says Philip.

«We love Her because She is "Mary". That's it!» remarks Peter.

[3] Jesus has been listening to them and He says: «You have all 346.3

* **say** as in *Song of Songs 2:10-14*.

spoken very well. Simon Peter is quite right: one loves Mary because She is "Mary". On our way to Caesarea I told you that only those who join perfect faith to perfect love will be successful in understanding the true meaning of the words: "Jesus, the Christ, the Word, the Son of God and the Son of man". But I can now tell you that there is another name full of meaning. And it is the name of My Mother. Only those who add perfect faith to perfect love will succeed in understanding the true meaning of the name "Mary", of the Mother of the Son of God. And the true meaning will begin to appear clearly to the true faithful and loving ones in a dreadful hour of torture, when the Mother is to be tortured with Her Son,when She co-redeems with the Redeemer, in the eyes of the whole world and forever and ever.»

«When?» asks Bartholomew, while they stop by the side of a large stream where many disciples drink.

«Let us stop here and eat our bread. It is midday. We shall be at lake Merom by evening and we shall be able to get boats and shorten our journey» replies Jesus evasively.

They all sit down on the tender grass on the bank of the stream, in the warm sunshine, and John says: «It is a pity to spoil these little flowers, which are so gentle. They look like little bits of the sky, which have fallen here, on these meadows.» There are hundreds and hundreds of myosotis.

«They will grow more beautifully tomorrow. They have bloomed to turn the earth into a dining room for their Lord» says his brother James to comfort him.

Jesus offers and blesses the food and they all eat happily. All the disciples, like sunflowers, are looking at Jesus, Who is sitting in the center of the row of His apostles.

346.4 [4] The meal is soon over, it was made tasty by serenity and pure water. As Jesus remains sitting, no one moves. The disciples move a little to come closer and hear what Jesus is saying to the apostles who have asked Him questions on what He said before about His Mother.

«Yes. Because it would be a great thing indeed to be My Mother according to the flesh. You must consider that Anne of Elkanah is remembered as Samuel's mother. And he was only a prophet. And yet his mother is mentioned because she bore him. Thus, Mary would be remembered with the greatest praise for giving

Jesus, the Savior, to the world. But it would be too little, as compared with what God exacts from Her to fill the measure required for the redemption of the world. Mary will not disappoint God's desire. *She has never disappointed Him.* She has given and will give Herself completely both with regards to requests of *total* love and to those of *total* sacrifice. And when She has accomplished the supreme sacrifice, with Me and for Me, and for the world, then the true faithful and loving believers will understand the real meaning of Her Name. And forever in the future each true faithful and Loving believer will be granted to know it. The Name of the Great Mother, of the Holy Nurse, Who will nourish all the children of Christ with Her tears, to bring them up for the Life in Heaven.»

«Tears, Lord? Must Your Mother weep?» asks the Iscariot.

«Every mother weeps. And Mine will weep more than any other.»

«Why? I made mine weep sometimes, because I have not always been a good son. But You! You never grieve Your Mother.»

«No. I do not grieve Her as Her Son. But I will deeply distress Her as Redeemer. There are two who will make My Mother weep endless tears: I, to save Mankind, Mankind by its continuous sinning. Every man who has lived, is living or will live, costs Mary tears.»

«Why?» asks James of Zebedee, who is obviously astonished.

«Because every man makes Me suffer to redeem him.»

«But how can You say that with regards to those who are already dead or not yet born? The living, the scribes, Pharisees, Sadducees may make You suffer through their charges against You, their jealousy, their wickedness. But nothing more than that» states Bartholomew confidently.

«John the Baptist was also killed... and he is not the only prophet killed by Israel, or the only priest of the eternal Will killed because he was disliked by those who disobeyed God.»

«But You are greater than a prophet than the Baptist himself, Your Precursor. You are the Word of God. The hand of Israel will not rise against You» says Judas Thaddeus.

«Do you think so, brother? You are wrong» replies Jesus.

«No. It cannot be! That cannot happen! God will not allow it! It would be a perpetual humiliation of His Christ!» Judas Thaddeus is so excited that he stands up.

Jesus also stands up and stares at his pale face and sincere eyes. He says slowly: «And yet, it will happen» and He lowers His right arm, which He had raised, as if He were swearing an oath.

346.5 [5] They all stand up and press closer round Him: a circle of sad incredulous faces; voices can be heard whispering: «Of course… if it were really so… Thaddeus would be right.»

«What happened to the Baptist was wrong. But it extolled the man, a hero till the very last. If instead it should happen to the Christ, it would diminish His fame.»

«Christ can be persecuted, but not humiliated.»

«The unction of God is upon Him.»

«Who would continue to believe in You, if they saw You at the mercy of men?»

«We will not allow that.»

James of Alphaeus is the only one who makes no comment. His brother chides him: «Are you not saying anything? Are you not reacting? Have you not heard? Defend the Christ against Himself!»

James does not reply, but he covers his face with his hands and moves aside weeping.

«He is a fool!» utters his brother.

«Perhaps not such a fool as you think» replies Ermasteus. And he goes on: «Yesterday, when explaining the prophecy, the Master spoke of a decomposed body that is recomposed and of a body that will rise from death by itself. I think that one cannot rise again, unless one dies first.»

«But one may die a natural death, or die of old age. And even that would be too much for the Christ!» retorts Thaddeus, and many say that he is right.

«Yes, but in that case it would not be a sign given to this generation, which is much older than He is» remarks Simon Zealot.

«Of course not. But He did not necessarily speak of Himself» retorts Thaddeus, who is obstinate in his love and respect.

«No one but the Son of God can rise by oneself from the dead, as no one but the Son of God can be born as He was born. I maintain that, as I saw the glory of His birth» says Isaac as a fully confident witness.

Jesus has been listening to them, looking at each while he was speaking, with His arms folded on His chest. He now makes a gesture that He wants to speak and He says: «The Son of man will be handed over into the power of men because He is the Son of God, but He is also the Redeemer of man. And there is no redemption without suffering. My body, flesh and blood will suffer, to make amends for the sins of the flesh and of the blood. I will suffer morally to make amends for the sins of intentions and passions. And I will suffer spiritually for the sins of souls. My suffering will be *complete*. Therefore at the appointed time I will be captured in Jerusalem and after suffering grievously at the hands of the Elders and High Pontiffs, of the scribes and Pharisees, I will be sentenced to disgraceful death. And God will let them do so, because it must be so, as I am the Lamb Who is to expiate the sins of the whole world. And in deepest anguish, which My Mother and few more people will share with Me, I will die on the scaffold, and three days later, exclusively through My own divine will, I will rise again to eternal glorious life as Man and once again I will be God in Heaven with the Father and the Spirit. But I must first suffer all infamy and My heart is to be pierced by Falsehood and Hatred.»

[6] A chorus of scandalized shouts spreads through the warm 346.6
scented springtime air.

Peter, who is also daunted and scandalized, takes Jesus by the arm and pulls Him aside and whispers in His ear: «Oh! Lord! Don't say that. It's not right. See? They are scandalized. You lose their esteem. On no account You must allow that; in any case such a thing will never happen. So why speak of it as something real? You must rise higher and higher in the eyes of men, if You want to assert Your authority, and eventually end by working a last miracle, such as crushing Your enemies. But You must never lower Yourself to the level of a punished criminal.» And Peter looks like a master or a sorrowful father kindly reproaching a son who has said something silly.

Jesus, Who was lightly bent to hear Peter's whispering, straightens Himself up and with a severe countenance and eyes blazing with anger, He shouts so that everybody may hear Him and learn the lesson: «Go away from Me, as you are now Satan advising Me to disobey My Father! But that is why I came! Not to be honored! By advising Me to be proud, disobedient and uncharitably severe you are spurring Me to evil things. Go away! You are scandalising Me! Do you not understand that greatness does not lie in honors but in sacrifice and that it is of no importance to be considered worms by men, if God considers us angels? You, foolish man, understand neither God's greatness nor His reasons, and you see, judge, feel and speak according to what is purely human.»

Poor Peter is crushed by the severe reproach and feeling humiliated he moves aside and weeps... But his tears are not the tears of joy of a few days ago. He weeps his heart out because he realizes that he has sinned and has grieved the person whom he loves. And Jesus lets him weep. He takes off His sandals, pulls His clothes up and wades the stream.

The others follow Him silently. No one dare say a word. Poor Peter is the last in the group and in vain Isaac and the Zealot endeavor to console him.

346.7 [7] Andrew turns around several times to look at him and then whispers something to John, who is utterly depressed. But John shakes his head in denial. Andrew then makes up his mind. He runs forward and reaches Jesus. He calls Him in a low trembling voice: «Master! Master!...»

Jesus lets him call several times. At last He turns around and with a severe countenance He asks: «What do you want?»

«Master, my brother is distressed... he is weeping...»

«He deserved it.»

«That is true, Master. But he is a man... One can make mistakes when speaking.»

«In fact what he said today was quite wrong» replies Jesus. But He is not quite so severe now and the sparkle of a smile mitigates His divine eyes.

Andrew takes heart again and redoubles his efforts in favor of his brother. «But You are just and You know that he erred through his love for You...»

«*Love must be light, not darkness.* He turned it into darkness and bandaged his soul with it.»

«That is true, Lord. But bandages can be removed if one wants. It is not as if the spirit itself were in darkness. Bandages are the outside. The spirit is the inside, the living nucleus... The inside of my brother is good.»

«Well, let him remove the bandages that he put on it.»

«He will certainly do so, Lord! He is already doing it. If You turn round You will see how disfigured his face is by tears, which You are not comforting. Why are You so severe with him?»

«Because it is his duty to be the "first", as I gave him the honor to be so. He who received much, must give much...»

«Oh! Lord! Yes, that is true. But do You not remember Mary of Lazarus? Or John of Endor? Or Aglae? Or the Beautiful woman of Korazim? Or Levi? You gave them *everything*... and they had only shown You their *intention* of being redeemed... Lord!... You heard my entreaties on behalf of the Beautiful woman of Korazim and of Aglae... Would You not listen to my entreaties on behalf of Your Simon and mine, who erred through his love for You?»

Jesus looks at His mild apostle who has become bold and insistent in favor of his brother, as he was silently insistent for the beautiful woman of Korazim and Aglae, and His face shines brightly: «Go and call your brother» He says «and bring him here.»

«Oh! Thank You, my Lord! I will go at once...» and he runs away as swiftly as a swallow.

[8] «Come, Simon. The Master is no longer angry with you. Come, 346.8
because He wants to tell you.»

«No. I am ashamed... He rebuked me only a little while ago... He wants me to reproach me again...»

«How little you know Him! Come on! Do you think that I would take you to Him to make you suffer again? I would not insist if I were not sure that a great joy is expecting you there. Come.»

«But what shall I tell Him?» Peter asks, setting out somewhat reluctantly: he is restrained by his human nature, but at the same time he is urged by his soul that cannot bear to be without Jesus' condescension and love. «What shall I say to Him?» he continues to ask.

«Nothing! Show Him your face and that will be sufficient» his brother says encouraging him.

All the disciples, as the two brothers overtake them, look at them smiling, as they understand what is happening.

They arrive where Jesus is. But at the last moment Peter stops.

Andrew wastes no time. With a strong push, as he is wont to do when driving his boat into the lake, he hurls him forward. Jesus stops... Peter raises his face... Jesus lowers His... They look at each other... Two large tears stream down Peter's flushed cheeks...

«Come here, My big rash boy, that I may act as a father and wipe your tears» says Jesus, and He raises the hand on which the scar made by the stone at Giscala is still visible and with His fingers He wipes the two tears.

«Oh! Lord! Have You forgiven me?» asks Peter: in a trembling voice, taking Jesus' hand in his own and looking at Him with loving imploring eyes, as a faithful dog that wants to be forgiven by its angry master.

I never condemned you...»

«But before...»

«I loved you. *It is love not to allow deviations of sentiments and wisdom to strike root in you. You must be the first in everything*, Simon Peter.»

«So... so, You still love me? You still want me with You? Not because I want to be the first, You know. I am happy to be even the last one, providing I am with You, at Your service... and I die at your service, Lord, my God!»

Jesus puts His hand around Peter's shoulders and draws him close to Himself.

And Peter, who has been holding the other hand of Jesus all the time, smothers it with kisses... He is happy and whispers: «How much I suffered!... Thank You, Jesus.»

«You had better thank your brother. And in the future make
346.9 sure you carry your burden with justice and heroism. [9]Let us
wait for the others. Where are they?»

They are standing where they were when Peter reached Jesus, to leave the Master free to speak to His mortified apostle. Jesus beckons them to come forward. With them there is a little group of peasants, who had left the work in the fields to come and speak to the disciples.

Jesus, still resting His hand on Peter's shoulder, says:

«After what has happened, you have understood that it is a serious matter to be at My service. I reproached him. But My reproach applies to all of you. Because the same thoughts were in most of your hearts, either fully developed or in germ. I have thus demolished them for you, and he who still cherishes them proves that he does not understand My Doctrine, My Mission or My Person.

I have come to be Way, Truth and Life. I give you the Truth through My teaching. I mark out the road, I point it out and level it for you through My sacrifice. But I give Life to you through My Death. And remember that whoever answers My call and follows Me to cooperate in the redemption of the world must be prepared to die to give Life to other people. Thus, whoever wants to follow me must be prepared to deny himself, his *old* self with its passions, inclinations, customs, traditions and thoughts, and follow Me with his *new* self.

Let every man take his cross, as I will take Mine. He must take it even if it looks too defamatory to him. He must let the weight of his cross crush his human self to free his spiritual self, which the cross does not fill with horror, on the contrary it is a support and an object of veneration because *the spirit knows and remembers.* And let him follow Me with his cross. And at the end of his life will an ignominious death be waiting for him, as it is waiting for Me? It does not matter. He must not grieve over that, on the contrary let him rejoice because the ignominy of the earth will change into a great glory in Heaven, whereas it will be dishonorable to act in a cowardly way in front of spiritual heroism.

You always state that you are prepared to follow Me and face death with Me. Follow Me, then, and I will lead you to the Kingdom along a hard but holy glorious road, at the end of which you will attain the immutable Life forever. That is "to live". To follow instead, the ways of the world and of the flesh is "to die". So he who wants to save his life on the earth will lose it, whereas he who loses his life on the earth, for My sake and for the sake of My Gospel, will save it. But remember: of what avail will it be to man to conquer the whole world, if he loses his soul?

[10] And be very careful, both now and in future, not to be ashamed of My words and My deeds. To do so would be "to die" as well. Because he who is ashamed of Me and of My words among this stupid, adulterous, sinful generation, of which I spoke to you, and in the hope of gaining protection and profit flatters it denying Me and My Doctrine and throwing My words 346.10

to the foul mouths of pigs and dogs — the recompense of which will be excrement and not money — will be judged by the Son of Man, when He comes in the glory of His Father with angels and saints to judge the world. I will then be ashamed of those adulterers and fornicators, of those cowards and usurers and will expel them from His Kingdom, because in the celestial Jerusalem there is no room for adulterers, cowards, fornicators, blasphemers and thieves. And I solemnly tell you that some of those who are now present among my disciples and women disciples will not savor death before seeing the Kingdom of God being established and its King crowned and anointed.»

They take to the road again talking animatedly while the sun is slowly setting in the sky...

347. Martyrdom Foreseen for Marjiam and Peter. The Blind Man at Bethsaida.

1st December 1945.

347.1 [1] They are not walking any longer, but are running in the fresh dawn, which is more pleasant and clearer than the previous mornings; sparkling dewdrops and multi-coloured petals fall on their heads and in the meadows, adding other hues to the countless shades of the little flowers growing on the banks of streams and in fields, and glistening on the grass like diamonds. They are running in the middle of warbling birds and in a light breeze that rustles among branches and caresses the hay and corn that grow higher and higher day by day; and they hear the cheerful babbling of brooks flowing within their banks and gently bending the stems of flowers touching their clear water. They are running as if they were going to a tryst. Even the elderly ones, such as Philip, Bartholomew, Matthew, the Zealot share the joyful haste of the younger ones. And the same is happening among the disciples, where the older ones vie with the younger ones in walking fast.

The meadows are still wet with dew when they reach the area of Bethsaida, enclosed in a little space between the lake, the
347.2 river and the mountain. [2]A youth bent under bundles of sticks is coming down from the wood in the mountain. He is coming

down very fast, almost running, but he cannot see the apostles from his position... He is singing happily while running under his burden of sticks, and as soon as he reaches the main road at the first houses in Bethsaida, he throws his load to the ground and straightens himself up to rest, pushing back his dark hair. He is tall, thin and erect, and his body, although slender and agile, is strong. He is a handsome looking adolescent.

«It's Marjiam» says Andrew.

«Are you mad? That's a man» replies Peter.

Andrew cups his hands to his mouth and calls him in a loud voice. The young man, who was about to bend to pick up his load, after fastening the belt of his short tunic, which barely reaches his knees and is open at his chest probably because it is rather tight turns round in the direction of the call and sees Jesus, Peter and the others who are looking at him, standing near a group of willows dipping into a large stream, the final left-hand tributary of the Jordan before the lake of Galilee, just outside the village. He drops the bundle, raises his arms and shouts: «My Lord! My father!» and he darts off.

Peter also dashes off, wading the brook in his sandals he just pulls his garments up, and then runs along the dusty road: leaving the wet marks of his sandals on the dry ground.

«Father!»

«Son!»

They embrace each other and Marjiam is really as tall as Peter and thus his dark hair falls on Peter's face when they kiss each other. But as Marjiam is so slender, he looks taller.

[3] Then Marjiam breaks away from the loving embrace and re- 347.3
sumes his race towards Jesus, Who is now on this side of the stream and is coming slowly forward surrounded by the apostles. Marjiam falls at His feet, with his arms raised and he exclaims: «Oh! My Lord, bless Your servant!»

But Jesus bends, lifts him up and presses him to His heart kissing both his cheeks and wishing him «everlasting peace and increase in wisdom and grace in the ways of the Lord.»

The apostles also give a hearty welcome to the boy, particularly those who have not seen him for months and they congratulate him on his growth.

But Peter!... If he had procreated him he would not have been

so pleased! He walks round him, looks at him, touches him, and asks the others: «Isn't he handsome? Isn't he well built? Look how straight he is! What a broad chest! And his straight legs!... A bit thin, not very sinewy as yet. But he is promising! Very good! And his face? Tell me whether he looks like the poor little fellow I carried in my arms last year, when he looked like a frail, miserable, sad, frightened bird... Well done, Porphirea! Ah! she has been very clever feeding him with plenty of honey, butter, oil, eggs
347.4 and fish liver. I must congratulate her at once. [4]Do You mind, Master? May I go to see my wife?»

«Go, Simon. I will soon be with you.»

Marjiam, whose hand is still in that of Jesus, says: «Master, my father will certainly tell mother to prepare a meal for You. Let me go and help her...»

«Yes, go. And may God bless you for honoring your father and mother.»

Marjiam runs away, picks up his bundle of firewood, puts it on his shoulder, reaches Peter and walks beside him.

«They look like Abraham and Isaac climbing the mountain» remarks Bartholomew.

«Oh! Poor Marjiam! That would be the last straw indeed!» says Simon Zealot.

«And poor brother of mine! I don't know whether he would have the strength to act as Abraham...» says Andrew.

Jesus looks at him and then looks at the grey head of Peter, who is moving away close to his Marjiam, and He says: «I solemnly tell you that the day will come when Peter will rejoice knowing that his Marjiam has been imprisoned, beaten, scourged, sentenced to death, and that he would have the heart to lay the boy on the scaffold himself to clothe him with the purple of Heaven and to fertilize the earth with the blood of a martyr, and he will be jealous and sorrowful for one reason only: that he is not in the place of his son and subordinate, because his election to Supreme Head of My Church will compel him to spare himself for the Church until I say to him: "Go and die for it". You do not know Peter yet. I do.»

«Do you foresee martyrdom for Marjiam and my brother?»

«Are you sorry, Andrew?»

«No. I am sorry that You do not foresee it also for me.»

«I solemnly tell you that you will all be clad with purple, except one.»

«Who?... Who?..»

«Let us be silent on the grief of God» Jesus says sadly but solemnly. And they are all silent, looking frightened and pensive.

[5]They walk along the first road in Bethsaida, among vegeta- 347.5
ble gardens full of fresh greenery. Peter, with other people of Bethsaida, is leading a blind man towards Jesus. Marjiam is not there. He must have stayed at home to help Porphirea. Among the people of Bethsaida and the relatives of the blind man, there are many disciples who have come from Sicaminon and other towns, and among them there are Stephen, Hermas, John the priest, John the scribe and many more. (It is now quite a problem to remember them all: they are so many).

«I brought him to You, Lord. He has been waiting here for several days» explains Peter, while the blind man and his relatives singsong: «Jesus, Son of David, have mercy on us!», «Touch with Your hand the eyes of my son, and he will see», «Have mercy on me, Lord! I believe in You!»

[6]Jesus takes the blind man by the hand and walks back a few 347.6
steps with him, to put him in the shade, as the street is flooded with sunbeams. He places him against a foliage-covered wall of the first house in the village and stands in front of him. He wets both His forefingers with saliva and rubs the man's eyes with his moist fingers, He then presses His hands against his eyes, with the base of each hand against an eye-socket and His fingers spread out among the hair of the poor fellow. He prays and then removes His hands, asking: «What do you see?»

«I see some men. They must be men. But that is how I imagined trees in bloom. But they are certainly men, as they are walking and making signs to me.»

Jesus imposes His hands once again, then He removes them asking: «And now?»

«Oh! Now I clearly see the difference between trees planted in the ground and those men who are looking at me... And I see You! How handsome You are! Your eyes are like the sky and Your hair seems sunbeams... and Your look and Your smile come from God. Lord, I adore You!» and he kneels down kissing the hem of His tunic.

«Stand up and come to your mother who for years has been your light and comfort and whose love you only know.»

He takes the man by the hand and leads him towards his mother, who has knelt down a few steps away in adoration, as shortly before she had done imploring.

«Stand up, woman. Here is your son. He now sees daylight and may his heart wish to follow the eternal Light. Go home and be happy. And live holily out of gratitude to God. But going through villages do not tell anybody that I cured you, lest the crowds should rush here and prevent Me from going where it is just that I should go, to confirm the faith and take light and joy to other children of My Father.»

And He quickly disappears along a little path among kitchen gardens, going toward Peter's house, which He enters greeting Porphirea kindly.

348. At Capernaum, Manaen Gives an Account of Herod's Fears. Towards Nazareth with the Women Disciples. The Transfigurations of Mary, the Immaculate.

2nd December 1945.

348.1 [1] When they set foot on the little beach of Capernaum they are welcomed by shouting children who vie with swallows, now busy building their new nests, so quickly they run from the beach to the houses screeching in their shrill voices, cheerful with the simple joy of children, to whom everything is a wonderful sight and a mysterious object: a little fish found dead on the shore, or a pebble smoothed by the waves and that, owing to its hue, looks like a precious stone, or a flower growing between two stones, or the iridescent scarab captured in flight. All wonderful things to be shown to their mothers so that they may take part in the joy of their children.

But those little human swallows have now seen Jesus and all their flights converge towards Him, Who is about to set foot on the beach. And it is a warm live avalanche of children, a gentle chain of tender little hands, it is the love of children's hearts that welcome Jesus, Who is pressed, surrounded and warmed, as if they were a gentle fire.

«Me! Me!»

«A kiss!»

«To me!»

«Also to me!»

«Jesus! I love You!»

«Don't go away anymore for such a long time!»

«I came here every day to see whether You were coming.»

«And I used to go to Your house.»

«Take this flower, it was for my mother, but I give it to You.»

«Another kiss to me, a big one. You did not kiss me the first time because Jael pushed me back...»

And their shrill voices continue to shout, while Jesus endeavors to walk in the midst of the loving net.

«Leave Him now! Go! That's enough now!» shout the apostles and disciples trying to loosen the press. Not a hope! They are like lianas equipped with suckers. They are detached here and they adhere there.

«Leave them! With a little patience we shall get there» says Jesus smiling and He takes extraordinarily short steps in order to proceed without treading on the children's bare feet.

[2] What frees Him from the loving press is the arrival of Ma- 348.2
naen with other disciples, among whom are the shepherds who were in Judaea.

«Peace to You, Master!» thunders Manaen who is imposing in his magnificent garment and no longer wears jewels on his forehead and fingers; a wonderful sword is instead hanging on his side and it excites the respectful admiration of the children, who, at the sight of the magnificent knight dressed in purple and carrying such a marvelous weapon on his side, move aside obviously frightened.

And Jesus can thus embrace him and Elias, Levi, Matthias, Joseph, John, Simeon and I do not know how many more. «How come you are here? And how did you know that I had landed?»

«We knew by the shouting of the children. They pierced walls like arrows of joy. But I came here thinking that Your next trip to Judaea is now close at hand and that also the women will be taking part in it... I want to be there as well... To protect You, my Lord, if I am not too proud in thinking so. There is a great deal of excitement in Israel against You. I regret having to say so. But

You are aware of it.»

348.3 [3] And while speaking thus, they reach the house and go in. Manaen continues his speech after the landlord and his wife have worshipped the Master.

«By now the excitement and interest in You have pervaded every place, rousing and drawing the attention even of the most dull-minded people, who are normally concerned with entirely different matters. The news of what You have worked has passed even through the filthy walls of Machaerus and has reached the lustful refuges of Herod, that is: his palace in Tiberias, the castles of Herodias and the splendid royal palace of the Asmoneans near the Sixtus market. Like a wave of light and power the news passes through dark vile barriers, it demolishes the piles of sins placed as trenches to cover up the foul love affairs of the Court and its cruel crimes, it darts like an arrow of fire writing words that are by far more serious than those written on the lewd walls of the lewd bed-chambers and throne and banquet halls at Belshazzar's feast. The news shouts Your Name and power, Your Nature and Your Mission. And Herod trembles with fear; Herodias tosses in her bed fearing that You may be the revenging King, who will take her wealth and freedom, if not her very life, leaving her at the mercy of the populace, who will take revenge for her many crimes. They tremble at Court, because of You. They tremble with human and superhuman fear. Since they cut off John's head, a fire seems to be burning the bowels of his murderers. They do not even enjoy any longer their previous miserable peace, the peace of pigs sated with orgies, who silence their reproachful consciences in drunkenness or in copulation. Nothing can appease them... They are persecuted... And they hate each other, after making love, disgusted with each other, accusing each other of committing a crime that now perturbs them as it overstepped the limit. Salome, as if she were possessed by a demon, is shaken by such eroticism that would degrade even a slave girl. The Royal palace stinks more than a sewer. Herod has asked me about You several times. And every time I always replied to him: "As far as I am concerned He is the Messiah, the King of Israel of the unique royal stock: David's. He is the Son of man fore-

* **at Belshazzar's feast**, in *Daniel 5*.

told by the Prophets, He is the Word of God, He, Who being the Christ, the Anointed of God, has the right to reign over all living beings". And Herod turns pale with fear as he realizes that You are the Revenger. And as his courtiers, in order to comfort him say that You are John, erroneously believed to be dead, thus making him faint with horror, or that You are Elijah or some other prophet of the past, he fights against his fear and the cry of his conscience devoured by remorse, saying: "No. He cannot be John! I had John beheaded and his head is safely kept by Herodias. And He cannot be one of the prophets. One does not live again after dying. Neither can He be the Christ. Who says that He is? Who dares to tell me that He is the King of the unique royal stock? I am the king! Nobody else is! The Messiah was killed by Herod the Great: He was drowned in a sea of blood, as soon as He was born. He was slaughtered like a little lamb... and He was only a few months old... Can you not hear Him weep? His bleating is always resounding within my head together with John's roar: 'It is against the Law for you to have her'... Is it against the Law for me?! No, it isn't! I am allowed everything, because I am 'the king'. I want wine and women here, if Herodias refuses my embraces, and let Salome dance to rouse my senses, which your fearful tales have frightened". And he gets drunk with the girl-mimes of the court, while in her rooms the mad woman howls curses against the Martyr and threats to You, and Salome, in her rooms, realizes what it means to be born of two lewd parents and to give assent to a crime and to have it committed by yielding one's body to the lubricious craving of a filthy man. When Herod comes to his senses, he wants to be informed about You and would like to see You. That is why he is in favor of my visits to You, as he hopes that I may take You to him which I will never do as I am not prepared to take Your holiness into a den of foul beasts. And Herodias would like to have You to strike You. And she shouts so holding her stiletto in her hands... And Salome would like to have You, as she saw You at Tiberias, without Your knowing it, last Ethanim and is mad for You... That is the Royal Palace, Master! But I am remaining there so that I can keep an eye on what they intend doing to You.»

«And I am grateful to you for it and the Most High blesses you. That is also a way to serve the Most High in His decrees.»

«That is what I thought. And that is why I came.»

«Manaen, since you have come, I ask you to do Me a favour. Do not come towards Jerusalem with Me, but go with the women. I shall go with My disciples along an unknown road and no one will be able to injure Me. But they are women and unprotected and he who is to accompany them is a meek soul and has been taught to offer his other cheek to anyone who should strike him. Your presence will be a safe protection. I understand that it is a sacrifice but we shall be together in Judaea. My dear friend, do not deny Me this favour.»

«Lord, every desire of Yours is law to Your servant. I am at the service of Your Mother and of the women disciples as from this moment, until You wish so.»

«Thank you. Also this obedience of yours will be written in
348.4 Heaven. [4]Now, while waiting for the boats, let us cure the sick people who are waiting for Me.»

And Jesus goes down into the kitchen garden where there are stretchers and sick people and He cures them at once, while Jairus and a few friends of Capernaum pay their respects to Him.

In the meantime the women — that is: Porphirea and Salome, Bartholomew's elderly wife and Philip's less elderly one with her young daughters — are busy preparing food for the large crowd of disciples whose hunger will be satisfied with the baskets of fish offered by the people of Bethsaida and Capernaum. And a great deal of gutting the still wriggling silvery fish, of washing them in basins and grilling them is done in the kitchen while Marjiam and some other disciples keep the fire going and bring pitchers of water to help the women.

The meal is soon ready and soon over. And, as sufficient boats have already been assembled, all they have to do is to embark for Magdala, on an enchanting lake which is so serene and angelical in the emerald green setting of its shores.

The hospitable house and gardens of Mary of Magdala welcome the Master and His disciples in the midday sun, and the whole of Magdala rushes to greet the Rabbi, Who is going towards Jerusalem.

348.5 [5]And the faithful crowd march nimbly and happily along the cool slopes of the Galilean hills, followed by a comfortable wagon in which there are Johanna with Porphirea, Salome, the wives of Bartholomew and Philip with the latter's two young daughters and the two cheerful little orphans adopted by Johanna, Matthias and Mary, whose aspects have altered beyond recognition from what they were five months ago. Marjiam is marching bravely with the grown up people, and as instructed by Jesus he is in the apostolic group, between Peter and John, and does not miss a word of what Jesus says.

The sun is shining in a very clear sky and gusts of warm wind carry the scents of woods, mint, violets, early lilies of the valley, rose-bushes full of flowers, and above all, the fresh lightly bitterish scent of the blossoms of fruit-trees, which everywhere pour a shower of snow-white petals on the grassland. They all have petals in their hair while they proceed among the continuous warbling of birds, among enticing songs and anxious calls from one thicket to another, between bold males and demure females, while sheep graze, fat through their maternity, and the first little lambs knock their little muzzles against the round udders to increase the secretion of milk, or they jump about the meadows covered with tender grass, like happy children.

[6] They soon reach Nazareth after Cana, where Susanna joins 348.6
the other women, taking with her the products of her land in baskets and vases and a whole shoot of red roses, all in bud and about to open, «to be offered to Mary» she says.

«I have some, too, see?» says Johanna uncovering a kind of box, in which many roses have been laid among damp moss: «They are the first and the most beautiful ones. But still nothing for Her, Who is so dear!»

I see that every woman has brought food for the Passover pilgrimage and with the food some have brought flowers, some plants for Mary's garden. Porphirea apologizes for bringing only a vase of camphor, which is magnificent with its tiny blue-green leaves that exhale their aroma even when they are lightly touched. «Mary wanted this balsamic plant...» she says. And they all praise her for the luxuriant beauty of the young tree. «Oh! I have watched over it all winter, protecting it from frost and hail in my room. Marjiam helped me to take it out in the sun every morning, and bring it in at night... And if there had been no boat and no wagon, that dear boy would have loaded it on his shoulder to carry it to Mary, to do Her and me a favour» says the humble woman, who takes heart more and more through Johanna's kindness and who is beside herself with the joy of going to Jerusalem with the Master, her husband and Marjiam.

«Have you never been there?»

«When my father lived I used to go every year. But later… My mother did not go anymore… My brothers would have taken me, but I was a help to my mother and she would not let me go. Then I married Simon and my health has not been very good. The journey would have taken Simon a long time and he was bored…So I stayed at home waiting for him… The Lord saw my desire and it was the same as if I offered my sacrifice in the Temple…» says the meek woman.

And Johanna, who is near her, lays her hand on her wonderful plaits, saying: «My dear!». And there is so much love, understanding and meaning in that adjective.

348.7 [7] There is Nazareth… there is the house of Mary of Alphaeus who is already in the arms of her sons; and with her hands, which are dripping and red as she is doing the washing, she caresses them, and then, drying her hands in her coarse apron, she runs to embrace Jesus… And there is the house of Alphaeus of Sarah, immediately before Mary's house. Alphaeus tells his oldest grandchild to run and tell Mary, and he strides towards Jesus holding an armful of grandchildren in his arms and he greets Him together with the children held in his arms like a bunch of flowers offered to Jesus. And there is Mary: She appears at the door, in the sunshine, wearing a light blue dress, which is slightly faded, with Her golden hair shining on Her virginal forehead and forming a heavy knot of plaits on Her nape; She falls on the chest of Her Son, Who kisses Her with all His love.

The others stop discreetly to leave them free in their first meeting. But Mary moves away, turns around, Her face, unaltered by age, is now rosy because of the surprise and Her bright smiles, and She greets with Her angelical voice: «Peace to you, servants of the Lord and disciples of My Son. Peace to you, sisters in the Lord and She exchanges a sisterly kiss with the women disciples, who have come off the wagon.

«Oh! Marjiam! I will no longer be able to hold you in My arms!

You are a man now. But come to the Mother of all good children, I can still give you a kiss. My dear! May God bless you and make you grow in His ways, as strongly as your young body is growing, and even more. Son, we must take him to his grandfather. He will be so happy to see him thus» She then says turning around to Jesus.

She then embraces James and Judas of Alphaeus. And She gives them the news that certainly pleases them most of all: «Simon this year is coming with Me, as a disciple of the Master. He told Me.»

And She greets one by one the more familiar ones, the more influential ones, saying graceful words to each of them. Manaen is led towards Her by Jesus, Who introduces him as Her escort in the journey to Jerusalem.

«Are You not coming with us, Son?»

«Mother, I have other places to evangelize. We shall meet at Bethany.»

«May Your will be done now and always. Thank you, Manaen. You: a human angel; our guardians: the angels in Heaven; and we shall be as safe as if we were in the Holy of Holies.» And She offers Her little hand to Manaen in a token of friendship. And the knight, who has been brought up in courtly manners kneels down to kiss the gentle hand offered to him.

[8] In the meantime the flowers and what is to be left in Nazareth 348.8
has been unloaded. The wagon is taken to one of the stables in town.

The little house looks like a rosary with the roses that the women disciples have strewn everywhere. But Porphirea's plant, laid on a table, is the one that is mostly admired by Mary, Who has it taken to a suitable place according to the directions of Peter's wife.

They cannot certainly all go into the little house or the kitchen garden, which is not an estate, but it seems to rise toward the sky and become airy, so many are the clouds of blossoms on the trees in the garden. And Judas of Alphaeus asks Mary smiling: «Have You picked Your branch for Your amphora today?»

«Most certainly, Judas. And I was contemplating it when you arrived...»

«And You were dreaming once again, Mother, of Your remote

mystery...» says Jesus, embracing Her with His left arm and drawing Her close to His heart.

Mary raises Her flushed face and says with a sigh: «Yes, Son, and I was dreaming again of the first throb of Your heart within Me...»

Jesus says: «Let the women disciples, the apostles, Marjiam, the shepherd-disciples, John the priest, Stephen, Hermas and Manaen stay here. The others can spread out looking for lodgings...»

«Many can stay with me...» shouts Simon of Alphaeus from the door where he has been stopped. «I am their fellow-disciple and I claim them.»

«Oh! brother, come in, that I may kiss you» says Jesus effusively, while Alphaeus of Sarah, Ishmael and Aser, the two disciples, formerly donkey drivers, of Nazareth, say: «Come to our houses!»

The disciples who have not been chosen to stay, go away and the door can be closed... but it is opened once again immediately afterwards, for the arrival of Mary of Alphaeus, who cannot stay away, even if her washing is going to be spoiled. They are about forty people and they spread through the warm peaceful garden, until food is handed out, and everybody finds it has a celestial flavor, so happy they are to take it in the house of the Lord, and handed out by Mary.

Simon comes back after settling the disciples and says: «You did not call me with the others, but I am Your brother and I am staying here just the same.»

348.9 «Very well, Simon, come here. [9]I wanted you to be here to meet Mary. Many of you know Mary as the "mother"; some as the "spouse". But no one knows Her as the "virgin" Mary. I want you to become acquainted with Her in this garden in bloom, to which your hearts desire to come when you are compelled to be far away, as to a resting place after your apostolate work.

I listened to you apostles, disciples and relatives speak, and I heard your impressions, your recollections and your statements concerning My Mother. I will transfigure all that, which is admirable although still very human, into a supernatural knowledge. Because My Mother is to be transfigured, before Me, in the eyes of the most deserving, to show Her as She is. You see a woman. A woman different from other women, because of Her holiness, but in actual fact you see Her as a soul enveloped in a body, just like all women Her sisters. But now I wish to reveal to you the soul of My Mother. Her true and eternal beauty.

Come here, Mother. Do not blush. Do not withdraw shyly, sweet dove of God. Your Son is the Word of God and He can speak of You and of Your mystery, of Your mysteries, O sublime Mystery of God. Let us sit down here, in the pleasant shade of the trees in blossom near the house, near Your holy room. Thus! Let us lift this fluttering curtain, so that waves of holiness and Paradise may come out of this virginal room, to saturate us all with Your virtues... Yes. Me as well. That I may smell of You, O perfect Virgin, so that I may be able to bear the stench of the world, in order that I may see purity after saturating My eyes with Your Purity... Marjiam, John, Stephen come here, and you, women disciples, stand directly in front of the open door of the chaste abode of the most Chaste amongst women. And you, My friends, stand behind. And You, My beloved Mother, here, beside Me.

[10] A little while ago I said to you: "the eternal beauty of the soul 348.10
of My Mother". I am the Word, and thus I can make use of words without erring. I said: eternal, not immortal. And I deliberately said so. He is immortal who, after being born, does not die. Thus the souls of the just are immortal in Heaven, the souls of sinners are immortal in Hell, because a soul, once it has been created, does not die but to grace. But a soul has life, it exists from that moment that God thinks it. It is the Thought of God that creates it. The soul of My Mother was thought by God *from everlasting*. It is therefore eternal in its beauty, in which God poured every perfection to receive delight and comfort from it.

* It is written in the Book of our ancestor Solomon, who foresaw You, and can thus be called Your prophet: "God possessed me from the beginning of His works, from the very beginning, before Creation. From everlasting I was firmly set, from the beginning, before the Earth came into being. The deep was not yet, and I was conceived. There were no springs to gush with water, the mountains were not yet settled on their huge mass, and I already was. Before the hills I came to birth. He had not yet

* **It is written**, in: *Proverbs 8:22-31.*

made the Earth, the rivers, or the poles of the world, and I already existed. When He prepared the sky and Heaven I was present. When with inviolable law He closed the abyss under the vault, when He fixed firm the celestial vault and He suspended there the sources of water, when he assigned the sea its boundaries and He ordered the water not to pass its limit, when He laid down the foundations of the earth, I was by His side arranging everything. I was always joyfully at play in His presence. I played in the universe".

Yes, Mother, with Whom God, Immense, Sublime, Virgin, Uncreated, was pregnant and carried You like a most sweet burden, rejoicing at feeling You stir within Him, when with Your smiles he created the Universe! He laboriously gave birth to You to give you to the world, most gentle soul, born of the Deity to be the "Virgin", the Perfection of Creation, the Light of Paradise, the Advice of God, Who looking at You forgave Sin, because You alone, by Yourself can love as all Mankind put together cannot love. In You is the Forgiveness of God! You are the Treatment of God, You are the caress of the Eternal Father on the wound that man inflicted on God! In You is the Salvation of the world, Mother of the Love Incarnate and of the granted Redeemer! The soul of My Mother! Merged in Love with My Father, I looked at You within Me, O soul of My Mother!... And Your splendor, Your prayer, the idea of being carried by You comforted Me forever and ever for My destiny of sorrow and inhuman experience of what the corrupted world is for the most Perfect God. Thank You, Mother! When I came I was already full of Your consolation, I descended perceiving You alone, Your perfume, Your song, Your love... Joy, My joy!

348.11 [11] Now that you know that one only is the Woman in Whom there is no stain, that one only Human Being costs the Redeemer no injury, listen to the second transfiguration of Mary, the Elect Daughter of God.

It was a clear afternoon in the month of Adar and the trees were in bloom in the silent kitchen garden, and Mary, Joseph's bride, had picked a flowery branch to replace the one that was in Her room. Mary, taken from the Temple to adorn a house of saints, had recently come to Nazareth. And with Her soul divided among Temple, house and Heaven, She was looking at the flowery branch, considering that by means of a similar branch, which had bloomed in an unusual manner, a branch cut off in this garden in the depth of winter and had bloomed as if it were springtime before the Ark of the Lord — perhaps the Sun-God beaming in His Glory had warmed it — God had revealed His will to Her... And She was thinking also that on the day of their wedding Joseph had brought Her other flowers, but never like the first one on the thin petals of which It was written: "I want You united to Joseph"... She was thinking of many things... And while thinking She ascended to God. Her hands were busy with distaff and spindle and were spinning a yarn that was thinner than the hair of Her young head...

Her soul was weaving a carpet of love, moving quickly, like a shuttle on a loom, from the earth to Heaven. From the needs of the house, of Joseph, to those of the soul, of God. And She sang and prayed. And the carpet was forming on the mystical loom, it rolled off from the earth to Heaven, it ascended to get lost up there... Formed with what? With the thin, perfect strong threads of Her virtues, with the flying thread of the shuttle, which She thought was "Hers", whereas it was God's: the shuttle of the Will of God, on which was rolled the will of the little, great Virgin of Israel, Unknown to the World, Known to God, rolled and made *one* with the Will of the Lord. And the carpet was adorned with the flowers of love, of purity, with palms of peace and palms of glory, with sweet-smelling violets, with jasmines... Every virtue flowered on the carpet of love, which the Virgin of God unrolled invitingly from the earth to Heaven. And as the carpet was not sufficient She thrust Her heart singing:* "Let My Beloved come into His garden and eat the fruit of His trees... Let My Beloved come down to His garden, to the bed of spices, to pasture in the gardens and gather lilies. I am My Beloved's and My Beloved is Mine. He pastures among the lilies!". And from infinite distance, among torrents of Light, a Voice came that human ear cannot hear and human throat cannot utter. And it said: "How beautiful You are, My love! How beautiful You are!... Your lips distil wild honey... You are a garden enclosed, a sealed fountain, My sister, My promised bride..." and the two voices joined together to sing the eternal truth: "Love is stronger than death. Nothing can

* **singing**... The expressions of the mystic dialogue are taken from: *Song of the Songs 5:1; 6:2-3; 4:1.11.12; 8:6-7.*

quench or drown 'our' love". And the Virgin was thus transfigured when Gabriel descended and called Her back to the Earth, with his ardor, and joined Her soul to Her body again, so that She might hear and understand the request of Him, Who had called Her "Sister" but wanted Her to be His "Bride".

And the Mystery took place there... And a modest woman, the most modest of all women, Who was not even aware of the instinctive incentive of the flesh, fainted before the Angel of God, because even an angel upsets the humility and modesty of the Virgin, and only when She heard him speak She calmed down, and She believed, and She said the word, whereby "*their*" love became Flesh and will defeat Death and no flood will be able to quench it or wickedness to submerge it...»

348.12 [12]Jesus bends gently over Mary Who has slid to His feet, almost ecstatically, in the recollection of the remote hour; shining with a special light, which seems to issue from Her soul, and He asks Her in a low voice: «Which was Your reply, Most Pure Mother, to him who assured You that by becoming Mother of God, You would not Lose Your perfect Virginity?»

And Mary, almost in a dream, slowly, smiling, Her eyes shining with joyful tears: «I am the handmaid of the Lord! Let It be done to Me according to your Word» and She reclines Her head on the knees of Her Son, adoring Him.

Jesus covers Her with His mantle, concealing Her from everybody's eyes and He says: «And it was done. All will be done until the end. Until Her next transfiguration and the one after that. She will always be the "Handmaid of God". She will always act according to what "the Word" says. My Mother! That is My Mother. And you ought to begin to become fully acquainted with Her holy Figure... Mother! Mother! Raise You face, My Beloved... Call Your devout admirers back to the Earth, where we are for the time being...» He says uncovering Mary after a little while, during which no noise was heard except the humming of bees and the gurgling of the little fountain.

Mary raises Her face wet with tears and whispers: «Why did You do that to Me, Son? The secrets of the King are sacred...»
«But the King can reveal them whenever He wishes. Moth- *

* **can reveal**, as stated in: *Tobit 12:7*.

* er, I did it, so that the words of the Prophet may be understood: "A Woman will enclose the Man in Herself", and the words of
* the other Prophet: "The Virgin will conceive and give birth to a Son". And also that My disciples, who are struck with horror at too many things that they consider degrading for the Word of God, may have, as counterbalance, many other things confirming them in the joy of being "Mine". Thus they will no longer be
scandalized and will conquer Heaven... [13]Now those who have to 348.13
go to the house where they are guests, may go. I am staying with the women and Marjiam. All the men must be here tomorrow at dawn, because I want to take you to a place nearby. We shall then come back and say goodbye to the women, and then we shall go to Capernaum to gather other disciples and tell them to follow the women...»

349. The Transfiguration on Mount Tabor. The Curing of a Lunatic Boy at the Foot of the Mount. Jesus Exhorts His "Voices".

3rd December 1945.

[1]Which man has never seen, at least once, a clear dawn in the 349.1
month of March? If such a man exists, he must be very unhappy, because he is unaware of one of the most beautiful charms of nature awakening in springtime, when she becomes the virgin girl as creation must have been on its first day.

In such graceful charm, which is pure from every point of view, from its fresh dewy herbs, to the little flowers that are opening, like babies who are born, to the first smile of daylight, to the birds that awake flapping their wings and utter their first chirps, which sound like questions and are a prelude to all their singing conversation of the day, to the very smell of the air that during the night has lost all pollution of dust, smoke and smell of human bodies through the lavation of dew and the absence of man, Jesus is proceeding with His apostles and disciples. Simon of Alphaeus is with them, too. They are going southwards, crossing the hills that encircle Nazareth and a torrent, and are

* **the words of a Prophet**: *Jeremiah 31:22.*
* **and the words of the other Prophet**: *Isaiah 7:14.*

walking across a narrow plain between the Nazarene hills and a
349.2 group of mountains to the east. [2]These mountains are preceded
by the semi-truncate cone of the Tabor, the top of which strange-
ly reminds me of the crocked-hat of our carabineers, seen in pro-
file: .

They reach it. Jesus stops and says: «Peter, John and James of Zebedee will come up the mountain with Me. The rest will spread out at its foot, going in groups towards the roads that run along it, to preach the Lord. I want to be back in Nazareth by evening. So do not go too far away. Peace be with you.» And addressing the three He had called, He says: «Let us go.» And He begins to climb without turning back anymore and with such a quick pace that Peter finds it difficult to follow Him.

When they rest for a moment, Peter, flushed and perspiring, asks Him panting: «But where are we going? There are no houses on the mountain. On the top there is only that old fortress. Do You want to go and preach there?»

«I would have gone up the other side. But you can see that I have turned My back to it. We are not going to the fortress, and those who are in it will not even see us. I am going to be united to My Father, and I wanted you to be with Me, because I love you. Come on, quick!»

«Oh! My Lord! Could we not go a little slower, instead, and speak of what we heard and saw yesterday, which kept us awake all night to talk about it?»

«*You always go quickly to the appointments with God.* Come on, Simon Peter. I will let you rest up there.» And He carries on climbing...

349.3 [3] (Jesus says: «Put here the Transfiguration seen on August 5th 1944, but *without the dictation added to it.* After copying the Transfiguration of last year, P.M. will copy what I am going to show you now.»).

5th August 1944.

349.4 [4] I am with my Jesus upon a high mountain. Peter, James and John are with Jesus. They climb higher up and their eyes rove over open horizons, the details of which are well defined even in the distance, in the beautiful clear day.

The mountain is not part of a range of mountains like the one in Judaea; it rises isolated, with the east in front, with respect to the place where we are, the north to the left, the south to the right, and at the rear to the west, the summit, which is about one hundred steps higher up. It is very high and the view extends over a very wide range.

The lake of Gennesaret looks like a strip of sky that has come down to be set in the green of the earth, an oval turquoise enclosed by emeralds of various shades, a mirror that trembles and ripples in a light breeze, and on which boats in full sail glide as nimbly as sea-gulls, lightly bent towards the blue water, exactly with the grace of the flight of a kingfisher skimming the water in search of prey. Then a vein flows out from the vast turquoise, it is pale blue where the river-bed is wider, and darker where the banks narrow and the water is deeper and in the shade of the trees that grow luxuriantly near the river, nourished by its water. The Jordan looks like an almost straight stroke of a brush in the greenery of the plain.

Some villages are scattered here and there on both sides of the river. Some are only a handful of houses, others are somewhat larger, with the appearance of little towns. The main roads are yellowish lines among the green. But here, on the side of the mountain, the plain is more cultivated and fertile and it is really beautiful. The various hues of the several growths are a most pleasant sight in the beautiful sunshine of a very clear day.

It must be springtime, perhaps the month of March, if I take into account the latitude of Palestine, because I see the corn, which is already high, although still green, waving like a blue-green sea and I see the crests of the early fruit-trees decorate this little vegetable sea with something like tiny white and rosy clouds, and meadows strewn with the flowers of the high hay, where grazing sheep look like piles of snow spread here and there on the green grass.

Just near the mountain, on the low short hills at its foot, there are two little towns, one to the south and the other to the north. The very fertile plain extends particularly and more widely to the south.

[5]Jesus after a short rest in the cool shade of a group of trees, a 349.5
pause which He certainly granted out of pity for Peter who clear-

ly has great difficulty in climbing, resumes going up. He goes almost to the top, where there is a grassy tableland with a semicircle of trees near the side of the mountain.

«You may rest, My friends. I am going over there to pray.» And He points to a large stone, a rock that appears on the surface of the mountain and is not near the slope, but it lies internally towards the summit.

Jesus kneels on the grass and rests His hands and head on the rock, in the same position that He will also take when praying in Gethsemane. The top of the mountain protects Him from the sun. The remaining part of the grass-covered clearing is in the bright sun as far as the bordering trees, where the apostles are sitting in the shade.

Peter takes off his sandals, shakes off dust and grit and remains barefooted, with his tired feet on the cool grass, almost lying down, with his head resting on an emerald green tuft as a pillow. James does the same, but in order to be comfortable he looks for a tree, against which he leans his mantle and rests his back. John remains sitting looking at the Master. But the calm of the place, the fresh breeze, silence and fatigue overcome him as well and he droops his head and eyes. None of them are fast asleep, but they are in the state of summer drowsiness that stuns people.

349.6 [6] They are roused by a brilliancy that is so striking that it overwhelms the brightness of the sun and spreads and penetrates even into the shade of bushes and trees where the apostles are.

They open their eyes and are astonished at seeing Jesus transfigured. He is *exactly* as I see in the visions of Paradise. Of course * He has no Wounds and there is no banner of the Cross. But the majesty of His Face and Body is the same, the brightness is also the same and His garment, too, is identical: from deep red it has changed into an immaterial fabric of diamonds and pearls, in

* **transfigured**. On a piece of paper attached to a typewritten copy, M.V. has written: *Note on the Transfiguration. In order to divert Satan's slyness and the snares of future enemies of the incarnated Word (not unknown to the Father), God enshrouded the Christ in traits common to every man born from a woman. And this not only during His childhood and boyhood when He was "the son of the carpenter", but also when He was the Master Whose only hallmarks were His sapience and His power to work miracles. Israel was familiar with Masters (the Prophets) and miracle workers. Hence it was necessary to test the faith of His "elects": apostles and disciples who were supposed to "believe without seeing" extraodinary and divine events. Following Jesus they were used to seeing the learned Man who also worked miracles, while in His human necessities, He*

which He is clad in Heaven. His Face shines with an extremely intense sidereal light in which His sapphire eyes are beaming. He looks taller, as if His glorification had increased His height. I cannot say whether the brilliancy, which makes even the tableland fluorescent, emanates entirely from Him, or whether His own is mingled with the brightness that all the light of the Universe and of Heaven has concentrated on Him. I can only say that it is something indescribable.

Jesus is now standing, I would say that He is raised off the ground because between Him and the green meadow there is something like a luminous vapour, a space consisting only of a light upon which He seems to be standing. But it is so bright that I may be wrong, and the fact that I no longer see any green grass under Jesus' feet may be due to the bright light that vibrates and waves, as it is often seen in bonfires. It is a snow-white incandescent light. Jesus is looking at the sky and smiling at a vision that enraptures Him.

The apostles are almost afraid and they call Him, as He is transfigured so much that He no longer appears to be their Master. «Master, Master» they call in low voices, full of anxiety.

He does not hear.

«He is in an ecstasy» says Peter trembling. «I wonder what He sees?»

The three are now standing up. They would like to approach Jesus, but they dare not.

[7] The light increases further because of two lights that descend 349.7
from the sky and take place at Jesus' sides. When they settle on the tableland, their veils open and two majestic bright personages appear. One is older than the other, with a sharp severe countenance, and he has a double-pointed beard. Two horns of light depart from his forehead and make me understand that he

---

was in everything similar to them. Now, after the distressing announcement of His future death on the cross, He reveals Himself in the full Glory of His Divine Nature, in order to confirm the faith of the three chosen apostles. Afterwards, the doubt that the knowledge of such a death had created could not persist. They had seen God. They had seen God in the Man who was to be crucified. It was the manifestation of His two natures hipostatically united. An undeniable manifestation which could not leave space to doubt. Furthermore, to the Son-God made manifest, the Father-God unites with His words and with Moses and Elijah representing Heaven. So, after shaking their faith with the announcement of His death, Jesus restores and increases their faith through His Transfiguration.

is Moses. The other one is emaciated, bearded and hairy, more or less like the Baptist, whom I would say he resembles in height, leanness, structure and severity. While the light emanating from Moses is white, like that of Jesus, particularly with regard to the beams issuing from their foreheads, the light of Elijah is like the bright flame of the sun.

The two Prophets take a reverential attitude before their God Incarnate and although He speaks to them with familiarity, they do not drop their respectful attitude. I do not understand even one of the words they speak.

The three apostles fall on their knees trembling and covering their faces with their hands. They would like to look, but they are afraid. At last Peter says: «Master, listen to me.» Jesus looks around smiling towards His Peter, who takes heart again and says: «It is wonderful to be here with You, Moses and Elijah. If You wish, we will make three tents, one for You, one for Moses and one for Elijah, and we will stay here to serve you...»

Jesus looks at him again and smiles more warmly. He looks also at John and James. A glance that is a loving embrace. Also Moses and Elijah stare at the three. Their eyes flash fire. They must be like rays piercing hearts.

The apostles dare not say anything else. Frightened as they are, they lapse into silence. They look as if they were inebriated, like people who are bewildered. But when a veil, which is neither fog, nor a cloud, nor a ray, envelops the three glorious personages behind a screen that is even brighter than the one that surrounded them previously, and hides them from the sight of the apostles, a powerful harmonious Voice vibrates filling the air, the three bow down with their faces on the grass.

«This is My beloved Son, in Whom I am well pleased. Listen to Him.»

Peter, on falling flat on his face, exclaims: «Have mercy on me, a sinner! It is the Glory of God descending!». James does not utter a single word. John whispers with a sigh, as if he were about to swoon: «The Lord is speaking!»

349.8 [8]Even when there is total silence again, none of them dare raise their heads. Thus they do not even see that the light has come back to its natural state of daylight and that Jesus is alone and has become the usual Jesus wearing His red mantle.

He walks towards them smiling, touches them and calls them by their names. «Stand up. It is I. Be not afraid» He says, because the three dare not raise their faces and are imploring mercy for their sins, fearing that the Lamb of God wants to show them to the Most High. «Stand up, now. I order you» repeats Jesus authoritatively. They look up and see Jesus smile.

«Oh! Master, my God!» exclaims Peter. «How shall we be able to live near You, now that we have seen Your Glory? How shall we be able to live among men and among ourselves, since we are sinners, and we have heard the Voice of God?»

«*You will have* to live beside Me and see My glory until the end. Be worthy of that because the time is close at hand. Obey My Father and yours. Let us now go back among men because I came to stay with them and to bring God to them. Let us go. Be holy, strong and faithful in remembrance of this hour. You will take part in My greater glory. * But do not speak now to anybody of what you have seen. Do not tell your companions either. When the Son of man has risen from the dead and gone back to the glory of the Father, then you will speak. Because it will be necessary to believe then, to take part in My Kingdom.»

«But is Elijah not to come to prepare people for Your Kingdom? So the rabbis say.»

«Elijah has already come to prepare the way for the Lord.

Everything is happening as was revealed. But those who teach Revelation do not know and do not understand it, neither do they see or recognise the signs of the time or the messengers of God. Elijah has come back once. He will come for the second time when the last time is close at hand to prepare the last for God. He now came to prepare the first for the Christ, and men refused to acknowledge him, they tortured him and put him to death. They will do the same to the Son of man, because men do not want to acknowledge what is good for them.»

The three lower their heads and become pensive and sad while descending the mountain with Jesus by the same road they came up.

---

* **do not speak now**... In an attached note M.V. specifies that: *The perfect prudence of Jesus made Him give this command in order to avoid fanatical veneration or hatred, both premature and noxious.* And the she adds: *The Elijah who 'has come back once' to whom Jesus alludes, was John the Baptist.*

[3rd December 1945].

349.9 [9]... And it is Peter again who says, while stopping half way down: «Ah! Lord! I also say what Your Mother said yesterday: "Why did You do that to us?", and I also say: "Why did You tell us that?". Your last words have destroyed in our hearts the joy of the glorious sight! This has been a great day of fear! First we were frightened by the great light that roused us, it was stronger than if the whole mountain had been ablaze, or the moon had descended to light up the tableland right in front of us; then Your sight and Your rising from the ground as if You were going to fly away. I was afraid that You, being disgusted with the iniquity of Israel, were going back to Heaven, perhaps by order of the Most High. Then I was frightened when I saw Moses appear, as the people of his days could not look at him without a veil, so brightly the reflection of God shone on his face, and he was still a man, whereas now he is a blessed spirit inflamed with God, and Elijah... Divine Mercy! I thought I had come to my last moment, and all the sins of my life, since the time I was a child and used to steal fruit in the pantry to the last one, when some days ago I gave You wrong advice, came to my mind. And trembling with fear I repented! Then I got the impression that those two just men were fond of me... and I dared to speak. But even their love frightened me, because I do not deserve the love of such spirits. And then!... The most dreadful of all fears! The voice of God!... Jehovah has spoken! He said to us: "Listen to Him!". You! And He proclaimed You: "His Beloved Son in Whom He is well pleased". What a fright! Jehovah!... to us!... It was certainly Your power only that kept us alive!... When You touched us, and Your fingers burnt like points of fire, I had the last fright. I thought that the hour had come when I was to be judged and that the Angel touched me to take my soul to the Most High... But how could Your Mother see... hear... and live, in that hour that You told us yesterday, and not die, and She was alone, a young girl, without You?»

«Mary, the Immaculate, could not be afraid of God. Eve was not afraid, while she was innocent. And I was there. I, the Father and the Spirit, We, Who are in Heaven and on the earth and everywhere, and Who had our Tabernacle in the heart of Mary» says Jesus gently.

«How wonderful!... But later You spoke of death... And our joy came to an end... But why all that just to us three? Was it not better to give the vision of Your glory to everybody?»

«Just because you become senseless when you hear Me speak of death, and death by torture, of the Son of man, the Man-God decided to fortify you for that hour and for the future, by means of the foreknowledge of what I will be after Death. Remember all that, so that you may tell people in due time... Have you understood?»

«Oh! yes, Lord. It is not possible to forget it. And it would be quite useless to tell people. They would say that we are "drunk".»

[10]They resume their way down towards the valley. But when 349.10
they arrive at a certain point, Jesus takes a very steep side path towards Endor, that is in the opposite direction to the place where He left the disciples.

«We will not find them» says James. «The sun is beginning to set. They will be gathering where You left them, waiting for You.»

«Come and do not worry about foolish thoughts.»

In fact, where the brushwood opens on to a grassland that slopes gently as far as the main road, they see at the foot of the mountain the whole group of the disciples, who are very excited and with them there are some curious wayfarers and some scribes who have come from I do not know where.

«Alas! Scribes!... And they are discussing already!» says Peter pointing at them. And he walks down the last few metres half-heartedly.

But the apostles down there have also seen them and they point them out to one another and then they begin to run towards Jesus shouting: «How come, Master, You are here? We were about to go to the appointed place. But we have been held back by a discussion with scribes and by the entreaties of a worried father.»

«What were you discussing?»

«We were disputing about a possessed man. The scribes sneered at us because we were not able to free him. Judas of Kerioth tried several times out of pique. But in vain. So we said to them: "Try yourselves". They replied: "We are not exorcisers". Some people coming from Caslot-Tabor happened to pass by and among them there were two exorcisers. But they did not succeed either. Here is the father coming to implore You. Listen to him.»

349.11 [11] A man in fact comes forward imploring and he kneels before Jesus, Who is still on the sloping meadow and is thus at least three metres higher up than the road and clearly visible to everybody.

The man says to Him: «Master, I went to Capernaum with my son, looking for You. I took my unhappy son to You, that You might free him, as You expel demons and You cure all diseases. He is often possessed by a mute spirit. When it takes him he can but shout hoarsely, like an animal that is choking. The spirit throws him on the ground, where he rolls grinding his teeth, foaming like a horse biting the bit, or he injures himself, or he risks dying drowned or burned or smashed, because the spirit more than once has thrown him into the water, in the fire or down the steps. Your disciples tried, but they were not successful. Oh! Good Lord! Have mercy on me and on my child!»

Jesus blazes with majesty while He shouts: «O wicked generation, O satanic crowd, rebel legion, incredulous and cruel people of Hell, how long will I have to be in touch with you? How long shall I have to put up with you?» He is so imposing that there is dead silence at once and the sneers of the scribes stop.

349.12 [12] Jesus says to the father: «Stand up and bring your son here.»

The man goes away and comes back with other men and in the middle of the group there is a boy about twelve or fourteen years old. He is a handsome boy, but looks rather dull-witted as if he were bewildered. There is a long red wound on his forehead and under it an old white scar. As soon as he sees Jesus Who stares at him with His magnetic eyes, he utters a hoarse cry and his whole body writhes convulsively and he falls to the ground foaming and rolling his eyes, so that only the white globes can be seen, while he rolls on the ground in a typical epileptic fit.

Jesus comes forward a few steps to be close to him and says: «How long has that been happening to him? Speak in a loud voice, so that everybody may hear you.»

And while the crowds press closer and the scribes go above Jesus to dominate the scene, the man shouting says: «Since he was a boy. I told You: he often falls on the fire, into water or down the steps or from trees, because the spirit attacks him suddenly and throws him about to kill him. He is covered with scars and burns.

He is lucky that the flames of the fireplace have not blinded him. No doctor, no exorciser, not even Your disciples have been able to cure him. But You, if, as I firmly believe, can do something, have mercy on us and help us.»

«If you can believe thus, everything is possible to Me, because everything is granted to those who believe.»

«Oh! Lord, I do believe! But if I do not believe sufficiently, increase my faith, so that it may be complete and I may obtain the miracle» says the man weeping, while he kneels beside his son, who has fallen into a more severe convulsive fit.

[13] Jesus straightens Himself up, takes two steps back, and while the circle of the crowd presses closer and closer, He shouts loudly: «Cursed spirit, who make this boy deaf and mute and torture him, I order you: go out of him and never go back into him.» 349.13

The boy, although lying on the ground, bounces frightfully, arches his back with feet and head on the ground, utters inhuman cries and, after a last bounce, he turns around, falls flat on his face striking his forehead and mouth against a large stone emerging from the grass, which becomes stained with blood, and lies motionless.

«He is dead!» many shout. «Poor boy!», «Poor father!» say the better ones pitying them. And the scribes sneering say: «The Nazarene has served you well!», or: «Master, how come? Beelzebub has made You cut a bad figure this time...» and they laugh spitefully.

Jesus replies to no one. Not even to the father, who has turned his son around and is wiping the blood off the injured forehead and lips, moaning and imploring Jesus. And the Master bends, takes the child by the hand. And the boy opens his eyes with a deep sigh, as if he were awaking from sleep, he sits up and smiles. Jesus draws him close to Himself, makes him stand up and hands him to his father, while the crowds cheer enthusiastically, and the scribes run away chased by the mockery of the crowd...

«And now let us go» says Jesus to His disciples. And after dismissing the crowds He goes round the side of the mountain towards the road along which He came in the morning.

[14] Jesus says: 349.14

«And here P.M. can now put the comment on the vision of August 5th 1944 (copybook A 930) beginning from the words: "I am not choosing you for the only purpose of making you acquainted with the sadness and the sorrows of your Master. Those who are able to stay with Me sharing My grief must share My glory as well". And you, My faithful little John, have a rest, because you well deserve it. May My peace bring joy to you.»

[5th August 1944].

349.15 [15] Jesus says:

«[...]. I am not choosing you for the only purpose of making you acquainted with the sadness and the sorrows of your Master. Those who are able to stay with Me sharing My grief must share My joy as well. *

When you are before your Jesus and He shows Himself to you, I want you to have the same feelings of humility and repentance as My apostles had. You must never be proud. You would be punished by losing Me. You must always bear in mind Who I am and who you are. You must always remember your faults and My perfection so that your heart may be cleansed by contrition. But at the same time you must put so much trust in Me.

I said: "Be not afraid. Stand up. Let us go. Let us go among men, because I have come to be with them. Be holy, strong and faithful in remembrance of this hour". I say so also to you and to all My favourites among men, to those who have Me in a special way.

Be not afraid of Me. I show Myself to you to elevate you all, not to incinerate you.

Stand up: may the joy of the gift give you energy and do not let it blunt your minds with the savour of quietism, considering yourselves already saved because I have shown Heaven to you.

Let us go together among men. I have invited you to superhuman deeds by means of superhuman visions and lessons, so that you may be of greater help to Me. I make you partners in My work. But I have never had and I never have a minute's rest. Because Evil never rests and Good must be always active to make void the work of the Enemy as much as possible. We shall rest when the Time is accomplished. Now we must proceed untiring-

---

* **you**... this dictation is addressed to M. Valtorta and to the chosen "voices".

ly, we must work continuously and sacrifice ourselves unremittingly for the harvest of God.

May My continuous contact sanctify you, may My continuous teaching fortify you and may My fond Love for you make you faithful against all snares. Do not be like the old rabbis who taught the Revelation but did not believe in it, to the extent of not being able to recognize the signs of the time and the messengers of old. Ensure that you recognize the precursors of the Christ in His second coming, because the powers of the Antichrist are on the march and, making an exception on the limit I have imposed on Myself, because I know that you drink in certain truths not with a supernatural spirit but out of thirst for human curiosity, I solemnly tell you that what many people think is the victory over the Antichrist, the peace now close at hand, will be only a pause to give the Enemy of the Christ time to acquire new strength, to dress his wounds and gather his army for a fiercer struggle.

Since you are the "voices" of your Jesus, of the King of kings, of the faithful and truthful king who judges and fights with justice and will defeat the Beast and his servants and prophets, ensure that you know what is your Good and follow it forever. Let no false appearance entice you, let no persecution terrify you. Let your "voices" repeat My words. Let your Lives be devoted to this work. And if on the earth you should share the same destiny as the Christ, as His Precursor and Elijah, a sanguinary destiny or a destiny subjected to moral torture, smile at the future safe destiny you will enjoy with the Christ, with His Precursor and His Prophet.

We shall be equal in our work, in our grief, in our glory. Here I am the Master and the Example. There I shall be the Reward and the King. To have Me will be your blessedness. It will mean forgetting sorrow. It will be what no revelation is yet sufficient to make you understand, because the joy of the future life is by far superior to the possibility of imagination of a human creature still joined to a human body.»

350. At Nazareth, a Lesson to the Apostles and Disciples on the Power to Defeat the Demons.

4th December 1945.

350.1 [1] They are now once again in the house in Nazareth: or, more precisely, they are scattered on the terrace of the olive-trees, waiting to part and go to rest. And they have lit a little bonfire to illuminate the night, because it is already dark and the moon rises late. It is a warm evening, «even too warm» state the fishermen, who foresee rain. And it is pleasant to be there, all together, the women in the flowery garden around Mary, the men up here; and Jesus on the edge of the terrace, between the two groups, replying to various questions of the disciples, while the women listen attentively. They must have spoken of the lunatic who was cured at the foot of the mountain and they are still making comments.

«It took You to do it!» exclaims His cousin Simon.

«Oh! But those falcons were not convinced even when they saw that their own exorcisers could not do anything, although they admitted that they had used the strongest formulae!» says Solomon, the ferryman, shaking his head.

«And even if they tell the scribes their conclusions, they will not persuade them.»

«Of course not! I got the impression that they spoke well, did they not?» asks one whom I do not know.

«Very well. They excluded all demoniac witchcraft from Jesus' power stating that they felt they were pervaded with a deep peace, when the Master worked the miracle, whereas when it comes from a wicked power, they said that they feel it is painful» replies Hermas.

350.2 [2] «However, it was a strong spirit! It did not want to go away! But why did it not always possess the boy? Was it an expelled or lost spirit, or was the boy so holy that he expelled it by himself?» asks another disciple whose name I do not know.

Jesus, without being questioned, replies: «I have explained several times to you that every disease, as it is a torment and * a disorder, may conceal Satan and Satan may hide himself in

* **I have explained several times**, for example in 122.8.

a disease, causing it and making use of it to torture a soul and make it curse God. The boy was ill, he was not possessed. He is a pure soul. That is why I was so pleased to free his soul from the most cunning demon who wanted to dominate it and make it impure.»

[3] «In that case, if it was only a simple disease, why did we not 350.3
succeed in curing it?» asks Judas of Kerioth.

«Of course it is obvious that the exorcisers could not do anything if he was not possessed! But we...» remarks Thomas.

And Judas of Kerioth, who is not prepared to swallow his humiliating failure, as he made several attempts with the child with the only result of getting him into a frenzy if not into a convulsive fit, says: «On the contrary, we seemed to be making things worse. Do you remember, Philip? You were helping me and you heard and saw how he gibed at me. He even said to me: "Go away! Of the two of us, you are the worse demon". Which made the scribes laugh at me behind my back.»

«And were you sorry for that?» asks Jesus with indifference.

«Of course! It is not pleasant to be gibed at. And it is not useful when one is Your apostle. One loses one's authority.»

«When you have God with you, you are authoritative even if the whole world sneers at you, Judas of Simon.»

«Very well. But increase our power, at least the power of Your apostles, so that we may not suffer such defeats again.»

«It is not right for Me to increase your power and it would be of no avail. You must do that by yourselves, in order to succeed. It is through your insufficiency that you failed, and also because you diminished what I gave you by means of unholy elements, which you wanted to add hoping to attain greater triumphs.»

«Are You referring to me, Lord?» asks the Iscariot.

«You know whether you deserve it. I am speaking to everybody.»

Bartholomew asks: «Then, what is necessary to cast out such demons?»

«Prayer and fasting. Nothing else is required. Pray and fast. And not only in your bodies. It is good for you that your pride has been left devoid of satisfaction. Satisfied pride makes mind and soul listless and prayer becomes tepid and inert, just as the body,
when it is too full, becomes sleepy and sluggish. [4]And now let us 350.4

go and have a well deserved rest. Tomorrow morning at dawn you will all be on the road to Cana, except Manaen and the shepherd disciples. Go. Peace be with you.»

But He keeps Isaac and Manaen and gives them special instructions for the following day, when the women disciples and Mary will begin their Passover pilgrimage with Simon of Alphaeus and Alphaeus of Sarah.

«You will go through Esdraelon, so that Marjiam may see his old grandfather. You will give the peasants the purse that I asked Judas of Kerioth to give you. And with the other purse, which I gave you a short while ago, you will assist any poor people you come across on your way. When you arrive in Jerusalem go to Bethany and tell them to wait for Me at the new moon of Nisan. I will not be very late after that date. I entrust the person Who is dearest to Me and the women disciples to you. But I am not worried as I know they will be safe. Go. We will meet at Bethany and will be together for a long time.»

He blesses them and, while they disappear in the night, He jumps down into the kitchen garden and goes into the house, in which the women disciples and His Mother are already tying with Marjiam the strings of the travelling bags and arranging everything for their absence, which they do not know how long it will last.

351. The Tribute to the Temple and the Coin in the Mouth of the Fish.

5th December 1945.

351.1 [1] The two boats that they took to go back to Capernaum are gliding on an extraordinarily calm lake: a real large slab of blue crystal, which becomes one smooth piece again, as soon as the two boats pass. But they are not the boats of Peter and James, but two boats which they probably hired at Tiberias. And I can hear Judas complaining because he is left without any money after this last cost.

«He has seen to everybody else. But what about us? What shall we do now? I was hoping that Chuza... But nothing... We are in the same state as a beggar, one of the many who beg for alms of pilgrims on the roads» he grumbles in a low voice to Thomas.

But the latter replies good-naturedly: «What does it matter, if it is so? I am not at all worried.»

«Of course! But when it is time to eat, you are the one who wants to eat more than anybody else.»

«Certainly! I am hungry. I am brave even in that respect. Well, today instead of asking any man for some bread and a dish of something, I will ask God directly.»

«Today! But tomorrow we shall be in the same situation; and the day after tomorrow it will be the same again; and we are going towards the Decapolis where we are unknown; and they are half-heathens there. And it is not only a question of bread, there are sandals that wear out, and the poor who pester you, and one could be taken ill...»

«And if you go on like this, you will have me as good as dead shortly and you will have to think about my funeral. Oh! how many worries! I... am not worried at all. I am happy and calm, just like a new-born baby.»

Jesus, Who appeared to be engrossed in thought, sitting on the prow almost on the edge, turns around and says in a loud voice to Judas who is astern, but He says it as if He were speaking to *everybody*: «It is very good to be penniless. The paternity of God will shine more brightly even in the most humble things.»

«Everything has been all right for You recently. It is all right if we cannot work miracles, it is all right if we get no offerings, it is all right if we have given away everything we had: in a few words, everything is all right... But I feel ill at ease... You are a dear Master, a holy Master, but as far as material life is concerned... You are worth nothing» says Judas without bitterness, as if he were criticising a good young brother, of whose improvident kindness he was proud.

And Jesus replies to him smiling: «It is my greatest quality to be a man worth nothing with regards to material life... And I say again: it is very good to be penniless» and He smiles broadly.

[2] The boat rubs the shingly shore and stops. They land while 351.2
the other boat comes close and is about to stop. Jesus goes towards the house with Judas, Thomas, Judas and James, Philip and Bartholomew.

Peter lands from the second boat with Matthew, the sons of

Zebedee, Simon Zealot and Andrew. But while everybody sets out towards the house, Peter remains on the shore to speak to the boatmen who brought them there and with whom he is perhaps acquainted, and later helps them to set sail. He then puts on his long tunic and walks up the shore towards the house.

351.3 [3] While he is crossing the market square two men go towards him and stop him saying: «Listen, Simon of Jonah.»

«I am listening. What do you want?»

«Your Master, only because He is such, does He or does He not pay the two drachmas due to the Temple?»

«Of course He does! Why should He not?»

«Well... because He says that He is the Son of God and...»

«And He is» retorts Peter decidedly and he is already flushing with rage. And he adds: «But, as He is also a son of the Law, and the best son the Law has, He pays His drachmas like every Israelite...»

«We have no proof of that. We are told that He does not pay and we advise Him to do so.»

«H'm» mumbles Peter who is on the point of losing his temper. «H'm... My Master does not need your advice. Go in peace and tell those who have sent you here that the drachmas will be paid at the first opportunity.»

«At the first opportunity!... Why not at once? Who can assure us that He will? He is always wandering about aimlessly!»

«He cannot pay at once because He is penniless. If you turned Him upside-down, not a penny would drop to the ground. We are all penniless, because we, who are not Pharisees, who are not scribes, who are not Sadducees, who are not rich, who are not spies, who are not asps, we give what we have to the poor, according to His doctrine. Have you understood? And now we have given everything, and until the Most High provides, we can die of starvation, or stand at the street-corner and beg. Inform those who say that He is also a glutton of that. Goodbye!» and he leaves them grumbling and seething with anger.

351.4 [4] He goes into the house and upstairs where Jesus is listening to one who begs Him to go to a house on the mountain beyond Magdala, where a man is dying.

Jesus dismisses the man promising to go there at once, and after the man has left, he turns towards Peter, who is sitting in a corner engrossed in thought, and says to him: «What is your opinion, Simon? As a rule, from whom do the kings of the earth take toll or tribute? From their sons or from foreigners?»

Peter starts and says: «How do You know, Lord, what I was going to say to You?»

Jesus smiles making a gesture as if to say: «Never mind»; He then says: «Answer My question.»

«From foreigners, Lord.»

«Well, then, the sons are exempt, as in fact is right. Because a son is of the same blood and household of his father and therefore he must pay only tribute of love and obedience to his father. So I, the Son of the Father, should pay no tribute to the Temple, which is the house of the Father. You gave them the right answer. But as there is a difference between you and them, which is: that you believe that I am the Son of God, while they and those who sent them do not, in order not to scandalise them, I will pay the tribute and at once, while they are still in the square collecting the money.»

«But how, if we have not one penny?» asks Judas, who has approached them with the others. «You can see whether it is necessary to have something!»

«We can ask the landlord to lend it to us» says Philip.

Jesus makes a gesture with His hand commanding silence and says: «Simon of Jonah, go to the beach and cast a line with a strong hook as far as you can. And as soon as a fish bites, draw the line. It will be a big fish. Open'its mouth on the shore and you will find a stater inside it. Take it, go to these two men and pay for Me and for you. Then bring the fish here. We will roast it and Thomas will give us the charity of a little bread. We will eat and then go at once to the man who is dying. James and Andrew: prepare the boats, we will go in them to Magdala and we will walk back in the evening in order not to interfere with the fishing of Zebedee and Simon's brother-in-law.»

[5]Peter goes away and shortly afterwards he is seen climbing 351.5
onto a half-beached boat; he throws a thin strong line, fitted with a little stone or lead at the end, to which is attached the real fishing-line. The water of the lake forms silvery spray when the weight sinks into it, then it becomes calm again when concentric

* **a stater**: a coin equal in value to the Jewish shekel or four drachmas.

circles slowly move away...

But shortly afterwards the little rope, which hung loose in Peter's hands, is pulled tight and vibrates... Peter pulls the cord, which is shaken more and more vigorously. With a last jerk the fishing line emerges with the catch that whirls over the fisherman's head and falls on the yellowish sand where it writhes tortured by the hook that rends its palate and by incipient asphyxia.

It is a magnificent fish, the size of a brill weighing at least three kilogrammes. Peter tears the hook from its fleshy lips, thrusts his finger into its throat and pulls out a large silver coin. He lifts it up holding it between his thumb and forefinger to show it to the Master, Who is at the parapet of the terrace. He gathers the thin rope, rolls it up, picks up the fish and runs away towards the square.

All the apostles are dumbfounded... Jesus smiles and says: «And we will thus remove a scandal...»

351.6 [6] Peter comes in: «They were coming here. And Eli, the Pharisee is with them. I endeavoured to be as kind as a young girl, and I called them saying: "Hey, messengers of the Fisc! Take this. That's four drachmas, isn't it? Two for the Master and two for me. We are now square, are we not? I will be seeing you in the Valley of Jehoshaphat, particularly you, my dear friend". They took offence at my mentioning the "Tax office". "We are of the Temple, not of the Tax office". "You collect taxes like excisemen. Every tax collector, as far as I am concerned, is of the Tax office" I replied. And Eli said to me: "You insolent one! Are you wishing me to die?". "No, my friend, never! I wish you a pleasant journey to the Valley of Jehoshaphat. Are you not going to Jerusalem for Passover? So we can meet there, my dear friend". "I do not wish and I do not want you to take the liberty of calling me your friend". "In fact it is too big an honour" I replied. And I came away. The amusing side is that half the people of Capernaum were there and they saw that I paid for You and for me. And that old snake will not be able to say anything now.»

The apostles could not help laughing on hearing the story and seeing Peter's miming. Jesus wants to be serious. But a light smile slips from His lips while He says: «You are worse than mustard» and He concludes: «Cook the fish and let us make haste. I want to be back here by sunset.»

352. The Greatest in the Kingdom of Heaven. A Parable for Little Benjamin of Capernaum. The Sacredness of Children. The Use of the Name of Jesus.

6th December 1945.

[1] And just when the sky and the lake seem to be catching fire 352.1
in the blazing sunset, they come back towards Capernaum. They are happy. They are speaking to one another. Jesus speaks very little, but He smiles. They point out that if the messenger had given more precise information, they could have saved some of the road. But they also say that it was worth the trouble, because a group of little children had their father cured when death was so close at hand, that his body was already getting cold, and also because they are no longer penniless.

«I told you that the Father would provide for everything» says Jesus.

«And was he an old lover of Mary of Magdala?» asks Philip.

«Apparently... According to what they told us...» replies Thomas.

«What did the man tell You, Lord?» asks Judas of Alphaeus.

Jesus smiles evasively.

«I have seen her with him several times, when I used to go to Tiberias with friends. I know it for sure» states Matthew.

«Yes, brother, tell us... Did the man ask You only to be cured or also to be forgiven?» asks James of Alphaeus.

«What a senseless question! When has the Lord granted a grace without exacting repentance?» says the Iscariot rather angrily to James of Alphaeus.

«My brother has not been speaking nonsense. Jesus cures or casts out demons and then He says: "Go and do not sin any more"» replies Thaddeus.

«Because He has already seen repentance in their hearts» insists the Iscariot.

«In possessed people there is neither repentance nor will to be freed. Not one of them has ever shown any such signs. If you go over each case, you will see that they either ran away, or they hurled themselves at us in a hostile attitude, or they tried to do both, and they did not succeed only because their relatives held them back» replies Thaddeus.

«And Jesus' power, too» confirms the Zealot.

«So Jesus takes into account the will of relatives who represent the will of the possessed person, who would like to be freed if he were not hindered by the demon.»

«How much subtlety! And what about sinners? I think He uses the same words, even when they are not possessed» says James of Zebedee.

«He said to me: "Follow Me" and I had not said one word to Him, with regard to my situation» remarks Matthew.

«But He read your heart» says the Iscariot, who always wants to be right, at all costs.

352.2 [2]«All right! But that man, who according to public opinion was a big lewd sinner, although not demoniac, or rather not possessed, because with all his sins he must have had a demon as teacher if not as possessor, and he was dying and so on, what did he ask for? I think this is a lot of idle talk... Let us go back to the first question» says Peter.

Jesus satisfies him: «That man wanted to be alone with Me, to be able to speak freely. He did not speak at once about his health... but about his soul. He said: "I am about to die, but actually I am not so ill as I made people believe in order to have You here quickly. I need to be forgiven by You to be cured. But that is all I need. If You do not want to cure me, I will resign myself. I deserved it. But save my soul" and he confessed his many sins. A nauseating chain of sins...» says Jesus, but His face shines with joy.

«And You are smiling, Master! I am surprised!» remarks Bartholomew.

«Yes, Bartholomew. I am smiling because they no longer exist, and because with his sins I learned also the name of his redeemer. The apostle was a woman in this case.»

«Your Mother!» many of them say. Some say: «Johanna of Chuza! As he often went to Tiberias, perhaps he knows her.» Jesus shakes His head. So they ask Him: «Who was it then?»

«Mary of Lazarus» replies Jesus.

«Did she come here? Why did she not come to see any of us?»

«She did not come. She wrote to her old partner in sin. I read her letters. They all supplicate him for one thing: to listen to her, to redeem himself, as she redeemed herself, to follow her in Virtue, as he had followed her in sin, and with heart-rending words they beg him to relieve Mary's soul of the remorse of seducing his soul. And she converted him. So much so, that he retired to the country to overcome the temptations of the town. His disease, which was more remorse of his soul than physical trouble, completed his preparation for Grace. That is all. Are you happy now? Do you understand now why I am smiling?»

«Yes, Master» they all reply. And when they see that Jesus quickens His steps, to be alone, they begin to whisper to one another...

[3]They are already in sight of Capernaum, when at the junction of their road with the one coming along the lake from Magdala, they meet the disciples, who have come on foot from Tiberias evangelizing. They are all there, with the exception of Marjiam, the shepherds and Manaen, who have gone from Nazareth towards Jerusalem with the women. The disciples are actually more numerous as they have been joined by other fellow-disciples, who have come back from their mission with new proselytes of the Christian doctrine. 352.3

Jesus greets them kindly but He immediately stands aside once again, deeply engrossed in meditation and prayer, a few steps ahead of the others. The apostles, instead, mix with the disciples, particularly with the more influential ones, that is, Stephen, Hermas, John the priest, John the scribe, Timoneus, Joseph of Emmaus, Ermasteus (who, according to what I understand, is making great progress on the way to perfection), Abel of Bethlehem in Galilee, whose mother is at the back of the crowd with other women. And the disciples and apostles ask questions and give information on what has happened since they parted. They thus talk of today's curing and conversion, and of the miracle of the stater in the mouth of the fish... And because of the circumstance which brought this miracle about, it rouses the interest of many and the discussion spreads from one row to the next one like fire set to straw...

[4]Jesus says: «You will put here the vision of March 7th, 1944: "Little Benjamin of Capernaum", without the comment. And you will continue with the rest of the lesson and of the vision. Go on.» 352.4

So I am omitting the last sentence: «The vision ends here etc.» It would be out of place as the vision goes on.

7th March 1944.

352.5 [5] I see Jesus walking along a country road surrounded and followed by His apostles and disciples.

The calm blue lake of Galilee, which is not far away, shines in the beautiful sunshine of spring or autumn, because the sun is not as strong as in summer. But I would say that it is springtime, because the countryside is very fresh, without the golden tired hues that are typical of autumn.

As it is getting dark, Jesus seems to be retiring to the hospitable house and He therefore turns His steps towards the village, which is already in sight. As He often does, Jesus is walking a few steps ahead of His disciples. Only two or three steps, not more, to be alone with His thoughts, as He needs tranquility after evangelizing for a full day. He is absorbed in thought while walking, holding in His hand a green twig, which He must have picked from some bush and He lightly whips the grass on the edge of the road with it; He is lost in thought.

Behind Him, on the other hand, the disciples have entered into an animated discussion. They are recalling the events of the day and they are rather heavy-handed in appraising other people's faults and shortcomings. They are more or less severe in the fact that those responsible for the collection of the Temple tribute exacted payment from Jesus.

Peter, who is always impulsive, states that it is a sacrilege because the Messiah is not obliged to pay the tribute: «It is asking God to pay Himself» he says. «And it is not right. And if they do not believe that He is the Messiah, it becomes a sacrilege.»

Jesus turns around for a moment and says: «Simon, Simon, there will be many people who will mistrust Me! Even among those who think that their faith in Me is safe and unshakable. Do not judge your brothers, Simon. Always judge yourself first.»

Judas smiling ironically says to Peter, who feels mortified and has lowered his head: «That's for you. Simply because you are the oldest, you always want to play the doctor. It is not true that one's merits are judged according to one's age. Among us there are some who are above you by knowledge and social power.»

They thus enter into discussions on their respective merits. And some boast *of being among the first* disciples, some base their preferential argument *on the influential position they gave up* to follow Jesus, and there are those who say that no one has the same rights as they have because *no one* has turned so much by changing from a publican to a disciple. The discussion lasts a long time and if I were not afraid of offending the apostles, I would say that it takes the tone of a real quarrel.

Jesus pays no attention to them. He does not seem to hear them. They have in the meantime reached the first houses of the village, which I know is Capernaum. Jesus proceeds, the others follow Him discussing all the time.

[6] A little boy of seven or eight years runs tripping after Jesus. 352.6
He overtakes the vociferous group of the apostles and reaches Him. He is a lovely boy with short curly dark-brown hair. His dark eyes shine intelligently in his little dark face. He calls the Master confidentially as if he were very familiar with Him. He says: «Jesus, will You let me come with You as far as Your house?»

«Does your mother know?» asks Jesus smiling at him kindly.

«Yes, she does.»

«Is it true?» although smiling, Jesus casts a piercing glance at him.

«Yes, Jesus, it is true.»

«Come then.»

The boy jumps for joy and takes the left hand of Jesus Who stretches it out to him. With how much loving reliance the child places his little swarthy hand into Jesus' long hand! I wish I could do the same myself!

«Tell me a nice parable, Jesus» says the boy skipping beside Jesus and looking up at Him, his face shining with joy.

Jesus also looks at him with a cheerful smile that opens His lips shaded by His moustache and His reddish golden beard, which shines like gold in the sun. His dark sapphire eyes sparkle with joy while He looks at the child.

«What will you do with a parable? It is not a game.»

«It is better than a game. When I go to bed, I think about it then I dream of it and the following day I remember it and I repeat to myself to be good. It makes me good.»

«Do you remember it?»

«Yes, I do. Shall I repeat to you all the ones You told me?»

«You are clever, Benjamin, more clever than men, who forget. As a prize I will tell you a parable.»

The boy no longer hops about. He walks seriously and as seriously as an adult, he does not miss one word or any inflexion of Jesus, Whom he watches carefully, without even worrying where he puts his feet.

352.7 [7] «A very good shepherd found out that in a certain place many sheep had been abandoned by bad shepherds, and they were in great danger along rough roads and in harmful pastures, and were wandering about closer and closer to dark ravines. So he went to that place and sacrificing *everything* he had, he bought the sheep and lambs. He wanted to take them to his own kingdom, because that shepherd was also a king, like many kings in Israel. In his kingdom those sheep and lambs would find wholesome pastures, cool water, safe roads and protected shelter against thieves and wild wolves. So the shepherd gathered all his sheep and lambs together and said to them: "I have come to save you, to take you where you will no longer suffer and where you will find no snares. Love me, follow me, because I love you so much and I have made every possible sacrifice in order to rescue you. But if you love me, I will not regret my sacrifice. Follow me and let us go". And they set out towards the kingdom of happiness, the shepherd before them and the sheep after him. The shepherd turned around every moment to make sure that the sheep were following him, to exhort those which were tired, to encourage the ones which were downhearted, to assist the sick ones and to caress the little lambs. How much he loved them! He used to give them his bread and salt, and he always tasted the water of fountains first, to make sure that it was good and he blessed it to make it holy. But the sheep — would you believe it, Benjamin? — the sheep became tired. First one, then two, then ten, then one hundred remained behind grazing and stuffing themselves with so much grass that they could no longer move, and they lay down in the dust and mud when they were tired and full. Some went close to the brinks of precipices, notwithstanding that the shepherd said to them: "Don't do that"; and as he stood near the most dangerous places to prevent them from going there, some bumped into him trying to make him fall into the precipice and they did that several times. And thus many fell into ravines and died miserably. Some butted each other and killed each other. Only one little lamb never went astray. It ran

about bleating as if to say to the shepherd: "I love you"; it always ran behind the good shepherd and when they arrived at the gates of his kingdom, they were the only two: the shepherd and the little faithful lamb. Then the shepherd did not say: "go in", but he said: "come" and he took it in his arms, close to his chest, and he took it inside calling all his subjects and saying to them: "Here. This little lamb loves me. I want it to be with me forever. And
you must love it because it is the pet of my heart". [8]And that is the 352.8
end of the parable, Benjamin. Now can you tell Me: who is that good shepherd?»

«It's You, Jesus.»

«And who is the little lamb?»

«It's me, Jesus.»

«But I will be going away now. You will forget Me.»

«No, Jesus. I will not forget You because I love You.»

«Your love will come to an end when you no longer see Me.»

«I will repeat to myself the words that You spoke to me and it will be the same as if You were present. I will love You and obey You thus. And tell me, Jesus: Will You remember Benjamin?»

«Always.»

«And how will You remember?»

«I will say to Myself that you promised to love and obey Me and I will thus remember you.»

«And will You give me Your Kingdom?»

«I will, if you are good.»

«I will be good.»

«What will you do? Life is long.»

«But Your words are very good, too. If I repeat them to myself and I do what they say I should do, I will be good all my life. And I will do that because I love You. When one loves, it is not difficult to be good. I do not find it difficult to obey my mother, because I love her. And it will not be difficult for me to obey You, because I love You.»

Jesus stops and looks at the little face, which is lit by love more than by the sun. Jesus' joy is so deep that another sun seems to be burning in His soul and shining through His eyes. He bends and kisses the forehead of the child.

[9]He has stopped near a humble house with a well in front. Je- 352.9
sus sits down near the well where He is joined by the disciples,

who are still arguing over their prerogatives.

Jesus looks at them. Then He calls them: «Come here, around Me and listen to the last lesson of the day, you who have shouted yourselves hoarse celebrating your own merits and believe that you will gain a position according to them. See this child? He is in the truth more than you are. His innocence gives him the key to open the gates of My Kingdom. In his simplicity of a child, he has understood that the strength necessary to become great lies in love and that obedience practised with love is required to enter My Kingdom. Be simple and humble, be affectionate not to Me only, but to one another, obey My words, all of them, *also the ones I am speaking to you now*, if you wish to reach the place that these innocent souls will enter. Learn from the little ones. The Father reveals the truth to them, but He does not reveal it to the wise.»

Jesus is speaking holding Benjamin against His knees, with His hands on the boy's shoulders. Jesus' countenance is majestic. He is serious, not angry, but serious. As it is of a Master. His fair-haired head is a blaze of light in the last sunbeams.

The vision ends here leaving me full of sweet happiness notwithstanding my sorrows.

[6th December 1945].

352.10 [10] So, the disciples have not been able to go into the house. This was normal because of their number and out of respect. They never go in unless they are all invited, or one in particular is invited by the Master. I notice in them great respect and reservedness, notwithstanding the kindness of the Master and His long lasting familiarity. Even Isaac, who I can say is the first disciple, never takes the liberty of approaching Jesus unless he is called by the Master with at least a smile.

Somewhat different, is it not to the rash almost farcical? manner in which many people deal with what is supernatural... This is my comment and I feel that it is correct, because I cannot suffer people to treat what is above us with manners that we would not use for men like ourselves, if they are only a little better than we are... Well!... And let us go on...

The disciples are scattered on the shore of the lake to buy fish and bread and whatever is necessary for supper. James of Zebedee comes back and calls the Master, Who is sitting on the terrace with John crouched at His feet in loving conversation... Jesus stands up and leans over the parapet.

James says: «How much fish, Master! My father says that You blessed the nets by coming here. Look: this is for us» and he shows a basket full of silvery fish.

«May God grant him grace for his generosity. Prepare it, because after supper we will go on the shore with the disciples.»

They do so. The lake is black at night, waiting for the moon, which rises late. And rather than see it, one can hear it grumble and lap on the shingly shore. Only the exceptionally bright stars of eastern countries are mirrored in calm waters. They sit in a circle round an upturned boat on which Jesus is sitting. And the little lamps of boats placed in the centre of the circle hardly illuminate the faces closer to them. Jesus' face is lit up from below by a lantern placed near His feet, and thus everybody can see Him well while He talks to this one or that one.

[11] At first it is a simple home-like conversation. But it soon takes 352.11
the tone of a lesson. Jesus says so openly:

«Come and listen. We shall be parting shortly and I wish to instruct you to perfect you further.

I heard you dispute today, and not always charitably. I have already given the seniors among you the lesson, but I want to give it to you as well, and it will do the seniors no harm to hear it again. Little Benjamin is no longer here, standing against My knees. He is sleeping in his bed and dreaming his innocent dreams. But perhaps his innocent soul is here among us just the same. But imagine that he, or some other boy, is here, as an example for you.

Each of you has in his heart a fixed idea, a curiosity, a danger. That is: to be the first in the Kingdom of Heaven; to know who the first will be; and at last the danger: the still human desire to hear the reply: "You are the first in the Kingdom of Heaven" uttered by your obliging companions or by the Master, above all by the Master, of Whose veracity and knowledge of the future you are aware. Is it not so? The questions tremble on your lips and dwell in the depth of your hearts.

Your Master, for your own good, yields to that curiosity, although He loathes giving assent to human curiosity. Your Master is not a charlatan to whom one can ask questions for a few coins in the uproar of a market. Neither is He possessed by the spirit of the Python, that assists Him in making money by divining, to comply with the narrow-mindedness of man who wants to know the future in order to decide how "*to act*". Man cannot act wisely by himself. God will assist him if man has faith in Him! And it is of no avail to know the future, or to think that one knows it, if one has no means to avert the prophesied future. There is one means only: to pray to the Father and Lord that His mercy may assist us. I solemnly tell you that a confident prayer can change punishment into blessings. But he who has resorts to men in order to avert the future, as a man and with human means, cannot pray at all or prays very badly. As this curiosity may teach you a good lesson, I will reply to it for this once, although I abhor curious and disrespectful questions.

352.12 [12] You are asking: "Which of us will be the greatest in the Kingdom of Heaven?".

I do not take into consideration the limitation "of us" and I extend the frontiers to the whole present and future world and I reply: "He is the greatest in the Kingdom of Heaven, who is the least among men". That is: he who is considered "the least" by men: the simple, the humble, the trustful, the unaware. That is a child, or he who can make his soul be like the soul of a child once again. Neither science, nor power, nor wealth, nor industry, not even good industry, will make you "the greatest" in the blessed Kingdom. It is necessary to be like children with regard to loving kindness, humility, simplicity and faith.

Watch how children love Me, and imitate them. How they believe in Me, and imitate them. How they remember what I say, and imitate them. How they do what I teach them, and imitate them. How they do not pride themselves on what they do, and imitate them. How they do not become jealous of Me and of their companions, and imitate them. I solemnly tell you that if you do not change your ways of thinking, of acting and of loving, and you do not re-mold them on the pattern of children, you will not enter the Kingdom of Heaven. They know the essential elements of My doctrine, as you know them, but how differently they practise what I teach! For every good action you accomplish, you say: "I did that". A child says to Me: "I remembered You today, I obeyed for Your sake, I loved, I refrained from quarrelling... and I am happy, because I know that You are aware when I am good and You are pleased". And watch children when they are at fault. How humbly they confess: "Today I was naughty. And I am sorry because I grieved You". And they do not find excuses. They know that I know. They believe. They are sorry because *I am* sorry.

Oh! How dear children are to My heart: there is no pride, no duplicity, no lust in them! I tell you once again: become like children if you wish to enter My Kingdom. Love children, as they are angelical examples still at your disposal. Because you ought to be like angels. As an excuse you may say: "We do not see angels". But God gives you children as examples, and you have children amongst you. And if you see a child who is physically or morally forlorn and who may perish, welcome him in My Name, because they are *greatly* loved by God. And he who welcomes a child in My Name welcomes Me, because I am in the innocent souls of children. And he who welcomes Me, welcomes Him Who sent Me, the Most High.

[13] And beware lest you should scandalise one of these little ones, 352.13
whose eyes see God. You must never scandalise anybody. But woe betide three times those who soil the innocent purity of children! Let them be like angels as long as possible. The world and flesh are too repugnant to souls coming from Heaven! And a child, through his innocence, is still entirely a soul. Respect the soul of a child and his body as you respect a sacred place. And a child is sacred also because he has God within himself. The temple of the Spirit is in everybody. But the temple of a child is the most sacred and intimate, it is beyond the double Veil. Do not even allow the wind of your passions to shake the curtains of their unawareness of concupiscence.

I would like a child in every family, among every gathering of people, to check the passions of men. A child sanctifies, brings solace and freshness through the simple glance of his innocent eyes. But woe to those who despoil children of their holiness through their scandalous behaviour! Woe betide those who teach children wickedness through their debauchery! Woe betide those who by means of their words and irony injure the faith children have in Me! It would be better if a millstone were tied round the neck of each of them and they were thrown into the sea to be drowned together with their scandal. Woe to the world that scandalises such innocent souls! There must indeed be scandals, but alas for the man who provides them.

No one is entitled to do violence to his body or to his life. Because life and body are given to us by God and He only is entitled to take them entirely or in part. I tell you that if your hand causes you to sin, it is better that you cut it off, and if your foot causes you to give scandal, it is better if you cut it off. It is better for you to enter into Life crippled or lame, than to be thrown into eternal fire with two hands and two feet. And if it is not sufficient to have one hand or foot cut off, have also the other hand or foot cut off, so that you may no longer scandalise, but you may have time to repent before being thrown into the unquenchable fire, which tortures like a worm forever. And if your eye should cause you to sin, tear it out and throw it away. It is better to be one-eyed, than be in hell with, both eyes. With one eye or without eyes you could see the Light in Heaven, whereas with two scandalous eyes you would see darkness and horror in hell. And nothing else.

352.14 [14]Remember that. Do not scandalise the little ones, do not despise them, do not deride them. They are worth more than you are, because their angels always see God, Who tells them the truth to be revealed to children and to those whose hearts are like those of children.

And love one another like children, without disputes and without pride. And be at peace with one another. Be peaceful-minded towards everybody. You are brothers, in the name of the Lord, not enemies. There must be no enemies among Jesus' disciples. The only Enemy is Satan. Be his fierce enemies and join battle with him and with the sins that install Satan in the hearts of men.

Be tireless in fighting Evil, whichever form it may take. And be patient. There is no limit to the activity of an apostle, because there is no limit to the activity of Evil. The demon never says: "That is enough. I am tired now and I am going to rest". He is indefatigable. He passes from one man to another as quick as thought, and even quicker, and he tempts and takes, he seduces and tortures and gives no peace. He attacks treacherously and demolishes, if one is not more than vigilant. At times he installs himself as conqueror, encouraged by the weakness of the person he assails, at times he enters as a friend, because the prey he is after already lives as an ally of the Enemy. Sometimes, when he is cast out of a man, he wanders around and assaults a better prey to avenge himself for the affront suffered at the hands of God or of a servant of God. But you must say what he says: "I will not rest". He does not rest in order to people hell. You must not rest in order to people Paradise. Give him no quarter. I foretell you that the more you fight him the more he will make you suffer. But you must not worry about that. He can overrun the earth, but he cannot enter Heaven. So he will not be able to trouble you there and all those who have fought him will be in Heaven...»

[15] Jesus stops abruptly and asks: «Why are you worrying John? 352.15
What do they want from you?»

John blushes and Bartholomew, Thomas and the Iscariot lower their heads seeing that they have been found out.

«Well?» asks Jesus peremptorily.

«Master, my companions want me to tell You something.»

«Tell Me, then.»

«Today, when You were with the sick man and we were going round the village, as You told us, we saw a man, who is not a disciple of Yours and whom we have never seen among those who listen to Your sermons, and he was casting out demons in Your name in a group of pilgrims going to Jerusalem. And he was successful. He cured a man who trembled so much as to be unable to work, and he made a girl recover the use of speech, which she had lost, because she was assailed in a forest by a demon in the form of a dog, which had tied her tongue. He said: "Go away, cursed demon, in the name of the Lord Jesus, the Christ, the King of the issue of David, the King of Israel. He is the Saviour and the Winner. Flee before His Name!" and the demon really fled. We resented that and we told him that he was not allowed to do so. He said to us: "Am I doing anything wrong? I honour the Christ by clearing His way from demons who are not worthy to see Him". We replied: "You are not an exorciser according to Israel and you are not a disciple of Christ. You are not allowed to do that". He said: "One is always allowed to do good things" and he rebelled against our order saying: "And I will continue to do what I am doing". That is what they wanted me to tell You, particularly because You just said that all those who fight Satan will be in Heaven.»

352.16 [16] «All right. That man will be one of them. He was right and you were wrong. The ways of the Lord are infinite and it is not true that only those who take the straight road arrive in Heaven. Everywhere, at all times, in countless different ways, there will be people who will come to Me, even along initially wrong ways. But God will see their good intentions and will lead them on to the right way. Likewise there will be some who through treble concupiscent inebriation will leave the good way to take one that will lead them far away and mislead them all together. So you must never judge your fellow-men. God only sees. Endeavour never to leave the right way, on which the will of God more than your own put you. And when you see one who believes and acts in My Name, do not call him stranger, enemy, or say that he is sacrilegious. He is a friendly faithful subject of Mine, because he believes spontaneously in My Name, and he believes more than many among you. That is why My Name on his lips works miracles like yours, and perhaps greater than yours. God loves him because he loves Me and will end by taking him to Heaven. No one who works miracles in My name can be My enemy or speak ill of Me. On the contrary he honours the Christ and bears witness to faith. I solemnly tell you that belief in My Name is sufficient to save your souls. Because My Name is Salvation. So I say to you: if you see him again, do not hinder him. But call him "brother", because he is such, even if he is still outside the enclosure of My Fold. He who is not against Me, is with Me. He who is not against you, is with you.»

«Have we sinned, Lord?» asks John sorrowfully.

«No. You acted out of ignorance, but without malice. So there is no sin. But, since you are now aware of the situation, it would be a sin in the future. And now let us go home. Peace be with you.»

352.17 [17] The dictation that follows the vision of little Benjamin (7.3.44) can be put here at the end of today's vision. As you wish.

[7th March 1944].

352.18 [18] Jesus then says:

«I will tell you also, what I told My little disciple. The Kingdom belongs to the faithful lambs who love and follow Me without getting lost in allurements. They love Me till the end.

And I say to you what I said to My senior disciples: "Learn from the little ones". The fact that you are learned, rich, bold, will not make you conquer the Kingdom of Heaven. Not if you are so from a human point of view. But you will conquer it, if you are supernaturally learned, rich and bold through the knowledge and practice of love. How love does enlighten one to understand the Truth! How it makes one rich to conquer it! How bold it makes one to conquer it! How much confidence and certainty it inspires!

Behave like little Benjamin, My little flower who scented My heart that evening and sang angelical music, which overwhelmed the scent of humanity seething in the disciples and the noise of human altercations.

And do you wish to know what happened later to Benjamin? He remained the little lamb of Christ, and when he lost his Great Shepherd, Who had gone back to Heaven, he became a disciple of the one who was more like Me, by whom he was baptised with the name of Stephen, My first martyr. He was faithful unto death and so were his relatives, conquered to Faith by their little apostle. Is he not known? Many people are known to Me in My Kingdom, but they are unknown to men. And they are happy for that. Worldly fame does not add even a tiny spark to the glory of the blessed souls.

Little John, always walk with your hand in Mine. You will proceed safely and when you arrive at the Kingdom I will not say to you: "Go in" but "Come" and I will take you in My arms to put you where My love has prepared a place for you and that your love has deserved.

Go in peace. I bless you.»

353. The Second Multiplication of the Loaves. The Spiritual Miracle of the Multiplication of the Words of Jesus, "Word of God".

28th May 1944, Whit Sunday, 2 a.m.

[1] A tranquil vision. I see a place which is neither a plain nor a 353.1

mountain. There are some mountains to the east, but they are rather far away. Then there is a little valley and minor flat risings of ground, like grass-grown tablelands. They seem to be the lower slopes of a group of hills. The ground is rather parched and bare. There is only short sparse grass scattered over the stony ground. Here and there is a small group of very low thorny bushes. The horizon opens wide and bright to the west. I can see nothing else. It is still daylight, but I would say that evening is approaching because the western sky is red in the sunset, whilst the mountains to the east are already violaceous in the incipient twilight. Deep crevices also look darker in the fading light, while higher parts are tinged with violet.

Jesus is standing on a large stone speaking to a *very huge* crowd dispersed on the tableland. His disciples are around Him. From His high position He dominates the crowds of people of every age and social condition around Him.

He must have worked some miracles because I hear Him say: «You must praise and be grateful to Him Who sent Me, not to Me. And your praise must not come from inattentive lips like the sound of rustling wind. True praise rises from your hearts and is the true feeling of your hearts. And it is pleasing to God. Let those who have been cured love the Lord faithfully. And the relatives of those who have been cured must love Him likewise. Do not misuse the gift of your recovered health. Fear more the diseases of your souls than those of your bodies. And do not sin. Because every sin is a disease. And some of them may bring about death. So, all of you who are now rejoicing, do not destroy the blessings of the Lord by committing sin. Your joy would come to an end because evil deeds destroy peace, and where there is no peace, there is no joy. But be holy and perfect, as the Father wants you to be, because He loves you and He wants to give a Kingdom to those whom He loves. But only those who are perfect through their loyalty to the Law will enter His holy Kingdom. May the peace of God be with you.»

353.2 [2] And Jesus falls into silence. He crosses His arms on His chest and watches the crowds around Him. He then looks around, at the clear sky which is becoming darker and darker in the fading light. He is pensive. He comes down from the large stone. He says to His disciples: «I feel sorry for these people. They have followed Me for three days. They have no more food supplies with them and we are far from any village. I am afraid that the weaker ones would suffer too much, if I send them away without feeding them.»

«And how do You want to do that, Master? You said it Yourself, that we are far from every village. Where can we find bread in this lonely place? And who would give us so much money to buy enough for everybody?»

«Have you not got any with you?»

«We have a few fish and some pieces of bread. What was left over from our meal. But it is not enough for anybody. If You give it to those who are near You, there will be a riot. You will deprive us and not help anybody» says Peter.

«Bring Me what you have.»

They bring a little basket with seven pieces of bread. They are not whole loaves. They look like thick slices of a large loaf. The little fish are a handful of tiny things burnt on the fire.

«Make the crowds sit down in groups of fifty people and tell them to be calm and quiet if they want to eat.»

The disciples, either climbing on stones or going round among the crowds, busy themselves to arrange the people as requested by Jesus. Through great efforts, they are successful. Some of the children whimper because they are hungry or sleepy, some whine because their mothers or some relatives have given them a slap to make them obey.

[3]Jesus takes the bits of bread, not all of them: one in each hand, 353.3
He offers them, puts them down and blesses them. He takes the little fish, they are so few that they are contained in the hollow of His long hands. He offers them, too, puts them down and blesses them.

«And now take them, go round the crowd and give everybody *plenty*.»

The disciples obey.

Jesus, standing, watches them and smiles: His white figure dominates the people sitting in wide circles all over the tableland.

The disciples move farther and farther, handing the food out all the time. And the basket is always full of food. The people eat while night falls and there is total silence and a great peace.

353.4 [4] Jesus says:

«And this is another thing which will annoy difficult doctors: the application of this evangelical vision. I will not make you meditate on My power and kindness, or on the faith and obedience of the disciples. Nothing of that. I want to show you the analogy of the episode with the work of the Holy Spirit:

See: I give My word. I give everything you can understand and assimilate to nourish your souls. But you have been made so dull by fatigue and inanition that you cannot assimilate all the nourishment which is in My word. You would need so much of it. But you are not able to receive much. You are so poor in spiritual strength! It burdens you without giving you blood or strength. And the Spirit then works the miracle for you. The spiritual miracle of the multiplication of the Word. It enlightens for you, and thus multiplies all its most secret meanings, so that you can feed on it and thus not collapse exhausted along the desert of life, thus you do not have to encumber yourselves with a load that would crush you without strengthening you.

Seven pieces of bread and a few fish!

I preached for three years and, as My beloved John says, "if all the parables I told and all the miracles I worked were to be written to give you substantial food, capable of taking you as far as the Kingdom, without fainting through weakness, the whole Earth would not suffice to contain all the volumes". And even if all that had been written, you could not have read so many books. You do not even read, as you ought to, the little which has been written about Me. And it is the only thing you should know, as you have known the more necessary words since your childhood. *

So Love comes and multiplies. He, too, Who is One with Me and the Father, "feels sorry for you who are dying from starvation" and with a miracle that is being repeated throughout centuries, He multiplies twice, ten times, a hundred times the nourishment of each word of Mine. You thus have an infinite treasure of celestial food. It is offered to you by the Charity. Draw from it without fear. The more you draw from it, the more it will grow, as it is the fruit of Love.

353.5 [5] God has no limit in His wealth and possibilities. You are rela-

* **says** in: *John 21:25.*

tive. He is not. He is infinite. In all His works. And also in His power to give you, every moment and for every event, the light you need, in any *particular moment*. And as on the day of Pentecost the Spirit infused in the apostles made their word understandable to Parthians, Medians, Scythians, Cappadocians, to the inhabitants of Pontus, to Phrygians, and made it like their mother tongues to Egyptians, Romans, Greeks and Libyans, so it will comfort you when you weep, it will advise you when you ask for advice, it will share your joy when you rejoice, through the same Word.

Oh! if the Spirit really elucidates the sentence to you: "Go in peace *and do not sin*", those words are really a reward for those who have not sinned, they are encouragement for those who are still weak but do not want to sin, they are forgiveness for repentant souls, and a mild merciful reproach for those who only show a shadow of repentance. And it is *only* a sentence. And one of the most simple ones. But how many there are in My Gospel! How many, which, like flower buds after a shower and springtime sunshine, open in large numbers on the branch where there was only one, and cover it all to the joy of those who admire it.

Rest now. The peace of Love be with you.»

354. In the Synagogue of Capernaum, the Sermon on the Bread from Heaven. The Desertion of Many Disciples.

[1]The vision of the second miracle of the loaves given on 28th May 1944 and relevant dictation are to be put before the vision of 7th December. 354.1

7th December 1945.

[2]The beach at Capernaum is crowded with people disembarking from a fleet of boats of all sizes. And the first to land spread among the crowds looking for the Master or an apostle or at least a disciple. And they ask after them... 354.2

A man at last replies: «The Master? The apostles? No, they are not here. They went away immediately after the Sabbath and have not come back. But they will come back, because some of the disciples are here. I spoke just now to one of them. He must be an important disciple. He speaks as well as Jairus! He went along the coast towards that house in the fields.»

The man who asked the question spreads the news and they all rush towards the house. But after about two hundred metres they meet on the beach a group of disciples coming towards Capernaum gesticulating animatedly. They greet them and ask: «Where is the Master?»

The disciples reply: «During the night, after the miracle, He went with His disciples by boat to the other side of the sea. We saw the sails in the moonlight going towards Dalmanuta.»

«Ah! We looked for Him at Magdala, at Mary's house, but He was not there! However... the fishermen of Magdala should have told us!»

«They probably did not know. He may have gone up the Arbela mountains to pray. He has been there before, last year, before Passover. I met Him there, by the great grace of the Lord to His poor servant» says Stephen.

«But is He not coming back here?»

«He will certainly come back. He has to give us instructions before sending us away. But what do you want?»

«We want to hear Him again, to follow Him and become His disciples.»

«He will be going to Jerusalem. You will find Him there. And in the House of God, the Lord will speak to you and you will
354.3 know whether you ought to follow Him. [3]Because you must know that, although He does not reject anybody, there are tendencies in us which reject the Light. Now, he who has so many of them as to be not only saturated with them — which is not a great evil because He is Light and when we firmly decide to become His loyal followers His Light penetrates into us and overwhelms darkness — but to be also deeply attached to them, as to one's own body, then it is better for him to refrain from coming, unless he is prepared to demolish his old being and form a completely new one. Consider, therefore, whether you have the strength to take on a new spirit, a new way of thinking and wanting. Pray in order to see the truth concerning your vocation. Then come, if you should so decide. And may the Most High, Who guided Israel in the "passage", guide you also in this "Pesach", so that you may *
follow in the wake of the Lamb, from the desert, towards the

eternal Earth, the Kingdom of God» says Stephen, speaking on behalf of all his companions.

«No, no! Now! At once! No one does what He does. We want to follow Him» shout the crowds in tumult.

Stephen smiles *meaningly*. He opens his arms and says: «Do you want to come because He gave you plenty good bread? Do you think that in future He will give you only that? He promises His followers what is His own lot: sorrow, persecution, martyrdom. Not roses, but thorns; not caresses, but slaps; not bread but stones are awaiting the followers of Christ. And I say so without becoming a blasphemer, because His true followers will be anointed with the holy oil made by His Grace and His suffering; and we shall be "anointed" to be the victims on the altar and the kings in Heaven.»

«Well? Are you jealous perhaps? If you are there, we want to be there as well. The Master belongs to everybody.»

«All right. I told you because I love you and I want you to know what it means to be "disciples", so that you may not become deserters later. Let us now go all together and wait for Him at His house. The sun is already setting and the Sabbath is about to begin. He will come to spend it here before departing.»

[4]And they go towards the town, talking. And many ask Ste- 354.4
phen and Hermas, who has joined them, many questions, as they are both placed in a very favourable light in the eyes of the Israelites, because they are Gamaliel's dearest pupils. Many ask: «But what does Gamaliel say about Him?», and some: «Did he send you?», and some: «Did he not regret losing you?», or: «What does the Master say of the great rabbi?»

The two disciples reply patiently: «Gamaliel speaks of Jesus of Nazareth as of the greatest man in Israel.»

«What? Greater than Moses?» exclaim some who are almost scandalised.

«He says that Moses is one of the many precursors of the Christ. But he is only the servant of the Christ.»

«So, according to Gamaliel, this man is the Christ? Is that what he says? If rabbi Gamaliel says that, the matter is settled. He is the Christ!»

---

* **passage**, already remember in 340.9.

«He does not say that. He cannot yet believe that, unfortunately for him. But he says that the Christ is on the earth because he spoke to Him many years ago. Both he and wise Hillel. And he is waiting for the sign that Christ promised him so that he may recognise Him» says Hermas.

«But how could he believe that that man was the Christ? What did He do? I am as old as Gamaliel, but I never heard of anyone doing the things that the Master does. If he is not convinced by these miracles, what miracles did he see in that Christ that he believed in Him?»

«He saw Him anointed with the Wisdom of God. So he says» replies Hermas once again.

«Well, then, what is this one according to Gamaliel?»

«The greatest man, master and precursor in Israel. If he could say: "He is the Christ", the wise and just soul of my just master would be saved» says Stephen and he concludes: «And I pray that that may happen, at all costs.»

«But if he does not believe that He is the Christ, why did he send you to Him?»

«We wanted to come. He let us come saying that it was a good thing.»

«Perhaps he wanted to find out things and report them to the Sanhedrin...» insinuates one.

«Man what are you saying? Gamaliel is honest. He does not play the spy for anybody, and particularly for the enemies of an innocent person!» objects Stephen and he is so indignant and almost beaming with holy indignation that he looks like an archangel.

«But he must have been sorry to lose you» states another man.

«He was and was not. As a man who was fond of us, yes. As a very righteous spirit, no. Because he said: "He is greater than I am and younger than I am. So I will be able to breathe my last breath peacefully, as far as your future is concerned, as I know that you are with the 'Master of masters'".»

«And what does Jesus of Nazareth say of the great rabbi?»

«Oh! He speaks but highly of him!»

«Is He not envious of him?»

«God does not envy» replies Hermas severely. «Do not make sacrilegious suppositions.»

«So He is God according to you. Are you sure?»

And the two reply together: «As we are sure that we are alive just now.» And Stephen concludes: «And believe it yourselves if you wish to possess eternal Life.»

[5] From the beach they go into the square, which they cross going towards the house. Jesus is at the door caressing some children. 354.5

The disciples and some curious people crowd around Him asking: «Master, when did You come?»

«A few minutes ago.» Jesus' countenance is still as majestically solemn, somewhat ecstatic, as when He is engrossed in prayer for a long time.

«Have You been praying, Master?» asks Stephen in a low voice out of respect, and for the same reason he has stooped.

«Yes, I have. What makes you understand that, My son?» asks Jesus laying His hand on the disciple's dark hair with a kind caress.

«Your angelical face. I am a poor man, but the expression of Your face is so clear that one can read on it the emotions and deeds of Your spirit.»

«Yours also is clear. You are one of those who remain children...»

«And what is there on my face, Lord?»

«Come aside and I will tell you» and Jesus takes him by the wrist and leads him into a dark corridor. «Charity, faith, purity, generosity, wisdom; God gave them to you and you have improved them and you will do so even more in the future. Finally, in accordance with your name, you have a crown: it is of pure gold with a large gem glittering in front. On the gold and on the gem there are two expressions engraved: "Predestination" and "Early Fruit". Be worthy of your destiny, Stephen. Go in peace with My blessing.» And once again He rests His hand on Stephen's dark hair while he kneels down and bends to kiss His feet.

[6] They go back to the others. 354.6

«These people have come to hear You...» says Philip

«It is not possible to speak here. Let us go to the synagogue. Jairus will be pleased.»

They go to the beautiful synagogue of Capernaum: Jesus leads the way and is followed by the procession of all the others.

Jairus greets Him and He enters, giving instructions to leave all the doors open, so that those who cannot go inside may hear Him from the street and square next to the synagogue.

Jesus goes to His place, in the friendly synagogue, in which, fortunately, there are no Pharisees today. They have probably already left for Jerusalem in full plumage. And He begins to speak.

«I solemnly tell you: You are looking for Me not to hear Me or because of the miracles which you have seen, but because of the bread that I gave you to eat to your fill and without any expense. That is why three quarters of you were looking for Me, and also out of curiosity and that is why you came from every part of our Fatherland. So there is no supernatural spirit in your quest, dominated by human spirit with its unsound curiosities or at least with childish curiosity, not because it is simple like that of children, but because it is maimed like the intelligence of a dull-minded person. And linked to such curiosity there is sensuality and vitiated feeling. Sensuality, as subtle as the demon whose daughter it is, hides behind appearances and seemingly good deeds, and vitiated feeling is simply a morbid deviation of sentiment, and like everything which is "disease" it needs and craves after drugs, which are not plain food, good bread, good water, unadulterated oil, the first milk which is sufficient to live and live well. Vitiated feeling needs extraordinary things to be roused, to feel the thrill of pleasure, the sickly thrill of paralysed people who need drugs to feel the sensation, which beguiles them into believing that they are still healthy and virile. The sensuality that wants to satisfy one's gluttony without work, in this case, with bread which was not hard-earned, but given by God's bounty.

354.7 [7] The gifts of God are not common ordinary things, they are special ones. One cannot claim them nor can one become lazy and say: "God will give them to me". It is written: "You shall eat bread moistened with the sweat of your forehead", that is the bread earned through hard work. If He Who is Mercy said: "I feel sorry for these people, who have followed Me for three days and have nothing left to eat and may faint on the way before they reach Hippo on the lake, or Gamala, or any other town", and He provided accordingly, that does not imply that He is to be followed just because of that. I am to be followed for much more than a little bread, which becomes excrement after it is digested. I am to be followed not for the food that fills the stomach, but for that which nourishes the soul. Because you are not only animals, which must browse and ruminate, or grout and get fat. You are souls! That is what you are! Your body is the garment, your being is the soul. It is the soul that lasts. Your body, like every garment, wears out and comes to an end and it is not worth taking care of, as if it were something perfect deserving every care.

Seek, therefore, what is just to attain, not what is unjust. Endeavour to get not the food that does perish, but that which lasts for eternal life. The Son of man will always give it to you, whenever you want it. Because the Son of man has at His disposal everything that comes from God, and He can give it; He is the Master, the generous Master of the treasures of the Father God, Who has impressed His seal on Him so that no honest eye may be confused. And if you have the food that does not perish, you will be able to do the works of God, having been nourished with the food of God.»

[8] «What shall we do to work the deeds of God? We keep the 354.8
Law and respect the Prophets. Thus we are already nourished with the food of God and we do the works of God.»

«That is true. You keep the Law. Or better still: you "*know*" the Law. But to know is not to practise. For instance, we know the laws of Rome, but no faithful Israelite puts them into practise, except in those specific cases when he is compelled to do so as a subject. Otherwise, I am referring to faithful Israelites, we do not put into practise the heathen customs of the Romans, although we know them. The Law which you know and the Prophets should, in fact, nourish you with God and make you capable of working the deeds of God. But in order to do so, they should have become one thing with you, like the air you breathe and the food you assimilate, which become your life and your blood. Instead they are like strangers to you, although they belong to your house, just like an object in the house, which is known and useful to you, but will not interfere with your life if it were lost. But try not to breathe for a few minutes, or to go without food for days... and you will see that you cannot live. And that is how your *ego* should feel in your malnutrition and asphyxia of the Law and Prophets known to you but not assimilated and thus not all one with you. This is what I have come to teach you and to give you: the juice, the air of the Law and of the Prophets, to give blood and breath back to your souls dying from inanition and asphyxia. You are like children whom a disease has made unable to tell what can nourish them: You have plenty food in front of you, but you do not know that it must be eaten to be changed into something vital that is, that it must *really become part of us*, through pure generous loyalty to the Law of the Lord, Who spoke to Moses and the Prophets on behalf of all of you. It is your duty, therefore, to come to Me to receive the air and juice of eternal Life. But that duty presupposes faith in you. Because if one has no faith, one cannot believe My words, and if one does not believe, one cannot come to Me and say: "Give me the true bread". And if you do not have the true bread you cannot work the deeds of God, because you are unable to do them. So in order to be nourished by God and to work the deeds of God, you must do the basic work, which is: to believe in Him Whom God sent.»

354.9 [9] «But what miracles do You work that we may believe that You have been sent by God and we may see the seal of God upon You? What do You do, that the Prophets have not already done although in a more modest form? In truth, Moses exceeded You, because he fed our ancestors with wonderful food not once but for forty years. It is in fact written that our forefathers ate manna in the desert for forty years, and it is written that Moses gave * them the bread of heaven to eat, as he was able to do so.»

«You are wrong. Not Moses but the Lord was able to do so. And in Exodus we read: "Now I will rain down bread from the heavens. Let the people go out and gather what is sufficient for each day, so that I may test whether the people will follow My law or not. And on the sixth day they will gather twice as much, out of respect for the seventh day, which is the Sabbath". And the Hebrews every morning saw the desert become covered with that "delicate thing that resembles what is pounded in a mortar and is like hoarfrost and coriander seed and has the lovely taste of flour kneaded with honey". So it was not Moses but God who supplied manna. *God can do everything.* He can punish and bless. He can grant and take away. And I tell you that He always

* **manna in the desert**, in *Exodus 16*. The following quotations are taken from: *Exodus 16:4-5.14.31*; *Wisdom 16:19-29*; *Sirach 45:1-6*.

prefers to bless and grant rather than punish and take away.

God, as the Book of Wisdom states, out of love for Moses — who, according to Ecclesiasticus, "was beloved by God and men, of blessed memory, and was made by God the equal of the holy ones in glory, and strong to the terror of his enemies, and was able to work miracles and stop them, and was raised high in the respect of kings, and was His minister before the people, and saw the glory of God and heard the voice of the Most High, and was the guardian of the precepts and of the Law of life and science" — God, I was saying, out of love for Moses, nourished His people with the bread of angels and from heaven untiringly sent them bread already prepared, containing every delight, satisfying every taste. And — remember what Wisdom says — as it came from heaven, from God, and demonstrated His sweetness towards His children, it tasted as each eater wished and produced the effects that each person wanted, and was thus useful to babies, whose stomachs are still delicate, and to adults enjoying good appetite and healthy digestions, and to delicate girls and to decrepit old people. And, to testify that it was not the work of man, it overturned the laws of elements, and the mysterious bread, which at sunrise melted like frost, endured fire. Or rather — it is still Wisdom speaking — fire forgot its own nature out of respect for the work of God, its Creator, and for the needs of the just people of God, so that, while it burns to torture, in this case it became mild to assist those who confided in God. Thus, by transforming itself in many ways, it served the grace of the Lord, nourishing everyone, according to the will of those who prayed the Eternal Father, so that the beloved children might learn that it is not the reproduction of fruit that nourishes men, but it is the word of the Lord that preserves those who believe in God. In fact it did not consume the sweet manna, as it was able to do, not even when it flared, whereas the mild morning sunshine could melt it, so that men should learn and remember that the gifts of God are to be sought from the very beginning of the day and of life, and that one must anticipate Light to receive them, and rise and pray the Eternal Father at daybreak.

That is what manna taught the Hebrews. And I am reminding you because that duty still lasts and will last forever. Seek the Lord and His celestial gifts without idling until the late hours of day or of life. Rise and praise Him before the rising sun does, and feed on His word, which consecrates, preserves and leads to True life. It was not Moses who gave you the bread of Heaven, but it was God the Father, and now I solemnly tell you that it is My Father Who gives you the *true* Bread, the new Bread, the eternal Bread which descends from Heaven, the Bread of mercy, the Bread of Life, the Bread that gives Life to the world, the Bread that satisfies every hunger and removes all languor, the Bread that gives eternal Life and eternal joy to those who eat it.»

354.10 [10] «Give us some of that bread, Lord, and we shall not die.»

«You will die as every man dies, but you will rise to eternal Life, if you feed *holily* on that Bread, because those who eat it become incorruptible. With regards to giving it, it will be given to those who ask My Father for it with pure hearts, upright intentions and holy charity. That is why I taught you to say: "Give us our daily Bread". But those who eat it unworthily will become swarms of infernal worms, like the baskets of manna kept contrary to instructions received. And the Bread of health and life will become conviction and death for them. Because the greatest sacrilege will be committed by those who place that Bread on a corrupt foul spiritual table and profane it by mixing it with the sink of their incurable passions. It would have been better if they had never taken it!»

354.11 [11] «But where is that Bread? How can one find it? What is its name?»

«I am the Bread of Life. You will find it in Me. Its name is Jesus. He who comes to Me will never be hungry again, and he who believes in Me will never be thirsty again, because celestial rivers will flow into him quenching all material ardour. I have already told you. And you have known Me by now. And yet you do not believe Me. You cannot believe that everything is in Me. And yet it is so. All the treasures of God are in Me. And everything pertaining to the earth has been given to Me; thus the glorious Heavens and the militant earth are united in Me and even the expiating and expecting mass of those who died in the grace of God are in Me, because all power has been given to Me and is in Me. And I tell you: everything the Father gives Me, will come to Me. And I will not reject those who come to Me, because I descended from Heaven not to do My will, but the will of He Who sent Me.

And this is the will of My Father, of the Father Who sent Me: that I may lose not even one of those He gave Me, but I may raise them from death on the last day. Now the will of the Father Who sent Me is that whoever knows the Son and believes in Him, will have eternal Life and I may raise him on the Last Day, seeing that he is nourished with faith in Me and is signed with My seal.»

[12]People begin to grumble both inside and outside the syna- 354.12
gogue because of Jesus' new hardy words. And the Master, after taking breath, looks with ecstatically shining eyes towards the people who are grumbling more loudly, that is towards the groups in which there are some Judaeans. He resumes speaking.

«Why are you grumbling among yourselves? Yes, I am the Son of Mary of Nazareth, the daughter of Joachim of the house of David, a virgin consecrated in the Temple and then married to Joseph of Jacob, of the house of David. Many of you have known the just parents of Joseph, a royal carpenter, and those of Mary, the virgin heiress of the royal stock. And you thus say: "How can He say that He descended from Heaven?", and you become doubtful.

I remind you of the Prophets who prophesied the Incarnation of the Word. And I remind you that it is a dogma, more for us Israelites than for any other people, that He, Whose name we dare not mention, could not become Flesh according to the laws of mankind, and an impoverished mankind at that. The Most Pure Uncreated One, if He humiliated Himself by becoming Man for the sake of man, could but choose the womb of a Virgin purer than lilies to clothe His Divinity with Flesh. The Bread that descended from Heaven in the days of Moses was placed in the gold
* Ark, which supported the Mercy Seat and was watched over by Cherubim, behind the veils of the Tabernacle. And the Word of God was with the Bread. And it was right that it should be so, because the deepest respect is to be paid to the gifts of God and to the tables of His most holy Word. So what will God have prepared for His own Word and for the true Bread that has come

---

* **the gold Ark**. Origin, description, events and contents of the *ark* of the Covenant are shown in: *Exodus 25:10-22; 26:33-34; 37:1-9; 40:20-21*; *Numbers 10:33-36; 17:25*; *Deuteronomy 10:1-5; 31:25-26*; *Joshua 3-4; 6:1-16*; *1 Samuel 3:3; 4:3-22; 5-6; 7:1-2*; *2 Samuel 6:1-17; 7:2; 11:11*; *1 King 3:15; 6:19-28; 8:1-9*; *2 Maccabees 2:4-5*. That the ark also contained the manna can be found in: *Hebrews 9:4*. In the work by Valtorta the ark represents Holy Mary (starting with 25.9 and ending with 642.8/9 and 649.11) but also Jesus (in 221.9 and 387.8).

from Heaven? A more immaculate and precious Ark than the gold one, to support the precious Mercy Seat of His pure will to immolate Himself, watched over by the cherubim of God, veiled by virginal purity, by perfect humility, sublime charity and all the most holy virtues.

So? Do you not yet understand that My Paternity is in Heaven, and that, consequently, I come from there? Yes, I descended from Heaven to fulfil the decree of My Father, the decree of salvation of men, according to what He promised at the same moment of condemnation and He repeated to Patriarchs and Prophets. And that is faith. And faith is given by God to souls of goodwill. No one, therefore, can come to Me unless My Father leads him to Me, as although He sees that he is in darkness, He knows that he is craving for light. It is written in the Prophets: "They will all be *
taught by God". So, that was decided. *It is God Who instructs them where to go to be taught by God.* Therefore, whoever has heard God speak in the depth of his righteous soul, has learned from the Father to come to Me.»

«And who has ever heard God or seen His Face?» ask many who begin to show signs of irritation and scandal. And they conclude: «You are either raving or You are a day-dreamer.»

«No one has seen God except Him Who came from God: He has seen the Father. And I am He.

354.13 [13] And now listen to the "Creed" of future Life, without which no one can be saved.

I solemnly tell you that he who believes in Me has eternal Life. I solemnly tell you that I am the Bread of eternal Life.

Your fathers ate manna in the desert and they died. Because manna was a holy but temporary food and gave life as was required to reach the Land Promised by God to His people. But the Manna Which I am, will have no limit of time or power. It is not only celestial but divine and produces what is divine: the incorruptibility and immortality of what God created to His image and likeness. It will not last forty days, forty months, forty years, forty centuries. But it will last until the end of Time and will be given to all those who hunger for what is holy and pleasing to the Lord, Who will rejoice at giving Himself incommensurably to

* **written**, as in: *Isaiah 54:13*; *Jeremiah 31:34.*

men, for whom He became incarnate, that they may have the Life which does not die.

I can give Myself, I can transubstantiate for the sake of men, so that the bread may become Flesh and the Flesh may become Bread, for the spiritual hunger of men, who without that Food would die of starvation and spiritual diseases. But if one eats this Bread with justice, one will live forever. The bread that I will give is My Body sacrificed for the Life of the world, it is My Love spread in the houses of God, so that all loving or unhappy souls may come to the Table of the Lord, and may find solace to their need to be united to God and relief to their sorrows.»

[14] «But how can You give us Your flesh to eat? Who do You think 354.14
we are? Blood-thirsty beasts? Savages? Murderers? Blood and crime disgust us.»

«I tell you solemnly that man is very often more cruel than beasts, that sin makes men savages, that pride makes them blood-thirsty murderers and that blood and crime will not disgust all the people present here. And also in future man will be the same because Satan, sensuality and pride make him brutal. Man therefore with greater care must rid himself of the dreadful germs through the infusion of the Holy One. *I tell you solemnly that if you do not eat the Flesh of the Son of man and you do not drink His Blood, you will not have Life in you.* He who eats My Flesh worthily and drinks My Blood has eternal Life and I will raise him up on the Last Day. For My Flesh is real Food and My Blood is real Drink. He who eats My Flesh and drinks My Blood lives in Me, and I live in him. As the living Father sent Me, and I live for the Father, so whoever eats Me will live also for Me and will go where I send him, and will do what I want, and will live austerely, as a man, and as ardently as a Seraph, and will be holy, because in order to be able to feed on My Flesh and My Blood, he will abstain from sin and will live ascending and finish his ascent at the feet of the Eternal Father.»

«He is mad! Who can live like that? In our religion only the priest is to be purified to offer the victim. He wants to make us victims of His madness. His doctrine is too painful and his language too hard! Who can listen to Him and practise what He says?» whisper the people present and many are disciples known as such.

354.15 [15] The crowds disperse making their comments. And when the Master is alone in the synagogue with His most faithful followers the number of disciples has diminished considerably. I cannot count them, but I would say that, more or less, they are about one hundred. So there must have been a remarkable defection also in the group of the old disciples by now at the service of God. Among those left there are the apostles, John the priest and John the scribe, Stephen, Hermas, Timoneus, Ermasteus, Agapo, Joseph, Solomon, Abel of Bethlehem of Galilee, and Abel the leper of Korazim, with his friend Samuel, Elias (the one who did not bury his father to follow Jesus), Philip of Arbela, Aser and Ishmael of Nazareth and some whose names I do not know. They are speaking to one another in low voices commenting on the defection of the others and the words of Jesus, Who with folded arms is leaning against a high lectern.

«Are you scandalised at what I told you? And if I told you that one day you will see the Son of man ascend to Heaven where He was before, and sit beside His Father? What have you understood, assimilated and believed so far? And how have you heard and assimilated? Only through your humanity? *It is the spirit that gives life and is important. The flesh is of no avail. My words are spirit and life, and they are to be heard and understood through the spirit to have life*. But there are many among you whose spirits are dead because they are without faith. Many of you do not really believe. And they are staying with Me in vain. They will not receive Life, but Death. Because they are staying with Me, as I said at the beginning, either out of curiosity, or for human pleasure, or worse still, for more worthless purposes. They have not been led here by My Father, as a reward to their goodwill, but by Satan. Nobody can really come to Me, unless it is granted to him by My Father. You may go, you who find it difficult to remain here, because you are ashamed, from a human point of view, to leave Me but you are more ashamed to stay at the service of One Who seems "mad and hard" to you. Go. It is better for you to be far away, than be here and do harm.»

Many of the disciples withdraw, among them there is John, the scribe Marcus, the possessed Gerasene, who was cured by Jesus and the devils possessing him were sent into pigs. The good disciples consult with one another and run after their faithless companions endeavouring to stop them.

[16] In the synagogue there is only Jesus with the chief of the synagogue and the apostles, 354.16

Jesus turns towards the twelve apostles, who are deeply humiliated and are standing in a corner and says to them: «Do you want to go as well?» He says so without bitterness and without sadness, but very seriously.

Peter replies with sorrowful transport: «Lord, where can we go? To whom? You are our life and our love. You alone have words of eternal Life. We know that You are the Christ, the Son of God. If You wish, send us away. But we will not leave You of our own free will, not even... not even if You should not love us anymore...» and Peter sheds large tears silently...

Andrew, John, Alphaeus' two sons also weep openly, and the others, who are either pale or flushed with emotion, do not weep, but are clearly suffering.

«Why should I send you away? Did I not choose you twelve?...»

Jairus has wisely withdrawn to leave Jesus free to console or reproach His apostles. Jesus, Who has noticed his silent withdrawal, sits down; He is tired, disgusted, grieved and depressed, as if the revelation He is about to make costs Him a greater effort than He can possibly bear, and He says: «And yet, one of you is a demon.»

His words drop slowly, frighteningly, in the synagogue, where only the light of the lamps seems to be cheerful... and no one dare speak. They look at one another with fearful disgust and painful inquisitiveness and each one examines himself with even greater anguish and uncertainty...

No one moves for a while. And Jesus remains alone, on His seat with His hands crossed on His knees and lowered face. He at last looks up and says: «Come. I am not a leper! Or do you think I am?...»

John then rushes forward and throwing his arms round Jesus' neck he says: «I will be with You, then, my only love, in Your leprosy. I will be with You in Your conviction, in Your death, if that is what You think is awaiting You...»; and Peter creeps at His feet, takes them in his hands and laying them on his shoulders he says sobbing: «Press them here, tread on me! But do not make me think that You do not trust Your Simon.»

When the others see that Jesus is caressing the first two, they come forward and kiss Jesus' clothes, His hands and hair... Only the Iscariot dares to kiss Him on His cheek.

Jesus springs to His feet and His movement is so sudden that He seems to be repelling him rudely, and He says: «Let us go home. Tomorrow night we will leave for Hippo by boat.»

355. The New Disciple Nicolaus of Antioch. The Second Announcement of the Passion.

9th December 1945.

355.1 [1] Jesus is all alone on the terrace of the house Thomas of Capernaum. The town is quiet on the Sabbath and its population is already greatly reduced, as the most zealous in practising their religion have already left for Jerusalem, as well as those who go there with their families and have children who cannot march long distances and thus compel adults to make frequent stops and short journeys. One thus misses the bright note of cheerful children, even more so on a rather cloudy day. Jesus is pensive. He is sitting on a low bench in a corner near the parapet, with His back to the staircase almost hidden by the parapet; He is resting one elbow on His knee and reclines His head on His hand with a tired almost painful gesture.

355.2 [2] He is interrupted in His meditation by the arrival of a little boy who wants to say goodbye to Him before leaving for Jerusalem. «Jesus! Jesus!» he calls at each step, as he cannot see Jesus because the low wall conceals Him from the sight of whoever is below. And Jesus is so engrossed in thought that He does not hear the light voice or the step of the child, which is as light as a dove's... so that when the boy arrives on the terrace, He is still in the same painful position. And the little boy is frightened. He stops on the threshold, puts a finger between his lips and thinks... he then makes up his mind and moves slowly forward... he is now almost behind Jesus' back... he bends to see what He is doing... and says: «No, lovely Jesus! Don't weep! Why? Because of those bad ugly men of yesterday? My father was saying to Jairus that they are not worthy of You. But You must not weep. I love You. And my little sister, and James and Toby, and Johanna, and Mary and Micah and all the children in Capernaum, they all love You. Don't weep anymore...» and he clasps Jesus' neck caressing Him and concludes: «Otherwise I will weep, too and I will weep during all the journey...»

«No, David, I am not weeping anymore. You have consoled Me. Are you alone? When are you leaving?»

«After sunset. We are going by boat as far as Tiberias. Come with us. My father loves You; You know?»

«Yes, I know, My dear. But I must go to other children... Thank you for coming to say goodbye to Me. I bless you, little David. Let us kiss each other goodbye and then you will go back to your mother. Does she know that you are here?...»

«No, she doesn't. I ran away because I did not see You with Your disciples and I thought that You might be weeping.»

«I am not weeping anymore, as you can see. Go back to your mother, who perhaps is looking for you and is worried. Goodbye. Watch the donkeys of the caravans. See? They stop everywhere.»

«Are You really not weeping anymore?»

«No. I am no longer grieved. You have comforted Me. Thank you, My child.»

The boy runs down the steps while Jesus watches him. He then shakes His head and goes back to His place in the same sorrowful meditation as before.

[3] Some time goes by. The setting sun appears now and again 355.3
when the cloudy sky clears.

A heavy step is heard coming up the staircase. Jesus looks up. He sees Jairus going towards Him. He greets him. Jairus replies respectfully.

«How come you are here, Jairus?»

«Lord! Perhaps I have done the wrong thing. But as You see the hearts of men You know that there was no ill-will in mine. I did not invite You to speak in the synagogue today. But I suffered for You so much yesterday, and I saw You suffer so much... that I did not dare. I spoke to Your disciples. They said to me: "He wishes to be alone"... But a little while ago Philip, David's father, came to me saying that his son had seen You weep. He said that You thanked him for coming to see You. So I came, too. Master, the people who are still in Capernaum, are about to meet in the synagogue. And my synagogue is Yours, Lord.»

«Thank you, Jairus. Other people will speak there today. I will come as a simple believer...»

«And You would not be obliged to come. The world is Your synagogue. Are You not really coming, Master?»

«No, Jairus. I am staying here with My spirit before the Father Who understands Me and finds no fault in Me.» Jesus' sad eyes shine with tears.

«Neither do I find fault in You... Goodbye, Lord.»

«Goodbye, Jairus.» And Jesus sits down once again, meditating.

355.4 [4]Jairus' daughter, in a white dress, goes upstairs as lightly as a dove. She looks around... She then calls in a low voice: «My Saviour!»

Jesus looks around, sees her, smiles and says: «Come near Me.»

«Yes, my Lord. But I would like to take You to the others. Why is the synagogue to be silent today?»

«There is your father and many others to fill it with words.»

«But they are words... Yours is the Word. Oh! My Lord! Through Your word You gave me back to my mother and father, and I was dead. But look at those who are now going towards the synagogue! Many of them are more dead than I was. Come and give them Life.»

«My dear daughter, you deserved it; they... No word can give life to those who choose death for themselves.»

«Yes, my Lord. But come just the same. There are also some who live more intensely when they hear You... Come. Give me Your hand and let us go. I am the witness of Your power and I am ready to bear witness also before Your enemies, even at the cost of being deprived of this second life, which in any case is no longer mine. You gave it to me, my dear Master, out of pity for a mother and a father. But I...» the girl, a beautiful girl, almost a young woman, with large bright eyes and a pure intelligent face, stops choked by tears, which from her long eyelashes stream down her cheeks.

«Why are you weeping, now?» asks Jesus laying His hand on her hair.

«Because... I was told that You say that You will die...»

«Everybody must die, my girl.»

«But not as You say!... I... oh! now I would not have liked to be brought back to life, in order not to see that, not to be there when... that horrible thing will happen...»

«In that case, you would not have been here either to comfort Me as you are doing now. Do you not know that a word, even one word only, of a pure soul who loves Me, takes all grief away from Me?»

«Does it? Oh! Then You must no longer be grieved because I love you more than I love my father, my mother and my own life!»

«It is so.»

«Then come. Don't be alone. Speak for me, for Jairus, for my mother, for little David, for those who love You. We are many, and we will be more. But do not be alone. It makes You sad» and through motherly instinct, like every honest woman, she ends saying: «No one will hurt You if I am near You. In any case, I will defend You.»

Jesus stands up and pleases her. With His hand in hers, they cross the street and enter the synagogue by a side door.

[5] Jairus, who is reading a roll in a loud voice, stops reading and 355.5
bowing lowly says: «Master, please speak to those whose hearts are righteous. Prepare us for Passover with Your holy word.»

«You are reading the Book of Kings, are you not?»

«Yes, Master. I was endeavouring to make them consider that those who part from the true God become idolaters of golden calves.»

«You are quite right. Does anybody wish to speak?»

The crowd begins to whisper. Some want Jesus to speak, some shout: «We are in a hurry. Let us say the prayers and dismiss the congregation. We are going to Jerusalem in any case and we will hear the rabbis there.» Those who shout thus are the deserters of yesterday who have been held up in Capernaum because of the Sabbath.

Jesus looks at them with deep sadness and says: «You are in a hurry. That is true. God also is in a hurry to judge you. You may go.» Then addressing the people who are reproaching them He says: «Do not rebuke them. Each tree bears its own fruit.»

* «Master! Repeat the gesture of Nehemia! Since You are the High Priest, speak against them!» shouts Jairus indignantly and

* **the gesture**, invoked by Jairus, is the threat made in *Nehemiah 5:13*; but Jesus's reply is an invocation of forgiveness as in *Nehemiah 5:19*.

the apostles, the faithful disciples and the people of Capernaum join in with him.

Jesus stretches out His arms crosswise; He is very pale and His countenance is most sorrowful, although very kind while He cries: «Remember Me, My God! Remember Me propitiously! And remember them propitiously, too! I forgive them!»

355.6 [6]The synagogue is soon empty, only those who are faithful to Jesus have remained... There is a stranger in a corner. A strong man whom no one notices and to whom no one speaks. On the other hand he does not speak to anybody. He stares at Jesus, so much so that the Master turns His eyes towards him and asks Jairus who he is.

«I do not know. He must be a passer-by.»

Jesus asks him: «Who are you?»

«Nicolaus, a proselyte from Antioch. I am going to Jerusalem for Passover.»

«Whom are you looking for?»

«For You, Lord, Jesus of Nazareth. I wish to speak to You.»

«Come, then.» And when he comes near, Jesus goes out with him into the kitchen garden behind the synagogue, to listen to him.

«I spoke in Antioch with a disciple of Yours, whose name is Felix. I have longed to meet You. He told me that you are often in Capernaum and that Your Mother lives in Nazareth. And that You go to Gethsemane or to Bethany. The Eternal Father has granted me to find You in the first place. I was here yesterday... And I was near You this morning, while You were weeping and praying near the fountain... I love You, Lord, because You are holy and meek. I believe in You. Your actions and Your words had already conquered me. But Your mercy of a little while ago, on the culprits, has finally convinced me. Lord, accept me in place of those who leave You! I will come to You with everything I have: my life, my wealth, everything.» He has knelt down while saying the last words.

Jesus gazes at him... then He says: «Come. As from today you belong to the Master. Let us go to your companions.»

They go back into the synagogue where the disciples and apostles are discussing animatedly with Jairus.

«Here is a new disciple. The Father has comforted Me. Love

him as your brother. Let us go and share with him our bread and salt. Then, during the night, you will leave for Jerusalem with him and we will go to Hippo by boat... And do not tell anybody which way I am going so that I shall not be held up.»

[7] In the meantime the Sabbath is over and those who want to 355.7
shun Jesus have gathered on the beach haggling over the price of boats to Tiberias. And they quarrel with Zebedee who does not want to hire out his boat, which is ready near Peter's to depart during the night with Jesus and the Twelve.

«I will go and help him!» says Peter who is annoyed.

To avoid too big a clash, Jesus holds him back saying: «We will all go, not just yourself.»

And they go... And they experience a bitter disappointment seeing the fugitives go away without even a nod, avoiding all contact in order to go away from Jesus... and they also hear some unpleasant epithets and acrid advice to the faithful disciples...

Jesus turns around to go back home after the hostile crowd has left, and He says to the new disciple: «Have you heard them? That is what you are to expect if you come with Me.»

«I know. That is why I am staying. I saw You one glorious day when the crowds cheered You and hailed You "king". I shrugged my shoulders saying: "Another poor day-dreamer! Another plague for Israel!", and I did not follow You because You looked like a king and I forgot all about You. I will now follow You because I see the promised Messiah in Your words and kindness.»

«You are really more just than many others. But once again I warn you. He who hopes that I am an earthly king, should go away. He who feels that he will be ashamed of Me before the world accusing Me, should go away. He who will be scandalised seeing Me treated as an evil-doer, should go away. I am telling you so that you may do so before being compromised in the eyes of the world. Imitate those who are escaping in those boats, if you feel that you cannot share My lot in disgrace, to be able to share it later in glory. Because this is what is about to happen: the Son of man is about to be accused and put into the hands of men, who will kill Him as a criminal and will believe that they defeated Him. But they will have accomplished their crime in vain. Because after three days I will rise from the dead and triumph. Blessed are those who will be able to stay with Me till the end!»

355.8 [8]They have now reached the house and Jesus entrusts the newcomer to the disciples, and goes upstairs where He was before. He goes into the upper room and sits down meditating.

Shortly afterwards the Iscariot goes upstairs with Peter. «Master, Judas has made me ponder on certain matters that I think are right.»

«Tell Me.»

«You have accepted this Nicolaus, a proselyte, whose past is unknown to us. We have already had so much trouble... and we are still experiencing it. And now? What do we know about him? Can we trust him? Judas quite rightly says that he may be a spy sent by our enemies.»

«Of course! A traitor! Why does he not want to tell us where he comes from and who sent him? I have asked him, but he only says: "I am Nicolaus from Antioch, a proselyte". I am very suspicious.»

«I would remind you that he came because he saw that I was betrayed.»

«It may be a lie! It may be treachery!»

«He who sees falsehood and treachery everywhere is a soul capable of such things, because he measures himself on his own model» replies Jesus seriously.

«Lord, You are offending me!» shouts Judas indignantly.

«Leave Me, then, and go with those who abandoned Me.»

Judas goes out slamming the door very rudely.

«But, Lord, Judas is not entirely wrong... In any case, I would not like that man... to mention John. It must be Felix, the man of Endor, who sent him to You...»

«It is certainly so. But John of Endor is a wise man and he resumed his old name. Do not worry, Simon. A man who becomes a disciple because he realizes that My human cause is lost, can but be a righteous spirit. Quite different from him who just went out and who came to Me because he was hoping to become the prince of a powerful king... and he cannot convince himself that I am King only for the spirit...»

«Do You suspect him, Lord?»

«I suspect no one. But I solemnly tell you that the apostle Judas of Simon, an Israelite and Judaean, will never go as far as Nicolaus, a disciple and proselyte.»

«Lord, I would like to ask Nicolaus after... John.»

«No, do not. John has not entrusted him with any task, because he is wise. Do not be the unwise one.»

«No, Lord, I was only asking You...»

«Let us go downstairs and hasten the supper. At the dead of night we will leave... Simon... do you love Me?»

«Oh! Master! What are You asking?»

«Simon, My heart is darker than the lake in a stormy night and as agitated as it...»

«Oh! Master of mine!... What shall I tell You, if I am more sullen and agitated than You are? I can only say: "Here is Your Simon. And if my heart can comfort You, take it". It is the only thing I have, but it is sincere.»

For a moment Jesus rests His head on Peter's wide strong chest and then stands up and goes downstairs with him.

356. Going Towards Gadara. Judas Iscariot's Heretical Theories and John's Loving Faith.

10th December 1945.

[1] Jesus is already beyond the Jordan. And from what I under- 356.1
stand, the town I can see on top of a green hill, is Gadara and it is the first town they reach after landing on the south-east coast of the lake of Galilee. In fact that is where they landed, as they did not disembark at Hippo, where they were preceded by the boats carrying the people hostile to Jesus. I think that they set ashore opposite Tarichea, where the Jordan flows out of the lake.

«You know the shortest road to Gadara, do you not? Do you remember it?» asks Jesus.

«Of course I do! When we are at the hot springs near the river Yarmuk, all we have to do is to follow the road» replies Peter.

«And where will you find the springs?» asks Thomas.

«Oh! Your nose will tell you where they are. They smell a mile away!» exclaims Peter turning up his nose in disgust.

«I did not know that you were troubled with pains...» remarks Judas Iscariot.

«Pains? Me? Never!»

«Hey! If you are so familiar with the hot springs at the Yarmuk, you must have been there.»

«I never needed hot springs to be fit! The poison in my bones always came out with the perspiration of my honest work... in any case, as I worked more than I enjoyed myself, there was always very little poison in me...»

«That one is for me, isn't it? I am guilty of everything...» says Judas angrily.

«Who bit you? You asked me a question and I replied to you, as I would have replied to the Master or to a companion. And I think that none of them, not even Matthew... who was a pleasure-seeking person, would have taken it amiss.»

«Well, I do!»

«I did not know that you are so touchy. But I apologise for the assumed insinuation. For the Master's sake, you know. He is so distressed by strangers that there is no need for us to vex Him further. Instead of running after your own touchiness, look at Him, and you will realize how much He needs peace and love.»

Jesus does not speak. He simply looks at Peter and smiles gratefully.

356.2 [2]Judas does not reply to Peter's fair remark. He is taciturn and irritated. He wants to appear kind, but the anger, bad mood, and disappointment of his heart are clearly revealed by his eyes, voice and countenance, and even by his overbearing gait, as he stamps the ground angrily giving vent to what boils within him.

But he strives to look calm and be kind, he does not succeed, but he tries... He asks Peter: «Well, then, how do you know these places? Perhaps you have been here for your wife?»

«No, we passed here when in the month of Ethanim we came to Hauran with the Master. I took His Mother and the women disciples to Chuza's estate. Coming via Bozrah, we passed by here» replies Peter sincerely and wisely.

«Were you alone?» asks Judas ironically.

«Why? Do you think that I by myself am not as good as several people when it is the case of showing how valient you are, and there is an important task to be done and one does it with all goodwill?»

«Oh! How proud you are! I would have loved to see you!»

«You would have seen a serious man accompanying holy women.»

«But were you *really* alone?» asks Judas with the true attitude of an inquisitor.

«I was with the Lord's brothers.»

«Ah! You are beginning to make admissions!»

«And you are beginning to get on my nerves! Can you tell me what is the matter with you?»

«That's true. It is a shame» says Thomas.

«It's time you stopped it» corroborates James of Zebedee.

«It is not right for you to sneer at Simon» states Bartholomew reproachingly.

«You ought to remember that he is the Head of us all» concludes the Zealot.

Jesus is silent.

«Oh! I am not sneering at anybody, and nothing is the matter with me. I just like to tease him a little...»

«That is not true! You are a liar! You ask sly questions because you want to reach some conclusion. A sly man thinks that everybody is sly. We have no secrets. We were all there, and we all did the same thing: what the Master told us. And there is nothing else. Is that clear?» shouts the other Judas who is really angry.

«Be quiet. You are like quarrelsome women. You are all wrong. And I am ashamed of you» says Jesus severely.

[3] There is total silence while they go towards the town on the 356.3
hill. Thomas breaks the silence exclaiming: «What a dreadful smell!»

«It's the springs. That is the Yarmuk and those buildings are the Roman Thermae. Beyond them there is a beautiful paved road that takes one to Gadara. Romans like to travel in comfort. Gadara is beautiful!» says Peter.

«It is even more beautiful because we will not find certain... beings here, at least not many of them» grumbles Matthew between his teeth.

They cross the bridge over the river in the pungent smell of sulphur water. They pass near the Thermae, among Roman vehicles, and they take a beautiful road, paved with large slabs, which takes to the town on the top of the hill, a beautiful town enclosed by walls.

John approaches the Master and asks: «Is it true that in old days a damned soul was hurled down into the bowels of the earth where those waters are? My mother used to tell us that when we were little children to make us understand that one must not commit sin, otherwise hell opens under the feet of a soul cursed by God and swallows the sinner. And then in memory and as a warning, cracks remain through which smell, heat and water of hell come up. I would be afraid to bathe in there...»

«Afraid of what, boy? It would not infect you. It is easier to be infected by those men who have hell within themselves and exhale the stench and poison of hell. But only those are contaminated who are inclined to become so by themselves.»

«Could I be contaminated?»

«No. Not even if you were among a crowd of demons.»

«Why not? What has he got which is different from everybody else?» asks Judas of Kerioth at once.

«He is pure in *every* way and thus he can see God» replies Jesus and Judas laughs maliciously.

John asks once again: «So those springs are not mouths of hell?»

«No. On the contrary they are good things made by God for His children. Hell is not enclosed in the earth. It is *on* the earth, John, in the hearts of men. And it expands further there.»

356.4 [4] «But does Hell really exist?» asks the Iscariot.

«What are you saying?» ask his companions who are thoroughly scandalised.

«I am asking: does it really exist? I don't believe it does, and I am not the only one.»

«Heathen!» they shout with horror.

«No. Israelite. Many of us in Israel do not believe such nonsense.»

«Well, how can you believe in Paradise?», «And in God's justice?», «Where do you put sinners?», «What about Satan?» many of the apostles object shouting.

«I say what I think. A short while ago I was blamed for being a liar. I am proving that I am sincere, even if what I say scandalises you and makes me hateful in your eyes. In any case I am not the only one in Israel, since Israel has improved in knowledge through contacts with Hellenists and Romans, who are of such opinion. And the Master, the only one whose opinion I respect, cannot reproach me or Israel, as He protects Romans and Greeks and is openly their friend... I base myself on the following philosophical concept. If everything is controlled by God, everything we do depends on His will, and He must reward us all in the same way, because we are only automata moved by Him. We are beings devoid of will. The Master Himself says so: "The Will of the Most High. The Will of the Father". That is the only Will. And it is so infinite that it crushes and destroys the limited will of creatures. Consequently, both the Good and the Evil, which we appear to do, is done by God, Who imposes it on us. Thus He will not punish us for evil deeds and His justice will be administered that way, because our sins are not voluntary but they are imposed by Him Who wants us to commit them, so that both good and evil may be on the earth. He who is bad is the means of expiation for those who are not so bad. And he suffers within himself as he cannot be considered good, and thus expiates his part of sin. Jesus said so. Hell is on the earth and in the hearts of men. I do not perceive Satan. He does not exist. Once I believed he existed. But for some time I have convinced myself that it is a lot of nonsense. And one attains peace through such belief.»

Judas expounds such... theory with so much ostentation that
the others stand breathless with astonishment... [5]Jesus is silent. 356.5
And Judas teases Him: «Am I not right, Master?»

«No.» His «no» is so sharp that it sounds like an explosion.

«And yet I... I do not perceive Satan, neither do I admit free will or Evil. And all the Sadducees are of my opinion as well as many other people in Israel. No, Satan does not exist.»

Jesus looks at him. His glance is so complex that it cannot be analyzed. It is the glance of a Judge, of a Doctor, of a grieved astonished man... There is everything in it...

Judas, who is already launched out, concludes: «Perhaps it is because I am better and more perfect than the others, that I have overcome the terror of men for Satan.»

And Jesus is silent. But Judas teases Him: «Speak! Why am I not terrified?»

Jesus keeps silent.

«Are You not replying, Master? Why? Are You afraid?»

«No. I am Charity. And Charity withholds its opinion until it is compelled to give it... Leave Me and go away» He says at last, because Judas tries to embrace Him, and when He is held by force in the arms of the blasphemer, He whispers to him: «You disgust Me! You do not see or perceive Satan, because he is all one with you. Go away, you demon!»

Judas kisses Him impudently and laughs, as if the Master had praised him secretly. He goes back to the others who are so aghast that they have stopped and he says to them: «See? I know how to open the Master's heart. And I make Him happy by showing Him my confidence and I learn. You, instead!... You never dare speak to Him. Because you are proud. Oh! I will know more about Him than anybody else. And I will be able to speak...»

356.6 [6] They reach the gates of the town. They all go in together, because Jesus has waited for them. But while going through the entrance hall, Jesus commands: «My brothers and Simon, go ahead and gather the people.»

«Why not I, Master? Are You not giving me any more missions to fulfil? Are they no longer necessary now? You gave me two, one after the other, and they lasted for months...»

«And you complained and said that I wanted to keep you away. Are you now complaining because I want to keep you with Me?»

Judas does not know what to reply and is silent. He goes ahead with Thomas, the Zealot, James of Zebedee and Andrew. Jesus stops to let Philip, Bartholomew, Matthew and John pass, as if He wished to be left alone. They do not interfere.

But the loving heart of John, whose eyes have often been shining with tears during the blasphemous dispute of Judas, compels the apostle to turn round shortly afterwards, just in time to see Jesus press His forehead with His hands, with a gesture of sorrow, and bend forward like one in great pain. Jesus does so thinking He was unobserved in the little lonely street, which is also dark owing to the many arches across it. Fair-headed John leaves his companions and goes back to his Master: «What is the matter, my Lord? Are You suffering once again as when we found You at Achzib? Oh! My Lord!»

«It is nothing, John! Help Me with your love. And do not say anything to the others. Pray for Judas.»

«Yes, Master. He is very unhappy, is he not? He is in darkness, and does not know. He thinks that he has attained peace... Is it peace?»

«He is very unhappy» says Jesus dejectedly.

«Don't be so sad, Master. Think of how many sinners have become good, although they were hardened in sin. Judas will do the same. Oh! You will certainly save him! I will spend the night praying for that. I will tell the Father to make me capable only of loving, I do not want anything else. I was hoping to give my life for You or to make Your power shine through my work. Now no longer so. I renounce everything, I choose the most humble and common life and I will ask the Father to give what is mine to Judas... to make him happy... so that he may turn to holiness... Lord... I should tell You something... I think I know why Judas is like that.»

«Come tonight. We will pray together and speak.»

«And will the Father listen to me? Will He accept my sacrifice?»

«The Father will bless you. But you will suffer...»

«Oh! No! It is enough for me to see that You are happy... and that Judas... and that Judas...»

«Yes, John. [7]Look, they are calling us. Let us run.» 356.7

The little street becomes a beautiful one, adorned with porches and fountains. And it is embellished with beautiful squares: each one being more beautiful than the others. It crosses another main street, which is just as beautiful, and at the end of it there is an amphitheatre. Several sick people have already gathered in a corner of the porches waiting for the Saviour.

Peter comes towards Jesus: «They have retained faith in what we told them about You in the month of Ethanim. They came at once.»

«And I will reward their faith at once. Let us go.»

And while the sun is setting and tingeing the marble buildings with red, He goes to heal those who are waiting for Him with faith.

357. The Night at Gadara. The Darkest Side of Judas Iscariot Disclosed. A Sermon on Divorce.

11th December 1945.

[1]The magnificent stars of a clear night in the month of March 357.1

are shining in the eastern sky and they are so large and bright that the vault of heaven seems to have stooped down like a canopy over the terrace of the house that welcomed Jesus. It is a very tall house, situated in one of the highest parts of the town, so that the infinite horizon spreads out before those who look in every direction. And if the earth disappears in the darkness of the night, which is not brightened by moonlight, as the moon is waning, the sky is glittering with countless stars. It is really the victory of the firmament which triumphantly displays its garden beds of stars, its Galatea grasslands, its planetary giants and forests of constellations in opposition to the fleeting vegetation of the earth, which, even when it is age old, is still *one hour* old, as compared with those that *exist* since God made the firmament. And when one is lost looking up there, and one's eyes roam along the wonderful avenues, where the trees are stars, one seems to hear the voices and songs of those splendid forests, of that huge organ of the most sublime cathedral, in which I like to imagine that the winds of racing stars are bellows and registers and the stars launched in their trajectories are voices. And one seems to perceive all that, particularly because the silence of the night, while Gadara is asleep, is total. No fountain whispers, no bird sings. The world is asleep, as well as all creatures. Men, who are less innocent than other creatures, are sleeping more or less peacefully in their dark homes.

357.2 [2] But a tall dark shadow, which is just visible because of the contrast of the white face and hands against its dark garment, comes out of the door of the room that opens onto the lower terrace, there is in fact another higher one on the upper room, and is followed by another lower shadow. They are walking on tiptoe to avoid awaking those who are perhaps sleeping in the room underneath and they climb on tiptoe the outside little staircase, which takes to the top terrace. They then take each other's hand and they go and sit down on the bench that lies against the high parapet surrounding the terrace. The low bench and the high parapet conceal everything from their eyes. Even if it were bright moonlight illuminating the world, they would see nothing. Because the town is completely concealed and also the dark shadows of nearby mountains are hidden in the darkness of the night. Only the sky is displayed to them with its springtime constellations and the magnificent stars of Orion: of Rigil and Betelgeuse, of Aldebaran, of Perseus, Andromeda and Cassiopeia and the Pleiades united like sisters. And Sapphirine Venus covered with diamonds, and Mars of pale ruby, and the topaz of Jupiter are the kings of the starry population and they palpitate as if they wished to greet the Lord, hastening their palpitations of light for the Light of the world.

Jesus raises His head to look at them and rests it against the high wall, and John imitates Him getting lost looking up there where the world can be ignored... Then Jesus says: «And now that this contemplation has cleansed us, let us pray.» He stands up and John does likewise. A long, silent, pressing prayer, said with all their souls, their arms stretched out crosswise, with their faces raised towards the east, where the first pale hint of moonlight appears. And then the «Our Father» said together, slowly, not once but three times, with increasing insistence in asking, as is clearly expressed by their voices. And their entreaty is so ardent that it separates their souls from their bodies, launching them along the ways of the Infinite.

Then there is silence. They sit down where they were before, while the moon whitens the sleeping earth more and more.

[3] Jesus lays His arm on John's shoulder and draws him towards 357.3
Himself saying: «So tell Me what you feel you must tell Me. What has My John seen, with the assistance of spiritual light, in the gloomy soul of his companion?»

«Master... I regret having said that to You. I will commit two sins...»

«Why?»

«Because I will grieve You by revealing what You do not know, and... because... Master, is it a sin to speak of the evil we see in other people? It is, isn't it? So, how can I speak about it, offending against charity!...» John is depressed.

Jesus enlightens his soul: «Listen, John. According to you, who is worth more, the Master or a fellow-disciple?»

«The Master, Lord. You are worth the most.»

«And what am I according to you?»

«The Beginning and the End. You are Everything.»

«Since I am Everything, do you think that I know everything?»

«Yes, my Lord. That is why there is a great contrast in me. Because I think that You know and suffer. And because I remember that one day You told me that at times You are the Man, only the Man, and thus the Father lets You know what it is to be a man, who must behave according to reason. And I also think that God, out of pity for You, may conceal this unpleasant truth from You...»

«Stick to that idea, John, and speak confidently. It is not a sin to confide what you know to Him Who is "Everything" for you. Because He Who is "Everything" will not be scandalised, will not grumble or lack charity, not even by thought, towards the unhappy fellow. It would be a sin if you said what you know to anyone who is not capable of being full of love, to your companions for instance, who would backbite and assail the culprit mercilessly, injuring him and themselves. It is therefore necessary to be merciful, the more merciful, the poorer the soul is in front of us, affected by many diseases. A doctor, a compassionate nurse, a mother are not much upset if a person is not seriously ill and they do not fight hard to cure him. But if a son, or a man, is seriously ill and his life is in danger, either because of intervening gangrene or paralysis, how they strive to cure him overcoming repugnance and fatigue. Is it not so?»

«Yes, it is, Master» replies John who has taken his usual position with his arm around the Master's neck and his head reclined on His shoulder.

«Well, not everybody knows how to be merciful to diseased souls. Consequently one must be careful in revealing their trouble so that the world may not shun them and hurt them through contempt. A sick man who realizes that he is being derided, becomes gloomy and gets worse. If instead he is nursed with cheerful hope, he may recover because the hopeful good humour of those nursing him inspirits him and stimulates the effect of medicines. But you know that I am Mercy and I will not humiliate Judas. So you may speak without scruple. You are not a spy. You are a son who with loving anxiety confides to his father the evil discovered in a brother so that the father may cure him. Come on...»

357.4 [4] John heaves a long sigh, then lowers his head further, letting it slide on to Jesus' chest, and says: «How grievous it is to speak of putrid things!... Lord... Judas is lewd... and tempts me to commit obscene things. I do not mind if he derides me. But it grieves me that he should come to You, filthy with his love affairs. Since he came, he has tempted me several times. When we happen to be alone — and he takes advantage of every opportunity — he does nothing but speak of women... and I am as disgusted with it as if I were immersed in some fetid matter that threatened to enter my mouth...»

«Are you deeply upset by that?»

«What? Upset? My soul shudders. Reason cries against such temptations... I do not want to be corrupted...»

«How does your body react?»

«It shrivels with disgust.»

«Nothing else?»

«No, Master, and I weep because I think that Judas could not cause a more serious offence to a man who has consecrated his life to God. Tell me: will that be detrimental to my offering?»

«No. Not more than a handful of mud thrown against a diamond plaque. It will not affect or penetrate the plaque. A cup of clean water poured over it is enough to clean it. And it becomes more beautiful than before.»

«Cleanse me, then.»

«Your charity and your angel cleanse you. There is nothing
left on you. You are a clean altar on which God descends. [5]What 357.5
else does Judas do?»

«Lord, he... Oh! Lord!» John's head slides lower.

«What?»

«He... It is not true that the money he gives You for the poor belongs to him. It is the money of the poor that he steals, to be praised for being generous, which is not true. He was wild because when You came back from mount Tabor, You took all the money away from him. And he said to me: "There are spies among us". I replied: "Spies of what? Have you stolen, perhaps?". "No" he replied to me, "but I am far-sighted and I have two purses. Someone told the Master and He ordered me to hand everything over, and He was so authoritative that I was compelled to do so". But it is not true, Lord, that he does so because he is provident. He does that to have money for himself. I could bear witness to that and I am almost certain that I would be telling the truth.»

«Almost certain! That uncertainty is indeed a slight fault. You cannot accuse him of being a thief, if you are not absolutely certain. The actions of men at times appear to be faulty, whereas they are good.»

«That is true, Master. I will not accuse him anymore, not even in my own mind. But it is true that he has two purses, and that the one he says belongs to him and he gives to You, is instead Yours and he does so to be praised. I would not do that, because I feel that it is not right.»

357.6 «You are right. [6]What else have you to tell Me?»

John raises his frightened face, opens his mouth to speak, then closes it and falls on his knees hiding his face in the tunic of Jesus, Who lays a hand on his head.

«So, speak up! You may have misjudged things. I will help you to consider them properly. You must also tell Me what you think of the probable causes of Judas' sinning.»

«Lord, Judas feels that he does not have the strength he would like to have to work miracles... You are aware that it has always been his ambition... Do You remember Endor? Instead... he is the one who works fewer miracles. Since he came back, he has not been able to do anything... and during the night he moans in his dreams, as if they were nightmares and... Master!»

«Come on. Tell Me everything.»

«And he curses... and practises witchcraft. This is not a lie and there is no doubt about it. I saw him myself. He chooses me as his companion, because I sleep soundly. Or rather, because I used to sleep soundly. Now, I must admit it, I watch him and my sleep is not so sound, because I hear him as soon as he moves... Perhaps I did the wrong thing. But I pretended to be asleep to see what he was doing. And twice I have heard and seen him do horrible things. I am not an expert in sorcery, but that is what it is.»

«Does he do that by himself?»

«Sometimes he does, sometimes he does not. I followed him at Tiberias. He went into a house. I inquired later who lives there. It is a man who practises sorcery with other people. And when Judas came out, almost at daybreak, I gathered from the words they spoke that they are familiar with one another and they are many... and not all strangers. He asks the demon to give him the power that You do not give him. That is why I renounce my part so that the Father may give it to him and he may sin no more.»

«You ought to give him your soul. But neither the Father nor I would allow that...»

[7] There is a long silence. Then Jesus says with a tired voice: 357.7
«Let us go, John. Let us go downstairs. We will rest until dawn.»

«You look more depressed than before, Lord! I should not have told You!»

«No. I already knew. But you have taken a load off your chest... and that is what matters.»

«Lord, must I avoid him?»

«No. Do not be afraid. Satan can do no harm to people like John. He terrorises them, but he cannot take away the grace that God continuously grants them. Let us go. I will speak in the morning and then we will go to Pella. We must make haste, because the river is already swollen with the thawing snow and the rain of the past days. It will soon be in spate, particularly because a haloed moon forebodes heavy rain...»

They go downstairs and disappear in the room underneath the terrace.

[8] It is morning. A morning in the month of March, when the sky 357.8
clears and becomes overcast alternately. But clouds overwhelm clearings, trying to take possession of the sky. The breaths of warm air make the air heavy with a veil of dust that is probably blown from the tableland.

«If the wind does not change, there is going to be rain» states Peter coming out of the house with the others.

Jesus comes out last; He says goodbye to the women of the house, while the landlord joins Him. They go towards a square.

After a few steps, they are stopped by a Roman non-commissioned officer who is with other soldiers. «Are You Jesus of Nazareth?»

«Yes, I am.»

«What are You doing?»

«I am going to speak to the crowds.»

«Where?»

«In the square.»

«A seditious speech?»

«No. Precepts of virtue.»

«Be careful! Don't tell lies! Rome has had enough of false gods.»

«If you come, too, you will see that I am not telling lies.»

The man who gave Jesus hospitality feels that he must put in a word: «Since when is a rabbi asked so many questions?»

«He has been denounced as an agitator.»

«Agitator? Him? You are making a blunder, Marius Severus. He is the meekest man on the earth. I can assure you.»

The officer shrugs his shoulders and replies: «So much the better for Him. But that is the denunciation that the centurion received. He may go. He has been warned.» And he turns around and goes away with his subordinates.

«Who has done that? I don't understand!» many of the people present say.

Jesus replies: «Never mind. It does not matter. Let us go while there are many people in the square. Later we shall go away from here, too.»

357.9 [9] The square looks like a business place. It is not a market, but not much different from a market, because there are warehouses around it, with all kinds of goods stored in them. And they are crowded with people. So there are many people also in the square and as some of them point out Jesus, a crowd soon gathers around the «Nazarene». In the crowd there are all kinds of people and of every country. Some are there out of veneration, some out of curiosity.

Jesus makes a gesture that He is about to speak.

«Let us listen to Him!» says a Roman coming out of a warehouse.

«Shall we not be listening to a lamentation?» replies his companion.

«Don't you believe that, Constant. He is not so boring as our usual orators.»

«Peace to those listening to Me! It is written in Ezra, in Ezra's prayer: "What shall we say now, my God, after what happened? *
Because, if we have deserted Your commandments, which You ordained through Your servants..."»

«Stop, You who are speaking. We will give You the subject» shout a handful of Pharisees who elbow their way through the crowd. The armed escort appears almost immediately and stops

* **prayer**, in: *Ezra 9:6-15*. The section indicated begins in verse 10.

at the nearest corner. The Pharisees are now before Jesus. «Are You the Galilean? Are You Jesus of Nazareth?»

«I am!»

«Praised be the Lord that we have found You!» Their ugly faces are so rancorous that they do not show much joy for the meeting...

The oldest one speaks: «We have been following You for several days, but You had always left when we arrived.»

«Why are you following Me?»

«Because You are the Master and we want to be instructed by You with regards to a dark passage of the Law.»

«There are no dark passages in the Law of God.»

«Not in the Law. But, eh! Eh!... "superimpositions", as You say, eh! eh!, have been made to the Law and have caused obscurity.»

«A dim light, at the most. And it is enough to turn one's mind to God to dispel it.»

«Not everybody can do that. We, for instance, are left in the dim light. You are the Rabbi, eh! eh! So help us.»

[10] «What is it that you want to know?» 357.10

«We want to know whether it is lawful for a man to repudiate his wife for any reason whatsoever. It is something that happens frequently and every time it causes a stir wherever it happens. People apply to us to know whether it is lawful. And we reply according to each case.»

«And you approve what happened in ninety per cent of the cases. And the remaining ten per cent, which you do not approve, concerns the poor or your enemies.»

«How do You know?»

«Because that is what happens in all human things. And I would add a third group of people: those who would be more entitled to it, if divorce were lawful: that is, *real* pitiful cases, such as incurable leprosy, life imprisonment, or unmentionable diseases...»

«So, according to You, it is never lawful.»

«Neither according to Me, nor according to the Most High, or anyone with a righteous soul. Have you not read, that the Creator, at the beginning of times, created man and woman? And He created them male and female; and it was not necessary for Him to do so, because He could have created a different way of procreation for the king of Creation, whom He made in His image and likeness, and it would have been a good way, even if it differed from every other natural way. And He said: "For this reason man will leave his father and mother and will join himself to his wife and they will become one body". So God joined them in one unity. Thus they are no longer "two", but "one" body only. So, what God united, because He saw that "it is a good thing", man must not divide, because if that should happen, it would no longer be a good thing.»

357.11 11 «Why then did Moses say: "If a man has taken a wife, but she does not find favour with him through something disgraceful, he will give her a writ of dismissal and send her away from his house"?»

«He said so because of the hardness of your hearts, to avoid, by means of his order, too serious disorders. That is why he allowed you to repudiate your wives. But it was not so from the beginning. Because a woman is worth more than an animal, which according to the caprice of its master or the free circumstances of nature, copulates with this or that male, a soulless body that copulates for procreation. Your wives have souls, as you do, and it is not fair that you should tread on them pitilessly. If in her condemnation it is said: "You will be subject to the power of your husband and he will lord it over you", that must take place according to justice and not with arrogance offending against the rights of a free soul worthy of respect. By repudiating your wives, which is not lawful, you give offence to the soul of your companion, to the twin body which joined yours, to the whole woman, whom you married, demanding honesty in her, whilst you, O perjurers, are dishonest, disabled, at times corrupt, when you go to her, and you continue to be so, taking every opportunity to strike her and give a wider scope to your unappeasable lust. Prostitutors of your wives! On no account can you separate from the woman who is joined to you according to the Law and Blessing. Only in the case that grace touches you, and you understand that woman is not a possession but a soul, and has therefore equal rights as yours to be recognised as part of man and not an object for his pleasure, and only in the case that your heart is so hard as not to be able to raise her to the dignity of wife, after enjoying her as a prostitute, only to remove the scandal of two who live together without the blessing of God on their union, you may send her away. Because in that case yours is not union but fornication often not honoured by the birth of children, because they are suppressed against nature or sent away as a disgrace. In no other case. Because if you have illegitimate children from your concubine, it is your duty to put an end to the scandal by marrying her, if you are free. I am not taking into consideration the case of adultery consumed to the detriment of an unaware wife. In that case the stones of lapidation and the fire of Sheol are holy. But for him who sends away his legitimate wife because he is satiated with her, to take another one, there is but one sentence: he is an adulterer. And also he who takes the repudiated woman is an adulterer, because if man has arrogated to himself the right to separate what God has joined, *the matrimonial union continues in the eyes of God, and cursed is the man who takes a second wife without being a widower.* And cursed is he who, after repudiating his wife and abandoning her to the dangers of life, which compel her to get married again to have her daily bread, takes her back when she becomes a widow of her second husband. Because, although she is a widow, she was an adulteress through your fault, and you would double her adultery. Have you understood, Pharisees, who are tempting Me?»

They go away thoroughly humiliated, without replying.

[12] «He is a severe man. If He were in Rome He would see that the 357.12
filth there is even more fetid» says a Roman.

Also some of the Gadara people grumble: «It is difficult to be men, if one must be so chaste!...»

And some say in louder voices: «If that is the situation of a man with respect to his wife, it is better not to get married.»

And the apostles also make the same remarks while they resume going towards the country, after leaving those of Gadara. Judas says so scornfully. James of Zebedee speaks with respect and consideration, and Jesus replies to both of them: «Not everybody understands that properly. Some in fact prefer to remain single in order to be free to indulge their vices. Some to avoid the possibility of sin, not being good husbands. But only few are granted to understand the beauty of being free from sensuality and also from the honest desire of woman. And they are the holiest, the freest, the most angelical on the earth. I am referring to those who become eunuchs for the Kingdom of God. Some men are born such. Some are made such. The former are monstrosities to be pitied, the latter are abuses to be repressed. But there is a third category: the voluntary eunuchs, who without any violence against themselves, and thus with double merit, comply with God's request and live like angels, so that the forlorn altar of the earth may still have flowers and incense for the Lord. They deny their inferior part satisfaction, so that their superior part may grow greater and bloom in Heaven in the flower-beds closest to the throne of the King. And I solemnly tell you that they are not mutilated, on the contrary they are gifted with what most men lack. Thus they are not the object of foolish sneering words, but of great veneration. Let those understand that who should understand it, and respect it, if they can.»

Those who are married among the apostles whisper to one another.

«What is the matter with you?» asks Jesus.

«And what about us? We were not aware of that, and we got married. But we would like to be as You say...» says Bartholomew on behalf of everybody.

«You are not forbidden to do so as from now onwards. Live continently, considering your companion as a sister and you will have great merit in the eyes of God. But quicken your steps, so that we may be at Pella before it begins to rain.» *

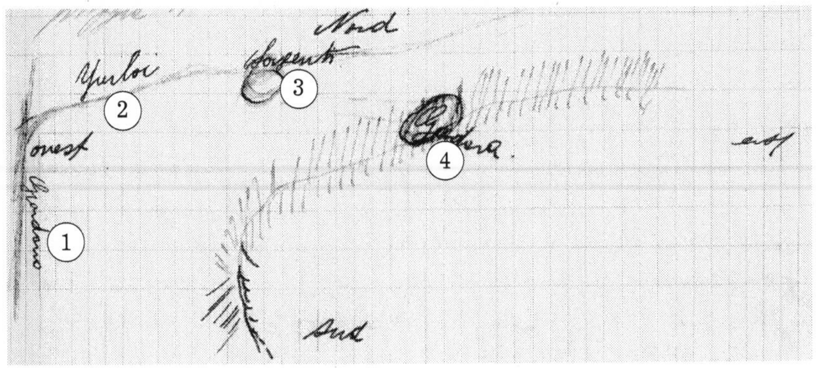

* **rain**: The drawing by M.V. shows: 1. the *Jordan*, running vertically; 2. the *Yarmuc*, along which course there are 3. the sulphurous water *springs*; 4. *Gadara*, on the top of a chain of hills. The four cardinal points are indicated as well.

358. At Pella. The Blind Youth Jaia.
The Anguish of the Mother of Mark of Josiah.

12th December 1945.

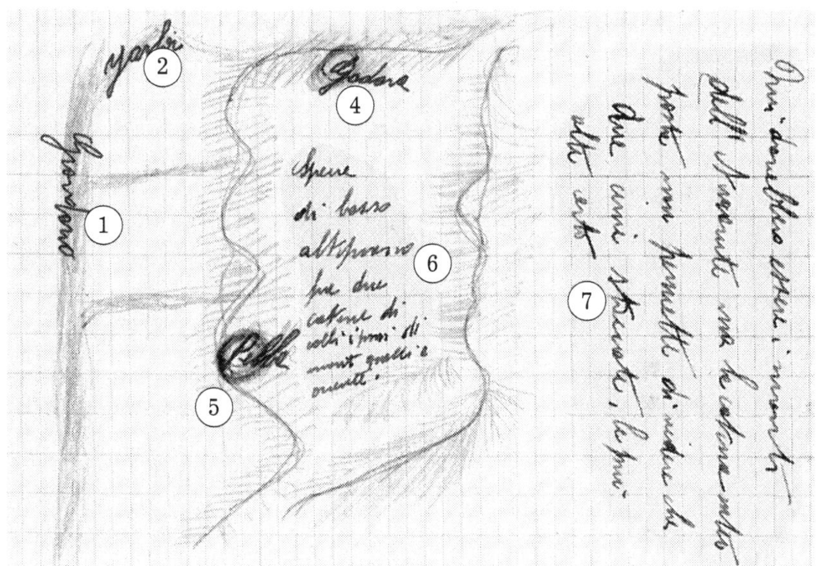

[1]The road which goes from Gadara to Pella runs through a fertile area between two rows of hills, one higher than the other. 358.1
They look like two huge steps of a staircase for fabulous giants, to climb from the Jordan valley up to the Hauran mountains. Where the road runs closer to the western mountain terrace, the view extends not only as far as the mountains on the other bank, which I think are those of southern Galilee and certainly those of Samaria, but it also reaches the beautiful green vegetation that forms a double hedge along both sides of the blue river. Where, instead, the road is closer to the eastern chain, then one loses sight of the Jordan valley, but the green mountain tops of the Samaria and Galilean chains can still be seen standing out against the grey sky. On a sunny day it would be a beautiful view

---

In the following drawing, which heads the next chapter, the same area is depicted. Two more nameless tributaries of the Jordan are marked, then: 5. *Pella*; 6. a note relative to the area at the centre saying: *"A kind of a low tableau limited by two chains of hills, more mountainous are those to the eats"*; 7. Another vertical note says: *"Here, the Auranite, mountains should be but the interposed chain only allows me to see two detached peaks, the highest certainly"*.

with charming bright hues. But today the sky is already overcast with low clouds, driven by sirocco, which is becoming stronger and stronger and blows fresh masses of clouds onto those already existing, lowering the sky with so much grey ruffled wadding, and thus the view loses its bright green shades, which look toned down as if they were seen through mist.

A village is reached now and again and left behind without anything remarkable happening. The Master is received and followed with indifference. Only beggars show interest in the group of Galilean pilgrims and ask for alms. And there are the usual blind people whose eyes in most cases have been destroyed by trachoma, or the almost blind people, who walk with lowered heads, as they cannot bear light, along the walls, all alone or in the company of a woman or a boy. In a village, where the road to Pella crosses the Bozrah-Gerasa road to the lake of Tiberias, there is a crowd of blind people who assail the caravans with their moaning, which resembles the whining of dogs and is interrupted now and again by howling. They are standing against the walls of the first houses, listening, in a group of misery, filth and rags, nibbling bread-crusts and olives, or dozing, while flies feed at will on their ulcerated eye-lids; but at the first noise of hooves or shuffling of feet they all stand up and move like a ragged chorus of an ancient tragedy, uttering the same words and making the same gestures to the new-comers. When a coin or a crust of bread is thrown to them, the blind or half blind people grope in the dust and filth for the offering.

358.2 [2] Jesus watches them and says to Simon Zealot and Philip: «Take some money and bread to them. Judas has the money, John the bread.»

The two go away promptly to do what they were told and they stop to speak, while Jesus comes forward slowly, as He is delayed by a line of donkeys, which bar the road.

The beggars are amazed at the greetings and kindness with which they are spoken to and assisted by the new-comers and they asks: «Who are you, who are so kind to us?»

«The disciples of Jesus of Nazareth, the Rabbi of Israel. He, Who loves the poor and the unhappy because He is the Saviour, and He passes by announcing the Gospel and working miracles.»

«This is the miracle» says one whose eyelids are dreadfully

ravaged. And he strikes his clean piece of bread, like an animal that understands and appreciates only material things.

A woman, who is passing by holding copper pitchers and has heard him, says: «Be quiet, you dirty sluggard.» She then addresses the disciples saying: «He is not from our village. He is quarrelsome and violent to his fellow-men. He should be driven away because he robs the poor of the village. But we are afraid he may take vengeance upon us», then in a very low voice, which can hardly be heard, she whispers: «They say that he is a robber and for years he has been robbing and killing, and he came down from the mountains of Caracamoab and Sela, which is now called Petra by the rulers, those who make roads in the deserts. They say that he is a deserter from the army of that Roman who came... to make Rome known... Helius, I think, and another name... If you give him a drink, he will tell you... Now he is blind and he happened to come here... Is that the Saviour?» she asks, pointing at Jesus, Who has gone straight on.

«Yes, He is. Do you want to speak to Him?»

«Oh! no!» says the woman with indifference.

The two apostles say goodbye to her and they set out to join
the Master. [3]But a riot breaks out among the blind people while 358.3
a child is heard weeping. Several people turn around and the woman seen previously, who is now standing at the door of her house, says: «It must be that cruel man taking the money from the weaker ones. He always does that.»

Jesus also turns around to look...

In fact a boy, or rather a youth, comes out of the group bleeding and weeping and he complains: «He took everything from me! And my mother has no more bread!»

Some pity him, some laugh at him...

«Who is he?» Jesus asks the woman.

«A youth from Pella. He is poor and comes here begging. They are all blind in the family, as they have infected one another. The father died and the mother stays at home. The youth asks passers-by and peasants for alms.»

The young fellow comes forward with his little stick, wiping his tears and the blood streaming down his forehead with the edge of his worn out mantle.

The woman calls him: «Stop, Jaia. I will wash your forehead

and give you some bread!»

«I had money and bread for several days! I have nothing now! Mother is waiting for me to have something to eat...» complains the unhappy youth while wiping his forehead with the water of the woman.

358.4 [4]Jesus moves forward and says: «I will give you what I have. Do not weep.»

«But, Lord! Why? How will we pay for our lodgings? What shall we do?» asks Judas anxiously.

«We will praise the Lord for keeping us healthy. It is a great grace.»

The youth says: «Oh! It is indeed. If I could see! I would work for my mother.»

«Would you like to be cured?»

«Yes, I would.»

«Why do you not go to a doctor?»

«None of them has ever cured us. We have been told that there is One in Galilee, Who is not a doctor, but can cure. But how can one go to Him?»

«Go to Jerusalem. To Gethsemane. It is an olive grove on the side of the mount of Olives near the road to Bethany. Ask for Mark and Jonah. Everyone in the district of Ophel will tell you. You can join a caravan. There are so many going by. Ask Jonah where Jesus of Nazareth is...»

«That's it! That is the name! Will He cure me?»

«He will, if you have faith.»

«I have faith. Where are You going, Who are so good?»

«To Jerusalem, for Passover.»

«Oh! Take me with You. I will not cause You any trouble. I will sleep in the open air and a piece of bread will be quite enough for me! Let us go to Pella... You are going there, are You not? And we will tell my mother, and then we will go... Oh! If I could see! Be good, Lord!...» And the youth kneels down searching for Jesus' feet to kiss them.

«Come. I will take you to the light.»

«May You be blessed!»

358.5 [5]They resume walking and Jesus' tapering fingers hold the youth by the arm to guide him with dispatch. And the youth asks: «Who are You? A disciple of the Saviour?»

«No.»

«But do You know Him, at least?»

«Yes, I do.»

«And do You think that He will cure me?»

«I do.»

«But... will He want money? I have none. Doctors ask for so much! We have gone to ruin to be cured...»

«Jesus of Nazareth wants but faith and love.»

«He is very good, then. But You are good, too» says the youth and to take the hand leading him and caress it, he feels the sleeve of the tunic. «What a fine garment You have! You are a gentleman! Are You not ashamed of me, as I am in rags?»

«I am ashamed only of sins, which disgrace man.»

«My fault is that at times I complain of my situation and I want warm clothes, bread, and above all sight.»

Jesus caresses him: «Those are not disgracing faults. But try to avoid even those imperfections and you will be holy.»

«If I get cured, I will no longer have them... Or... I do not get cured, and You will know, and will You prepare me for my destiny, and teach me to become holy like Job?»

«You will be cured. But afterwards, above all afterwards, you must always be happy with your condition even if it is not one of the most pleasant ones.»

They arrive at Pella. The kitchen gardens, which are always met outside towns, show the fertility of the soil through their luxuriant vegetation. Some women working in the fields or busy with their laundry greet Jaia and say to him: «You are back early today. Had you a good day?» Or: «Have you found a protector, poor son?» An elderly woman shouts from the far end of her kitchen garden: «Jaia! If you are hungry there is a plate of soup for you. Or for your mother. Are you going home? Take it.»

«I am going to tell my mother that I am going with this kind gentleman to Jerusalem to be cured. He knows Jesus of Nazareth and will take me there.»

[6] The road, near the gate of Pella, is crowded with people. There 358.6
are some merchants and also some pilgrims.

A fine looking woman travelling on a donkey's back, in the company of a maidservant and a servant, turns around on hearing Jesus being mentioned, then draws rein, stops the donkey, dismounts and goes towards Jesus. «Do You know Jesus of Nazareth? Are You going to Him? I am going too... To have a son cured. I would like to speak to the Master because...» she bursts into tears under her thick veil.

«What is the matter with your son? Where is he?»

«He is from Gerasa. But now he is going towards Judaea. He wanders about like one possessed... Oh! What have I said!»

«Is he possessed?»

«Lord, he was and he was cured. Now... he is worse than before because... Oh! I can only tell Jesus of Nazareth!»

«James, take the boy between you and Simon and go on with the others. Wait for Me on the other side of the gate. Woman, you can send your servants on. We will be able to speak to each other, just the two of us.»

The woman says: «But You are not the Nazarene! To Him only I will speak. Because He only can understand and have mercy.»

They are now alone. The others have all gone ahead on their own. Jesus waits until the road is clear and then says: «You may speak. I am Jesus of Nazareth.»

The woman utters a deep groan and is about to fall on her knees.

«No. People must not know for the time being. Let us go. There is a house that is open over there. We will ask them to let us rest and we will be able to speak. Come.»

Along a lane between two kitchen gardens they go to a house of common people where children are romping on the threshing floor.

«Peace be with you. Will you allow Me to let this woman rest here for a few minutes? I must speak to her. We have come from far away to speak to each other and God has made us meet before the appointed place.»

«Come in. A guest is a blessing. We will give you milk and bread and some water for your tired feet» says an old woman.

«It is not necessary. All we need is a quiet place where we can talk.»

«Come» and she takes them to a terrace decked with a vine blossoming with emerald-green leaves.

358.7 [7] They are left alone. «Speak, woman. I have already said that God made us meet before the end of our journey, for your relief.»

«There is no more relief for me! I had a son. He became possessed. He behaved like a wild beast among sepulchres. Nothing stopped him. Nothing cured him. He saw You. He adored You with the demon's lips and You cured him. He wanted to come with You. But You thought of his mother and you sent him to me, to restore my life and mind, which the grief of a possessed son made vacillate. And You sent him also to preach You, since he wanted to love You. Oh!... to be a mother once again... and of a holy son! Of a servant of Yours! But tell me! When You sent him back to me, did You know that he was... that he would become a demon again? Because he is a demon who has left You after receiving so much good, after knowing You, after being chosen for Heaven... Tell me! Did You know? But I am raving! I am speaking but I have not told You why he is a demon... For some time he has become like a madman again, oh! only a few days! but much more grievous to me than the long years when he was possessed... And then I thought I could never be more grieved than then... He came... he destroyed the faith that Gerasa had for You through Your merit and his, and he spoke infamously of You. And he is preceding You towards the ford of Jericho, doing harm to You!»

The woman who has never removed the veil behind which she is sobbing desolately, throws herself at Jesus' feet imploring: «Go away! go away! Don't let them insult You! I came away in full agreement with my sick husband, praying God that I would find You. He heard my prayer! Oh! May He be blessed for that! I do not want You, the Saviour, to be ill-treated because of my son. I will not allow that! Oh! why did I bring him into the world? He betrayed You, Lord! He misreports Your words. The demon has taken him once again. And... oh! Most High and Holy Lord! Have mercy on a mother! And he will be damned. My son! Previously it was not his fault if he was possessed by demons. It was a misfortune, which befell him. But now that You had cured him, now that he had known God and had been taught by You! Now he wanted to be a demon and no power will free him again! Oh!» The woman is lying on the ground, a heap of clothes and flesh shaken by sobs. And she moans: «Tell me, tell me, what must I do for You, for my son? To make amends! To save him! No. To make amends! You can see that my grief is atonement. But to save him! I cannot save the disowner of God. He is damned... And what is that to me, an Israelite? It's torture.»

358.8 [8] Jesus bends. He lays a hand on her shoulder. «Stand up, calm down! You are dear to Me. Listen, poor mother.»

«Are You not cursing me because I gave birth to him?!»

«Oh! no! You are not responsible for his error, and for your own relief you must know that you can bring about his salvation. The ruin of sons can be repaired by mothers. And that is what you will do. Your grief, since it is sincere, is not sterile, it is prolific. The soul you love will be saved through your suffering. You are expiating for him, and with such righteous intention that you are the indulgence of your son. He will go back to God. Do not weep.»

«But when? When?»

«When your tears will dissolve in My Blood.»

«Your Blood? So it is true what he says? That You will be killed because You deserve death?... Horrible blasphemy!»

«The first part is really true. I shall be killed to make you worthy of Life. I am the Saviour, woman. And salvation is granted through word, through mercy and through holocaust. That is what is required for your son and that is what I will give. But... help Me. Give Me your grief. Go with My blessing. Keep it in your heart, so that you may be merciful and patient with your son, and remind him thus, that *Another One* was merciful to him. Go, go in peace.»

«But You must not speak at Pella. Don't speak in Perea. He has set them against You. And he is not alone. But I see and speak only of him...»

«I will speak by means of a deed. And it will suffice to demolish the work of the others. Go home in peace.»

«Lord, now that You have absolved me for giving birth to him, look at my face, that You may know what the face of a mother is like when her heart is torn to pieces» and she uncovers her face saying: «Here is the face of the mother of Mark of Josiah, the denier of the Messiah and the torturer of his mother» and then she lowers the thick veil over her face disfigured by weeping and moans: «No other mother in Israel will be as deep in grief as I am!»

358.9 [9] They leave the hospitable house and take to the road again. They enter Pella and the woman joins her servants and Jesus His disiples. But the woman follows Him, as if she were fascinated, while Jesus follows the youth who is going towards his hovel situated in a basement of a building leaning against the side of the mountain, which is typical of this town built on mountain-terraces, so that the ground on the western side is the first floor of the eastern side, but in actual fact, it is ground even there, because one can reach it from the overhanging road, which is on the same level as the top floor. I do not know whether I have made myself understood.

The boy shouts in a loud voice: «Mother! Mother!»

A blind woman, who is still young and moves about freely and easily, as she is familiar with the surroundings, comes out of the dark miserable cave. «Are you already back, my son? Have the alms been so bountiful as to allow you to come back while the sun is still high?»

«Mother, I found one who knows Jesus of Nazareth, and who says he will take me to Him to be cured. He is very kind. Will you let me go, mother?»

«Of course, Jaia! Even if I have to remain alone, you may go, and may you be blessed and look at the Saviour also on my behalf!» The consent and the faith of the woman are total.

Jesus smiles. He says: «Woman, do you not doubt Me or the Saviour?»

«No I don't. If You know Him and are His friend, You must be good, too. And with regards to Him!... Go, son. Don't wait a moment. Give me a kiss and go with God.»

They kiss each other, groping...

Jesus leaves a loaf of bread and some coins on the coarse table. «Goodbye, woman. You can buy food for yourself with what I left here. Peace be with you.»

10 They come out. The group resumes walking while the first 358.10
drops of rain fall.

«Are we not stopping? It is raining...» say the apostles.

«We will stop at Jabesh-Gilead. Walk on now.»

They pull their mantles over their heads and Jesus covers the head of the boy with His own. The mother of Mark of Josiah follows Him with her servants, on her little donkey. She seems to be unable to part from Him.

They leave Pella. They advance into the green country, Which looks sad in the rainy day.

After about a kilometre Jesus stops. He takes the head of the blind boy in His hands and kisses his blind eyes saying: «And now go back. Go and tell your mother that the Lord rewards those who have faith and tell the people in Pella that I am the Lord.» He lets the boy go and moves away quickly.

But within less than three minutes the boy shouts: «But I can see! Oh! Don't run away! You are Jesus! Let me see You as the first thing!» and he falls on his knees on the wet road.

The Gerasene woman and her servants on one side, the apostles on the other run to see the miracle.

Jesus also comes back, slowly, smiling. He bends to caress the boy. «Go, go to your mother and believe in Me... always.»

«Yes, my Lord... But nothing for my mother?! Is she to remain in the dark, although she believes as I do?»

Jesus smiles more broadly. He looks around and on the roadside He sees a bunch of daisies wet with rain. He bends and picks them, He blesses them and hands them to the boy. «Pass them on your mother's eyes, and she will see. I am not coming back. I must go on. Let those who are good follow Me with their souls and speak of Me to those who are doubtful. Speak of Me to the people of Pella, whose faith is wavering. Go. God is with you.»

He then turns to the woman of Gerasa: «And you follow him. This is the reply of God to all those who are trying to weaken the faith of men in the Christ. And let that strengthen *your* faith and Josiah's. Go in peace.»

They part. Jesus resumes His march southwards. The boy, the Gerasene woman and the servants go northwards. The heavy rain separates them like a veil of smoke...

359. In Matthias' Hut Beyond Jabesh-Gilead.

13th December 1945.

359.1 [1] The deep woody valley where Jabesh-Gilead is situated is resounding with a swollen little torrent, which flows foaming towards the nearby Jordan. The dim twilight and dull day increase the gloomy sight of the woods and the village thus looks sad and inhospitable at first sight.

Thomas, who is always good-humoured, notwithstanding that his garments are just as wet as if they had been taken out of a washing tub and he is covered in mud from head to foot, says: «H'm! I would not like this village to revenge itself on us for the
* unpleasant surprise they received from Israel. Well, let us go and suffer for the Lord.»

The people do not kill them, that is true, but they drive the apostles away from everywhere, calling them thieves and worse names, and Philip and Matthew have to run as fast as they can, to get rid of a big dog, which a shepherd has set on them, when they knock at the door of his sheep-fold, asking for shelter for the night «at least under the shed of the sheep».

«What shall we do now?»

«We have no bread.»

«And no money. And without money one can find no bread and no lodgings.»

«And we are wet to the skin, frozen and starving.»

«And it is getting dark. We shall be a lovely sight tomorrow morning, after a night in the wood.»

Seven of the Twelve are grumbling openly, three are clearly dissatisfied, even if they do not say so. Simon Zealot is proceeding with his head lowered and the expression of his face is undecipherable. John is greatly embarrassed and with grievous countenance he casts rapid glances at Jesus and the grumblers alternately. Jesus continues to go personally to knock from door to door, as the apostles refuse to do so, or they do so fearfully, and He patiently walks along the little streets, which have become slippery foul quagmires. But He meets with refusal everywhere.

[2] They are at the end of the village, where the valley widens out 359.2
on the pastures of the Trans-Jordan plain. There are still a few houses... and each one is a disappointment...

«Let us look in the fields. John, can you climb up that elm-tree? From the top of it you will be able to see.»

«Yes, my Lord.»

«The elm-tree is slippery because of the rain. He will not be able to climb it and he will hurt himself. And we will thus have an injured companion as well» grumbles Peter.

---

* **unpleasant surprise**, narrated in: *1 Maccabees 5:9-36.*

And Jesus replies meekly: «I will climb it, then.»

«Certainly not!» they shout in chorus. And the fishermen shout louder than the others, adding: «If it is dangerous for us fishermen, what do You expect to do if You have never climbed up masts or ropes?»

«I was going to do it for your sake, to find shelter for you. I do not mind. It is not the rain that troubles Me...» How much sadness! What a sad appeal for loving understanding there is in His voice!

Some listen and become silent. Bartholomew and Matthew say: «It is now too late to do anything. A decision should have been taken earlier.»

«Of course! And not be guided by whim, by deciding to depart from Pella, when it was already raining. You have been obstinate and imprudent and now we are all paying for it. What can You do now? If our purse had been full, all the houses would have been open to us! But You!... Why do You not work a miracle, at least one miracle for Your apostles, since You work miracles even for undeserving people?» says Judas of Kerioth, gesticulating like a madman; he is so aggressive that the others, although they more or less agree with him, feel it is necessary to remind him to respect the Master.

Jesus is already like the Convict looking meekly at His executioners. And He is silent. This silence, which for some time has become more and more frequent in Jesus, foreshadowing His «great silence» before the Sanhedrin, Pilate and Herod, makes me feel so sorry for Him. It reminds me of the silent pauses in the moaning of a dying man, which are not due to soothing of pain, but are the prelude to death. Jesus' silences seem to be much more eloquent than words, as they express all His grief at men's lack of understanding and love. And because of His meekness which does not react and of the lowered posture of His head, He looks as if He were already put in chains and handed over to the hatred of men.

«Why don't You speak?» they ask Him.

«Because I would utter words which your hearts would not understand just now... Let us go. We will walk not to freeze... And forgive Me...»

He turns around quickly, leading the group, while some of

its members pity Him, some accuse Him, some contradict their companions.

[3]John remains slowly behind, deliberately avoiding notice by 359.3
anyone. He then goes towards a very tall tree,a poplar, I think, or an ash-tree, and after taking off his mantle and tunic, he begins to climb it, half naked as he is, with some difficulty, until the first branches make his ascent easier. He climbs up as swiftly as a cat. At times he slips, but he immediately collects himself and is almost at the top. He scans the horizon in the last light of the day, which is clearer here in the open plain, than in the valley, also because the dark clouds have thinned out. He looks carefully in every direction and at last he makes a gesture of joy. He slides down to the ground very rapidly, puts his clothes on and begins to run. He reaches his companions, overtakes them and is soon beside the Master. Panting because of the effort of climbing and running he says: «There is a hut, Lord... a hut to the east... But we will have to go back... I climbed up a tree... Come...»

«I am going with John this way. If you want to come, do so, otherwise go on as far as the next village on the river. We will meet there» says Jesus seriously and decisively.

Drenched with rain, they all follow Him through the fields. «But we are going back to Jabesh!»

«I can't see any houses...»

«I wonder what the boy has seen!»

«Perhaps a shed.»

«Or the hut of a leper.»

«We shall get soaked through. These fields are like sponges» grumble the apostles.

[4]But it is neither a shed nor a leper's hut what appears behind 359.4
a group of trees. It is a hut, a low large hut like a poor sheep-fold, half of the roof is thatched and the mud walls can hardly support the four pillars made of coarse stone. A pile-work enclosure is around the hovel and inside it there are vegetables dripping water.

John gives a shout. An old man appears. «Who is it?»

«Pilgrims going to Jerusalem. Give us shelter in the name of God!» says Jesus.

«Certainly. It's my duty. But you are unlucky. I have little room and no beds.»

«It does not matter. You will at least have a fire.»

The man bestirs himself at the gate and opens it. «Come in and peace be with you.»

They go through the tiny kitchen garden. They go into the only room which is kitchen and bedroom at the same time. A fire is lit in the fireplace. There is tidiness and poverty, and not one utensil more than is necessary.

«See! Only my heart is large and ornate. But if you wish to make the best of it... Have you any bread?»

«No. Just a handful of olives...»

«I have not got enough bread for everybody. But I will prepare something with milk. I have two sheep. They are enough for me. I will go and milk them. Will you give me your mantles? I will hang them up in the fold, at the rear. They will dry a little and tomorrow we will do the rest with the fire.»

The man goes out laden with the damp clothes. They are all standing near the fire enjoying its warmth.

The man comes back with a coarse mat, which he lays on the floor. «Take your sandals off. I will wash the mud off them and hang them up so that they may dry. And I will give you some warm water so that you may wash your feet. The mat is coarse, but it is clean and thick. You will feel it is more comfortable than the cold floor.»

He takes a cauldron full of greenish water, in which some vegetables are boiling, and pours half of it into a basin and half into another vessel. He then adds cold water and says: «There you are. It will refresh you. Wash yourselves. This is a clean cloth.»

In the meantime he busies himself at the fireplace. He makes up the fire, pours the milk into a pot, which he places on the fire. And as soon as it begins to boil he adds some seeds, which look like ground barley or hulled millet. And he stirs the mush.

359.5 [5] Jesus, Who is one of the first to wash Himself, approaches him: «May God grant you grace for your charity.»

«I am only giving back what I received from Him. I was a leper. I was a leper from my thirty-seventh to my fifty-first year of age. Then I became cured. But in the village I found that my wife and relatives had died and my house had been plundered. In any case I was the "leper"... So I came here. And I built my home here, by myself and with the help of God. At first I made a hut with bog grass, then a wooden one. Then I built the walls... Something new each year. Last year I built the fold for the sheep. I bought them selling the mats and wooden utensils that I make. I have an apple-tree, a pear-tree, a fig-tree and a vine. I grow vegetables in the front of the house and I have a small barley field in the rear. I have four couples of doves and two sheep. I will have lambs before long. And I hope they are ewe-lambs this time. I bless the Lord and I ask for no more. And who are You?»

«A Galilean. Have you a prejudice against them?»

«None, although I am of Judaean extraction. If I had had children, I could have had one like You... I now act as a father to my doves... I have become accustomed to being alone.»

«And at Festivities?»

«I fill the mangers and go. I hire a donkey. I rush there, I do what I have to do and come back. I never had as much as a leaf stolen. God is good.»

«Yes, both to those who are good and those who are not so good. But good people are under His wings.»

«Yes, Isaiah also says so... He protected me, He did.»

«But you were a leper» remarks Thomas.

«And I became poor and was left alone. But this is a grace of God, to become a man again and to have a roof and bread. Job was my model in misfortune. I hope to deserve the blessing of God, as he did, not in wealth, but in grace.»

«You will receive it. You are a just man. [6]What is your name?» 359.6

«Matthias.» He takes the pot off the fire and puts it on the table. He adds butter and honey and puts it back on the fire and says: «I have only six pieces of crockery between plates and bowls. You will have to eat in turn.»

«And what about you?»

«The host is the last to be served. First the brothers sent by God. Here you are. It is ready. And this will do you good.» And he pours ladelfuls of steaming mush into four plates and two bowls. There is no shortage of wooden spoons.

Jesus advises the younger to eat.

«No, You must eat, Master» says John.

---

* **says so**, for example in *Isaiah 3:10*, which is one of the various points where the concept is affirmed.

* **misfortune**, as related in *Job 1-2*.

«No. Judas had better have his fill, so that he may realize that there is always food for the children.»

The Iscariot changes colour but he eats.

«Are You a rabbi?»

«Yes, I am, and these are My disciples.»

«I used to go to the Baptist, when I was at Bethabara. Do You know anything about the Messiah? They say that He exists and that John pointed Him out. When I go to Jerusalem I always hope to see Him. But I have never been successful. I fulfil the rite and I do not stop there. Probably that is why I never see Him. I am isolated here and then... The people in Perea are not good. I spoke to some shepherds who come here to pasture. They knew Him and told me about Him. What wonderful words! I wonder how beautiful they must be when spoken by Him!...»

Jesus does not reveal Himself. It is His turn now to eat and He does so peacefully near the good old man.

«And now? What shall we do for beds? I give you my bed. But it is one only... I will go to the sheep-fold.»

«No, we will go there. Hay is good enough for those who are tired.»

The meal is over and they decide to lie down in order to be able to leave at dawn. But the old man insists and Matthew, who has a bad cold, sleeps in his bed.

359.7 [7] But it is raining torrents at dawn. How can they leave in such heavy rain? They listen to the old man and stay. In the meantime they brush their clothes and dry them, they grease their sandals and rest. The old man cooks barley again in milk for everybody and he puts some apples under the ashes. That is their meal and they are eating it when they hear a voice from outside.

«Another pilgrim? What shall we do?» says the old man. But he gets up, wraps himself in a coarse woollen water-resistant blanket and goes out. It is warm in the kitchen, but there is no good humour in it. Jesus is silent.

The old man comes back with his eyes wide open. He looks at Jesus and then at the others. He seems to be afraid... he looks uncertain and inquisitive. At last he says: «Is the Messiah among you? Tell me, because the people of Pella are looking for Him to adore Him because of a great miracle He worked. They have been knocking all night at the doors of all the houses as far as the river, as far as the first village... Now, on their way back, they thought of me. Somebody pointed out my house to them. They are outside, in wagons. A large crowd!»

Jesus stands up. The Twelve say: «Don't go. If You said that it was wise to avoid staying at Pella, there is no sense in showing Yourself now.»

«So! O Blessed! You are Blessed and He Who sent You to me. And I received You! You are Rabbi Jesus, Who... Oh!» The man is on his knees, with his forehead on the floor.

«Yes, I am. But let Me go to those who are looking for Me. Then I will come to you, My good man.» He frees His ankles from the hands of the old man and goes out into the flooded kitchen garden.

[8] «Here He is! Hosanna!» They jump out of the wagons. There 359.8
are men and women the young blind fellow cured yesterday and his mother, and also the Gerasene woman. They kneel down, without paying any attention to the mud and they implore: «Come back with us to Pella.»

«No, to Jabesh» shout other people, obviously from that place. «We want You! We are sorry that we drove You away!» shout those from Jabesh.

«No, to Pella with us, as Your miracle is still alive there. You have given light to their eyes. Give light to our souls.»

«I cannot. I am going to Jerusalem. You will find Me there.»

«You are angry because we expelled You.»

«You are disgusted because You know that we believed the slander of a sinner.»

Mark's mother covers her face weeping.

«Jaia, please tell Him Who loved you to come back.»

«You will find Me in Jerusalem. Go and persevere. Do not be like the winds, which blow in every direction. Goodbye.»

«No. Come. We will abduct You, if You do not come.»

«You shall not raise one hand against Me. That is idolatry, not faith. Faith believes even without seeing. It perseveres even when it is persecuted. It grows greater even without miracles. I am staying with Matthias, who believed without seeing anything and who is a just man.»

«At least accept our gifts: money and bread. We have been

told that You gave everything You had to Jaia and his mother. Take a wagon. You can travel in it. You will leave it at Jericho, with Timon, the hotel keeper. Take it. It is raining and will rain. You will be sheltered and will travel quicker. Give us a sign that You do not hate us.»

They are on the other side of the fence, Jesus is on this side: they look at one another and those on the other side are full of excitement. Behind Jesus there is old Matthias, on his knees, with his mouth wide open, and then the apostles, who are all standing.

Jesus stretches out His hand saying: «I will accept your offerings for the poor. But I will not accept the wagon. I am the Poor One among the poor. Please do not insist. Jaia, and you, woman, and you from Gerasa, come here, that I may give you a special blessing.» And when they approach Him, as Matthias has opened the fence, He caresses, blesses and dismisses them. He then blesses all those who have crowded at the gate to give the apostles money and foodstuffs and He dismisses them.

359.9 [9] He goes back into the house...

«Why did You not speak to them?»

«The miracle of the two blind people is My sermon.»

«Why did You not accept the wagon?»

«Because it is better to travel on foot.» And He addresses Matthias: «I would have rewarded you with My blessings. I can now add a little money to cover the expenses that you have met...»

«No, Lord Jesus... I don't want it. I did that wholeheartedly. And I am doing it now to serve the Lord. The Lord does not pay. He is not obliged to pay. I am the one who received, not You! Oh! this day! It will come with me, with its recollections, as far as the next life!»

«You are right! You will find your mercy towards pilgrims written in Heaven, as well as your prompt faith... As soon as it clears up a little, I will leave you. Those people might come back. They insist as long as they are roused by miracles, then they become as torpid as they were before, or even hostile. I will proceed. So far I have stopped trying to convert them. I now come and pass by, without stopping. I am going towards My destiny, which urges Me. God and man urge Me and I can no longer stop. Love and hatred spur Me. Let those who love Me, follow Me. But the Master will no longer run after indocile sheep.»

«Do they not love You, divine Master?» asks Matthias.
«They do not understand Me.»
«They are wicked.»
«Lust makes them dull.»

Old Matthias no longer dare be as confidential as he was previously. He seems to be standing in front of an altar. Jesus, on the contrary, since He is no longer the Unknown One, is less reserved and speaks to the old man as if he were a relative.

The hours thus go by until early afternoon. The clouds begin to dissipate, promising the end of the rain. Jesus gives the order to depart. And while the old man goes to get the dry mantles, He puts some coins in a box and has some bread and cheese put into a kitchen cupboard.

The old man comes back and Jesus blesses him. He then takes to the road again, turning around now and again to look at the white head leaning over the dark fence.

360. The Proceeding Hindered by Foul Weather. The Night Spent in a Cave. Rose of Jericho.

14th December 1945.

[1]The plain on the eastern bank of the Jordan is like a lagoon 360.1
because of the continuous rain, particularly where Jesus and the apostles are just now. They have just crossed a torrent that flows down from a narrow gorge in the nearby hills, which seem to form a Cyclopean dam, from north to south, along the Jordan, interrupted now and again by narrow valleys in which torrents inevitably flow. It looks as if God had placed a range of hills here, shaped like a huge scallop-edge, as a contour to the large Jordan valley. I would say that it is a rather monotonous scallop-edging, as its projections, aspects and distances are so much alike. The apostolic group is between the last two torrents, which have over-flown their banks and are thus wider, particularly the southern one, as it conveys an imposing mass of water from the mountains and it roars turbulently towards the Jordan. One can also hear the roar of the river, particularly where it bends naturally, which I would say are like continuous narrowings, or the confluence of affluents, cause obstructions to the wa-

ter. Well, Jesus is in this truncated triangle, formed by three watercourses in flood, and it is *
not an easy task to lift one's feet out of that quagmire.

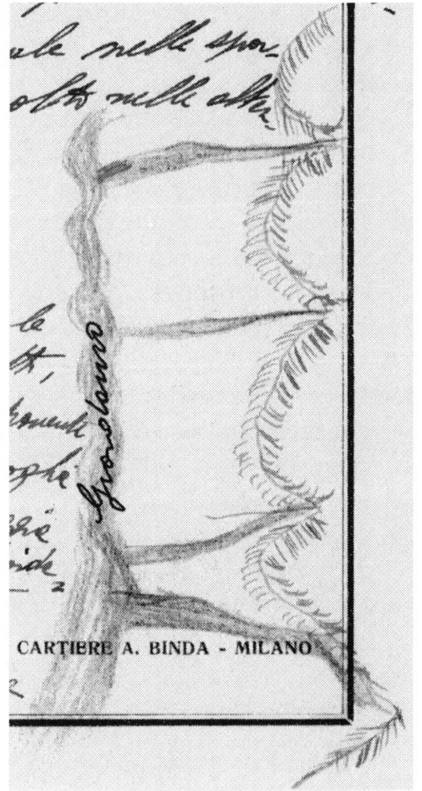

360.2 [2]The apostolic humour is duller than the weather. And that says everything. Each one wishes to express his own opinion. And everything they say implies reproach, although expressed as advice. It is the moment of sentences like: «I told you», or «If you had done what I suggested» etc., which annoy so much anybody who has made a mistake and is already depressed at having made it.

Some say: «It was better to cross the river in the Pella area and then proceed on the other side, which is not so bad», or «We ought to have taken the wagon! We wanted to be clever, and then...», and some remark: «If we had stayed up on the mountains, there would not have been all this mud!»

John says: «You are prophets of past events. Who foresaw all this rain?»

«This is its time. It should have been foreseen» remarks Bartholomew.

«In past years it was not like this before Passover. I came to you and the Kidron was certainly not in spate and last year we had a spell of drought. You are complaining and you have forgotten how much we suffered from thirst in the Philistine plain!» says the Zealot.

* **a truncated triangle, formed by three watercourses**, that in the drawing made by MV are the last two tributaries to the south and the part of the Jordan between one and the other. The name *Jordan* is written in the large course of water to the West, while to the East the hilly system is dotted.

«Eh! Of course! The two wise men have spoken and they contradict us!» says Judas of Kerioth ironically.

«You ought to be quiet. You are good only at criticising. But at the right moment, when one should speak to a Pharisee or the like, you are always silent, as if your tongue had been tied» Thaddeus says to him angrily.

«Yes. He is right. Why did you not answer one word to those three snakes in the last village? You were aware that we had been to Giscala and Meiron, that we behaved respectfully and that it was the Master Himself Who wanted to go there, as He respects the great dead rabbis. But you did not say anything! You know how He expects us to respect the Law and priests. But you did not say one word! But you are speaking now, because there is the opportunity of speaking ironically of the best ones among us and you are criticising what the Master does» insists Andrew, who is usually patient, but today is very irritable.

«Will you be quiet! Judas is wrong, he who is the friend of * many, too many Samaritans…» Peter says.

«Me? Who are they? Mention their names, if you can.»

«Yes, my dear! All the Pharisees, Sadducees and powerful people of whose friendship you brag so much and who certainly know you. They never greet me. But they greet you!»

«You are jealous! But I am one of the Temple, you are not.»

«Thanks be to God, I am a fisherman. Yes, and I am proud of it.»

«So stupid a fisherman that you could not even foresee this weather.»

«No! I said: "If the new moon of Nisan is wet, rain in torrents one may expect"» replies Peter.

«Ah! I caught you! And what do you say, Judas of Alphaeus? And you, Andrew? Peter also, our Head, criticises the Master!»

«I am not criticising anybody. I quoted a proverb.»

«Which is criticism and reproach for anyone who can understand it.»

«Yes… but I don't think that will help to dry the ground. We are now here and we will have to stay here. Let us spare our breath to get our feet out of this quagmire» says Thomas.

---

* **Peter says.** It is an adding which M.V. made while correcting the typewritten copy.

360.3 [3] And what about Jesus? Jesus is silent. He is a little ahead of everybody, wallowing in mud or looking for emerging turves. But even they splash water up to half of one's shin, as soon as one treads on them, as if they were bladders and not turves. He is silent and lets them speak, discontented as they are, behaving just like men, nothing more than men, whom the least inconvenience makes irritable and unfair.

The most southern of the rivers is now close at hand, and when Jesus sees a man on muleback pass along the flooded bank, He asks him: «Where is the bridge?»

«Further up. I am crossing there as well. The other one, the one further down the valley, the Roman bridge, is already under water.»

They all grumble again... in chorus. But they hasten to follow the man who is speaking to Jesus.

«But You had better follow the mountain path» he says. And he concludes: «Come back to the plain when you find the third river after the Yaloc. You will then be near the ford. But make haste. Don't stop. Because the river is swelling hourly. What a terrible season! Frost first, then rain. And so heavy! It's a punishment of God. But it is just! When we do not stone the blasphemers of the Law, God punishes us. And we have many of them! You are a Galilean, are You not? So You will know the One from Nazareth, Whom good people are now leaving because He is the cause of all troubles. His words attract thunderbolts! Such punishments! You should hear what those, who were with Him, say about Him. The Pharisees are right in persecuting Him. He must be a great robber. And he must frighten people as if he were Beelzebub. I wanted to go and hear Him, because previously they spoke so highly of Him. But... it was the men of his gang who spoke so. People without scruples like Him. Good people are now abandoning Him. And quite rightly. I am not going to see Him anymore. And if by chance I should come across Him, I will pelt Him with stones, as it is our duty to do so with blasphemers.»

«Stone Me, then. I am Jesus of Nazareth. I am not running away, neither will I curse you. I have come to redeem the world by shedding My Blood. Here I am. You may sacrifice Me, but become a just man.»

Jesus says so opening His arms a little towards the ground,

He speaks slowly, meekly and sadly. But if He had cursed the man, He would not have impressed him more; in fact he draws reins so abruptly that the mule swerves and nearly falls from the embankment into the river in spate. Jesus seizes the bit and holds the animal, just in time to save man and mule.

The man does nothing but repeat: «You! You!...» and seeing the gesture that has saved him, he shouts: «But I told You that I would stone You... Do You not understand?»

«And I tell you that I forgive you and that I will suffer for you as well, to redeem you. That is the Saviour.»

The man looks at Him again, he spurs his mule and runs away... He flies away... Jesus lowers His head...

[4] The apostles feel that it is necessary to forget mud, rain and 360.4
all the other miseries, in order to comfort Him. They gather around Him and say: «Do not grieve! We are in no need of bandits. And that is what he is. Because only a wicked person can believe such slander and be afraid of You.»

«But» they also say «how unwise of You, Master! And if he hurt You? Why say that You are Jesus of Nazareth?»

«Because it is the truth... Let us go towards the mountains as he suggested. We will lose a day, but you will get out of the quagmire.»

«And You, too» they remark.

«Oh! It does not concern Me. It is the quagmire of dead souls that worries Me» and tears stream down His face.

«Do not weep, Master. We grumble, but we love You. If we should meet Your slanderers, we will take vengeance upon them.»

«You shall forgive, as I do. But let Me weep. I am the Man, after all! And it grieves Me to be betrayed, disowned, abandoned!»

«Look at us, consider us. We are few but good. None of us will betray or abandon You. Believe us, Master.»

«Certain things should not even be mentioned! The thought that we may betray You, is an insult to our souls!» exclaims the Iscariot.

But Jesus is distressed. Silent slow tears stream down the pale cheeks of His tired emaciated face.

They approach the mountains. «Shall we go up there or shall we go along the foot? There are villages half way up the hills.

Look. On both sides of the river» they point out to Him.

«It is getting dark. Let us try and reach a village, any village at all.»

Judas Thaddeus, whose eye sight is very good, scans the sides of the mountains. He approaches Jesus and says: «In case of need there are fissures in the mountains. Can You see them there? We can take shelter in them. It will be better than being in mud.»

«We will light a fire» says Andrew to console everybody.

«What? with damp wood?» asks Judas of Kerioth ironically.

No one replies to him. Peter whispers: «I bless the Eternal Father that neither the women nor Marjiam are with us.»

360.5 [5] They cross the bridge, a very old one, at the foot of the valley and they go along its southern side, on a mule-track, to a village. It is getting dark very quickly, so much so that they decide to take shelter in a large cave to avoid a heavy shower. The grotto is probably used as a shelter place by shepherds, because there is straw, dirt and a rough fireplace.

«It is of no use as a bed. But to light a fire...» says Thomas pointing at the dirty twigs spread on the ground together with dry ferns and branches of juniper and similar plants. He draws them with a stick close to the fireplace, and once he has made a heap of them he sets them alight.

Smoke and foul smell rise from the fire together with the smell of resins and juniper. Yet the warmth of the fire is pleasant and they all form a semi-circle around it, eating bread and cheese in the flickering light of the flames.

«We could have tried to reach the village» says Matthew, who is hoarse and is suffering from a cold.

«What? To go through the same trouble as three nights ago? No one will drive us away here. We will sit on those logs over there and keep the fire going as long as we can. We can now see that there is plenty of wood in here! Look! And straw! It is a sheep-
360.6 fold, which they use in summer or when they migrate. [6]And what is this? Where does this take to? Take a branch on fire, Andrew, as I want to see» says Peter, who is moving about curiously. Andrew obeys. They slip through a narrow fissure in a wall of the grotto.

«Make sure there are no unpleasant beasts in there!» shout the others. «Or lepers» says Thaddeus.

After a moment Peter's voice can be heard: «Come, come in

here. It's much better here. It is clean and dry and there are some wooden benches and firewood. It's a palace for us! Bring some of the burning branches, so that we may light a fire at once.»

It must be a shelter for shepherds. And this is the grotto where some sleep while the others, who are on guard, watch the sheep. It is an excavation in the mountain, much smaller than the other one, and probably made by man, or at least enlarged and reinforced by means of poles supporting the vault. A very old rustic chimney is bent in the shape of a hook towards the outer cave, to draw the smoke that otherwise would have no outlet. Rough benches and straw are placed against the walls, in which there are some hooks to hang up lamps, clothes or bags.

«Lovely! Let us make a big fire! We shall be warm and our mantles will dry. Give me your belts: we will join them together and hang our mantles on them» says Peter, while he sorts out benches and straw. And he concludes: «And now we will sleep and keep the fire burning in turns, so that we shall have light and shall be warm. What a grace of God!»

Judas grumbles between his teeth. Peter turns around angrily. «This is a royal palace, as compared to the grotto in Bethlehem, where the Lord was born. If He was born there, we can spend a night here.»

«And it is also more beautiful than the grottos at Arbela. There was nothing beautiful there, except our hearts, which were kinder then» says John and he gets lost in his mystical remembrance.

«And it is also much better than the one where the Master stayed to prepare Himself for the office of a preacher» says the Zealot gravely, looking at the Iscariot as if he wanted to tell him to stop it.

Jesus is the last to speak: «And it is by far warmer and more comfortable than the one in which I did penance for you, Judas of Simon, in this month of Tebeth.»

«Penance for me? Why? There was no need of it!»

«Really, you and I ought to spend our lives in penance to free you from what overburdens you. And still... it would not be enough.»

The sentence, pronounced calmly but decidedly, drops like a thunderbolt on the dumbfounded group... Judas lowers his head and withdraws to a corner. He dare not react.

360.7 [7] «I will remain awake and look after the fire. You can sleep» orders Jesus after some time.

And shortly afterwards, the heavy breathing of the tired Twelve, lying on the benches among the straw, mingles with the crackling of the fire. And when the straw falls off anyone, leaving his body uncovered, Jesus gets up and covers him again, with the loving care of a mother. And He weeps while contemplating the hermetic faces of some of His sleeping apostles, some in fact are placid, some worried. He looks at the Iscariot, who seems to be grinning also in his sleep, with a grim countenance and clenched fists... He looks at John sleeping with one hand under his cheek, while his rosy face is veiled by his fair hair, and he looks as serene as a child in a cradle. He looks at the honest face of Peter at the severe face of Nathanael, at the pock-marked face of the Zealot and at the aristocratic one of His cousin Judas. And He contemplates for a long time James of Alphaeus who is so much like a very young Joseph of Nazareth. He smiles upon hearing the monologues of Thomas and Andrew, who appear to be speaking of the Master. He carefully covers Matthew who is breathing with difficulty, and He gets more straw with which He covers his feet, after warming it near the fire. He smiles hearing James proclaim: «Believe in the Master and you will have Life»... and continue to speak to people in his dream. And He bends to pick up a bag in which Philip keeps dear souvenirs, and lays it gently under his head. And in the intervals He meditates and prays...

360.8 [8] The Zealot is the first to awake. He sees Jesus near the fire in the pleasantly warm grotto. And from the pile of wood of which there is hardly anything left, he understands that many hours have gone by. He gets up from his straw-bed and approaches the Master on tip-toe. «Master, are You not going to sleep? I will watch.»

«It is dawn, Simon. I was out there a little while ago and I saw that the sky is beginning to grow light.»

«Why did You not call us? You are tired, too!»

«Oh! Simon! I needed to think... and to pray so much» and He leans His head on the apostle's chest.

The Zealot, standing close to the Master, Who is seated, caresses Him and sighs. He asks: «To think of what, Master? There is no need for You to think, as You know everything.»

«I need not think of what I have to say, but I must think of what I have to do. I am disarmed against the shrewd world, because I do not possess the wickedness of the world or the cunning nature of Satan. And the world defeats Me... And I am so tired...»

«And sorrowful. And we help in increasing Your grief, dear Master, Whom we do not deserve. Forgive me and my companions. I ask you on behalf of everybody.»

«I love you so much... I suffer so much... Why do you not understand Me so often?»

[9] Their whispering awakes John, who is closest to them. He 360.9
opens his blue eyes, looks around in amazement, he then remembers and gets up at once, and he comes behind the two who are talking. He hears Jesus' words: «Your love and your understanding would be quite enough to make all hatred and misunderstanding become a mere trifle, which I could easily bear... Instead you do not understand... And that is My first torment. And a very heavy one! But it is not your fault... You are men... You will regret not having understood Me, when you can no longer make amends... And as you will then expiate your present superficiality, meanness and dullness, I forgive you and I say before time: "Father, forgive them, because they do not know what they are doing or the grief they are causing Me".»

John slides forwards on to his knees, he embraces the knees of his grieved Jesus and is on the point of bursting into tears when he whispers: «Oh! My Master!»

The Zealot, on whose chest Jesus' head is still resting, bends to kiss His hair saying: «And yet we love You so much! But we would expect in You the ability to defend Yourself and us and to triumph. It disheartens us to see that You are a man, subject to men, to the inclemency of the weather, to misery, to wickedness, to the needs of life... We are foolish. But it is so. As far as we are concerned You are the King, the Triumpher, God. We fail to understand Your sublime self-abnegation to all that for our sake. Because You only are capable of loving. We are not...»

«Yes, Master. Simon is right. We cannot love as God loves: as

You do. And we mistake for weakness what is infinite goodness and infinite love and we take advantage of it... Increase our love, increase Your love, and as You are its source, let it overflow, as rivers are now overflowing, soak us in it, sate us with it, like the meadows along the valley. No wisdom, no worth or austerity is required to be perfect as You want us. Love is sufficient... Lord, and I confess, also on behalf of everybody, that we do not know how to love.»

«You, the two who understand more, are accusing yourselves. You are humility. But *humility is love*. Only a screen prevents the others from being like you. And I will demolish it. Because I am King, Victor and God forever. But now I am the Man. My forehead is already weighed under the torture of My crown. It has always been a torturing crown to be the Man... Thank you, My friends. You have comforted Me. Because this is the advantage
360.10 of being men: to have a loving mother and loyal friends. [10]Let us call your companions. It is no longer raining. Our mantles are dry and our bodies well rested. You may eat and then let us go.»

He raises His voice slowly until the words «let us go» become a definite order. They all get up and regret having slept all the time while Jesus was watching. They tidy themselves, they have something to eat, take their mantles, put out the fire, and go out on the damp path and begin to descend down to the mule-track that follows the hillside and is not a quagmire because of its steepness. The light is still dim because the sky is overcast and there is no sunshine. But it is sufficient to see.

360.11 [11]Andrew and the two sons of Alphaeus are ahead of them all. At a certain moment they stop, they look and run back. «There is a woman. She seems to be dead! She bars the way.»

«Oh! What a nuisance! It's a bad start. What shall we do now? We will have to purify ourselves!» It is the first grumbling of the day.

«Let us go and see whether she is dead» says Thomas to Judas Iscariot.

«I'm certainly not going» replies the Iscariot.

«I will come with you, Tom» says the Zealot and he goes ahead.

They approach her, then bend and Thomas runs back shouting.

«She was probably murdered» says James of Zebedee.

«Or she died from the cold» replies Philip.

But Thomas joins them and shouts: «She has on the torn garment of lepers...» and he is so frightened that he seems to have seen the devil.

«But is she dead?» they ask him.

«Who knows? I ran away.»

The Zealot stands up and comes at once towards Jesus. He says: «Master, a leper sister. I do not know whether she is dead. I do not think so. Her heart seems to be beating.»

«Did you touch her?!» shout many of them, moving away.

«Yes I did. I am not afraid of leprosy since I have been with Jesus. And I feel sorry for her because I know what it is to be a leper. Perhaps the poor woman has been struck, because her head is bleeding. Perhaps she came down here looking for food. It is dreadful, you know, to die of starvation and to have to defy men to get some bread.»

«Is she run down?»

«No, and I do not know why she is among lepers. She has neither scabs nor sores nor gangrene. Perhaps she has not been here very long. Come, Master, please. Have mercy on a leper sister as you had on me!»

«Let us go. Give Me some bread, cheese and the little wine that is still left.»

«You are not going to let her drink where we drink!» shouts the Iscariot struck with terror.

«Be not afraid. She will drink from My hand. Come, Simon.»

[12] They go... but curiosity spurs the others to follow them. With- 360.12
out being annoyed at the water on the foliage and that drops on their heads from the shaken branches, and without minding the soaking moss they climb up the hillside to see without being near the woman. And they see Jesus bend, take her by her armpits and make her sit against a rock. Her head hangs, as if she were dead.

«Simon, hold her head back so that I may pour a little wine into her mouth.»

The Zealot obeys without fear and Jesus, holding the gourd high up lets a few drops of wine fall between her half-open deathly pale lips. And He says: «The poor woman is frozen! And she is soaked.»

«If she were not a leper, we could take her where we were» says Andrew who is deeply moved.

«That would be the last straw!» exclaims Judas.

«But if she is not a leper! There is no sign of leprosy on her.»

«She has the garment. That's enough.»

The wine in the meantime has its effect. The woman sighs wearily. Jesus pours some into her mouth ensuring that she swallows it. The woman opens her dimmed frightened eyes. She sees the men. She tries to stand up and run away shouting: «I am infected!» But her strength does not support her. She covers her face with her hands moaning: «Don't stone me! I came down because I am hungry.... No one has thrown anything to me for three days...»

«There is bread and cheese here. Eat it. Do not be afraid. Drink a little wine out of My hand» says Jesus pouring some wine into the hollow of His hand and giving it to her.

«But are You not afraid» says the poor wretch who is dumbfounded.

«I am not afraid» replies Jesus. And He smiles standing up but He remains near the woman who eats the bread and cheese avidly. She looks like a starving animal. She pants in her anxiety to nourish herself.

360.13 [13]Then, after she appeases the gnawing hunger of her empty stomach, she looks around... She counts in a loud voice: «One... two... three... thirteen... So? Oh! Who is the Nazarene? You are, are You not? You are the only one who can pity a poor leper...» The woman goes on her knees with difficulty owing to her weakness.

«Yes, I am. What do you want? To be cured?»

«Also that... But I must tell You something first... I knew about You. Some passers-by told me some time ago... A long time ago? No. It was in autumn. But for a leper... every day is a year... I would have liked to see You. But how could I come to Judaea to Galilee? They call me "the leper woman". But I have only one sore on my breast and I got it from my husband, who married me when I was a virgin and healthy, but he was not healthy. But he is a mighty one... and can do anything, even saying that I had betrayed him as I was ill when I married him. He thus repudiated me to take another woman with whom he had fallen in love. He denounced me as a leper and as I wanted to exculpate myself, I was pelted with stones. Was that fair, Lord? Yesterday evening a man passed through Bethjabbok saying that You were coming and that he was coming to drive You away. I was there... I came down as far as the houses because I was hungry. I would have rummaged among dunghills to find something to eat... I, who was once "the lady", would have tried to snatch some sour chicken-feed from poultry...»

She weeps... Then she resumes: «My anxiety to find You, to say to You: "Flee!", and for me: "Have mercy on me!", made me forget that, contrary to our law, dogs, pigs and poultry are allowed to live near houses in Israel, but a leper cannot come down to ask for some bread, not even if a woman is a leper only by name. And I came down, asking where You were. As I was in the shade they did not see me at once and they said to me: "He is coming along the embankment of the river". Then they saw me and they gave me stones instead of bread. I ran away in the night to come and meet You and to escape the rogues. I was hungry, cold and afraid. I fell where You found me. Just here. I thought I was going to die. Instead I found You Lord, I am not a leper. But this scab here on my breast prevents me from going back among the living. I do not ask to become once again Rose of Jericho as in the days of my father, but at least to be allowed to live among men and to follow You. Those who spoke to me in October told me that You have women disciples and that You were with them... But first save Your own life. Do not die, You are so good!»

«I will not die until My hour comes. [14]Go over there, to that 360.14
rock. There is a safe grotto. Have a rest and then go to the priest.»

«Why, Lord?» asks the woman trembling with anxiety.

Jesus smiles: «Become once again the Rose of Jericho that blooms in the desert and is always alive, even when it appears to be dead. Your faith has cured you.»

The woman half-opens her dress over her breast, she looks and shouts: «There is nothing now! Oh! Lord, my God!» and she prostrates herself on the ground.

«Give her bread and some food. And you, Matthew, give her a pair of your sandals. I will give her a mantle. She will then be able to go to a priest, after she has refreshed herself. Give her also the offering for the purification, Judas. We will wait for her at Gethsemane to give her to Eliza, who asked Me to let her have a daughter.»

«No Lord I do not want to rest. I will go at once, immediately.»

«Go down to the river, then. Wash yourself and put on the mantle...»

«Lord, I will give my leper sister one. Let me do it and I will take her to Eliza. I will be cured a second time as I will see myself in her and so happily» says the Zealot.

«Do as you wish. Give her what she needs. Woman, listen to Me carefully. You will go and be purified, then you will go to Bethany and you will look for Lazarus, and you will ask him to give you hospitality until I arrive. Go in peace.»

«Lord! When will I be able to kiss Your feet?»

«Soon. Go. But you must be aware that only sin disgusts Me. And forgive your husband, because through him you found Me.»

«That is true. I forgive him. I am going... Oh! Lord! Do not stop here where they hate You. Remember that I walked all night, although I was exhausted, to come and tell You and that if I had met other people, instead of meeting You, I might have been stoned like a snake.»

«I will remember. Go, woman. Burn your clothes. Go with her, Simon. We will follow you and will join you at the bridge.»

360.15 [15] They part.

«Now we must all purify ourselves. We are all unclean.»

«It was not leprosy, Judas of Simon. I can assure you.»

«Well, I will purify myself. I do not want uncleanness on me.»

«What a snow-white lily!» exclaims Peter. «If the Lord does not feel unclean, how can you feel so?»

«And because of a woman who the Lord said was not a leper? But what was the matter with her, Master? Did You see her scab?»

«Yes. A fruit of male lewdness. But it was not leprosy. And if the man had been honest, he would not have rejected her, because he was more affected by disease than she was. But lewd people take advantage of everything to satisfy their lust. Judas, if you wish, you may go. We will meet at Gethsemane. And purify yourself! But the first purification is sincerity. You are a hypocrite. Remember that. But you may go.»

«No, I will stay. If you say so, I believe You. So I am not unclean and I will stay with You. You mean that I am lustful and that I was taking advantage of the situation to... I am now proving that You are my love.»

They go quickly down the hill.

15th December.

[16] Jesus says: «You will put here the vision of the "Miracle of the Jordan in flood", which you had on September 17th, 1944.» 360.16

361. Mary Magdalene Warns Jesus of a Plot Against Him. Miracle on the Jordan in Flood.

17th September 1944.

[1] At last I can write what has kept my mental sight and hearing busy as from early dawn this morning, making me suffer from the strain in hearing the noise of worldly matters from outside and in the house, while I *must* see and hear the things of God, and making me impatient of everything different from what my spirit sees. 361.1

How much patience is required... not to lose my patience while waiting for the moment to say to Jesus: «Here I am! Now You can go on!» Because — I have said so many times and I will repeat it — when I cannot continue or begin to write what I see, the scene stops at the very beginning or when I am interrupted, and is resumed again when I am free to follow it. I think that God wants that so that I may not omit any detail or make even a slight error, what might happen if I had to write some time after seeing.

I can assure you in all conscience that what I write, because I see or hear it, I do write it while seeing or hearing.

So here is what I have been seeing as from this morning, and my internal warner tells me that it is the beginning of a beautiful long vision.

[2] In very stormy weather Jesus is walking along a very muddy country road. The road is a little river of yellowish sticky mud, which splashes at each step, it is as slippery as soft soap, it sticks to sandals, it sucks them like a sucker and at the same time it slips under them, making it thus most painful to walk. 361.2

It must have rained continuously during those days. And the

sky promises more rain, covered as it is with dark low clouds blown by sirocco or north-east winds, which make the air so heavy that it tastes, in one's mouth, sickly sweet, like a sweetish coating. No relief is brought by the wind that blows bending grass and branches, then stops and everything becomes heavily immobile in the stormy sultriness. Now and again a huge cloud bursts and large warm drops, which seem to be coming from a hot shower, reach the ground forming bubbles in the mud that splashes garments and legs even more.

Although Jesus and His apostles have pulled up their tunics, bagging them at their waists with the cords used as belts, the lower part of their tunics is completely splashed with mud, which is damp at the bottom but almost dry higher up. Their mantles also, which they carry as high as possible, and have folded in half, both to keep them clean and to have double protection against the short but heavy showers, are completely soiled. On their feet and their legs, up to half their shins, they seem to be wearing thick coarse woollen stockings, it is instead mud encrusted on them.

361.3 [3] So far the beginning. It now continues.

The disciples complain a little of the weather and of the road, and we may as well say so, of the Master's not very healthy liking for going about in such weather.

Jesus does not seem to hear. But He does. And two or three times He turns slightly around — they are walking in single row to keep to the left hand side of the road, which is a little higher than the right hand side and thus not so muddy — to look at them. But He does not say anything.

The last time it was the oldest of the disciples who said: «Oh! poor me! With all this dampness that is drying on me I am going to be tortured by pain! I am old! I am no longer thirty years old!»

And Matthew grumbles, too: «And what about me? I was not used to this... When it rained at Capernaum, and you know very well, Peter, I did not go out. I put servants at the tax-bench and they brought me the people who had to pay. I organised a proper service for that. Of course... who would venture to go out in nasty weather? H'm! Only a melancholy fellow, but no one else. Markets and marches are done in good weather...»

«Be quiet! Because He will hear you!» says John.

«No, He will not hear us! He is thinking and when He thinks... we practically do not exist» says Thomas.

«And when He puts an idea into His head, there is no reason whatsoever that may move Him from His determination. He will do what He wants. He trusts no one but Himself and that will be
His ruin. If He only consulted a little with me... [4]I am aware of 361.4
so many things!» says Judas with the self-sufficiency of a «sagacious man who is more clever than anybody else».

«What do you know?» asks Peter at once and he has turned as red as a beetroot. «You know everything! What friends have you got? Are you perhaps a great man in Israel? Away you go! You are a poor man like me and the others... A little more handsome... But handsomeness of youth is a flower that lasts one day! I was handsome, too!»

A hearty laugh of John clears the atmosphere. Also the others laugh and joke at Peter's wrinkles, at his legs, which are wide apart like the legs of every sailor, at his goggle-eyes reddened by the winds of the lake.

«You may laugh, but it is so. In any case, do not interrupt me. Tell me, Judas. What friends have you got? What do you know? If you know what you want us to believe that you know, you must have friends among Jesus' enemies. And who has friends among enemies, is a traitor. Hey! boy! Be careful, if your handsomeness matters to you! Because if it is true that I am no longer handsome, it is also true that I am still strong and I would have no difficulty in giving you a thrashing» says Peter.

«What a manner of speaking! The language of a rude fisherman!» says Judas with the contempt of an offended prince.

«Yes, sir, and I am proud of it. A fisherman, but as sincere as my lake, which, if it is going to be stormy, does not say: "I'll be dead calm", but it stirs and puts such clouds as witnesses in the vault of heaven, that if one is not a fool or drunk, one realizes its meaning and acts accordingly. You... you look like this mud that seems to be hard, but look» (and with a sudden jerk of his foot he splashes the mud up to the chin of the handsome Iscariot).

«Peter! Your manners are disgusting! The Master's words on charity have a lovely effect on you!»

«The same applies to you with regards to His words on humility and sincerity. Come on. Spit it out! What do you know?

Is it true that you know or do you give yourself airs to make people believe that you have powerful friends? You are a poor worm!»

«I know what I know, and I am not going to tell you to start a brawl, which you, being a Galilean, would like. I would repeat that if the Master were less obstinate, it would be much better. And He ought to be less violent. People get tired of being offended.»

«Violent? If He were, He should throw you into the river, *at once*. He should make you fly over those trees. You would thus wash off the mud that soils your profile. I wish it would help to wash your heart, which, if I am not mistaken, is more crusty than my muddy legs.» As Peter, in fact, is hairy and short, his legs are very muddy. Both his and Matthew's legs seem to be made of clay up to their knees.

361.5 [5] «Will you stop it!» says Matthew.

John who has noticed that Jesus has slackened His pace, suspects that He may have heard, and quickening his pace, he overtakes two or three companions, he reaches Jesus and walking beside Him, he calls Him: «Master!» very gently, as usual, and with a loving glance, looking up at Him, as he is shorter also because he is in the middle of the road, beyond the little rising of the ground on which they are all walking.

«Oh! John! You have reached Me!» says Jesus smiling at him.

John, studying His face with love and anxiety to find out whether He has heard, replies: «Yes, my dear Master. Do You want me?»

«I always want you. I would like all of you with hearts like yours! But if you continue to walk where you are, you Will get drenched.»

«It does not matter, Master! Nothing matters, as long as I am near You!»

«Do you always want to be with Me? Do you not think that I am imprudent and I may cause trouble to you as well? Do you not feel offended because I do not listen to your advice?»

«Oh! Master! So You have heard!» John is dismayed.

«I heard *everything*. From the very first words. But do not be upset about that. None of you is perfect. I knew since I chose you. And I do not expect any of you to become perfect rapidly. You will all have to change from wild to domestic beings by means of two grafts...»

«Which ones, Master?»

«One is blood the other is fire. Afterwards you will be the heroes of Heaven and will convert the whole world, beginning from yourselves.»

«Blood? Fire?»

«Yes, John. Blood: *Mine*...»

«No Jesus!» John interrupts Him with a deep groan.

«Be calm, My friend. Do not interrupt Me. Be the first to listen to this truth, because you deserve it. The Blood *is Mine*. You already know. That is why I came. I am the Redeemer... Think of the prophets. They did not leave out one iota in describing My mission. I will be the Man described by Isaiah. And the Blood, that I will shed will fecundate you. But I will not confine Myself to that. You are so imperfect and weak, dull and timorous, that I, sitting gloriously beside the Father, will send you the Fire, the Strength that proceeds from My being through generation by the Father and that binds the Father and the Son in an indissoluble ring, making Three of One: the *Thought*, the *Blood*, the Love. When the Spirit of God, or rather, the Spirit of the Spirit of God, the Perfection of Divine Perfections, will come to you, you will no longer be as you are. But you will be new, powerful, holy... But for one of you Blood and Fire will be of no avail. Because Blood will have for him the power of damnation and he will forever know another fire, in which he will burn belching blood and swallowing blood, because he will see blood wherever he lays his material or spiritual eyes, having betrayed the Blood of a God.»

«Oh! Master! Who is it?»

«You will know one day. For the time being, forget about it. And for the sake of charity do not even endeavour to inquire into it. Investigation presupposes suspicion. You must not suspect your brothers, because suspicion is already lack of charity.»

«I will be satisfied if You assure me that neither James nor I will betray You.»

«Oh! Not you! Nor James. You are My comfort, My good John!» and Jesus lays an arm on his shoulders, draws him to Himself and they walk thus together.

361.6 [6] They are silent for some time. The others are also quiet. Only the shuffling of their feet in the mire can be heard. They then hear another noise. It is a rustling gurgling noise, I would say the deep snoring of a person affected by catarrh. It is a monotonous grumbling interrupted now and again by light crashes.

«Can you hear that?» says Jesus. «The river is close at hand.»

«But we will not arrive at the ford before night. It will soon be dark.»

«We will sleep in a hut somewhere. And we will cross the river tomorrow. I would have liked to arrive there earlier, because the flood is increasing hourly. Listen! The reeds on the banks are breaking under the pressure of the swollen water.»

«They kept You so long in those villages of the Decapolis! We said to the sick people: "The next time!" but...»

«He who is ill, wants to be cured, John. And he who pities them, cures them *at once*, John. It does not matter. We will cross over just the same. I want to do the other side before going back to Jerusalem for Pentecost.»

They become silent once again. It gets dark very quickly, as is usual on wet days. It becomes more and more difficult to walk in the deepening twilight. And also the trees along the road increase the darkness with their foliage.

«Let us cross to the other side of the road. We are now very close to the ford. We will look for a hut.»

They cross over and are followed by the others. They cross a little muddy ditch, with more mud than water, which flows gurgling towards the river. They almost grope their way among the trees making for the river, the noise of which is becoming louder and louder.

361.7 [7] A first moonbeam pierces the clouds, it penetrates between two clouds and descends making the miry water of the Jordan shine, in a spot where the river is swollen and very wide. (If my reckoning is correct the river is about fifty/sixty metres wide. I am not very clever with regards to measurements, but I think that my house could have gone into that river-bed nine or ten times and it was about five and a half metres wide). It is no longer the beautiful calm blue Jordan, the quiet low water of which leaves the fine sand on the banks uncovered, where the reef-thickets begin to grow and rustle continuously. The water has now submerged everything and the first reef-thickets have been bent and broken and thus are not visible with the exception of an odd leaf that undulates on the surface of the water and seems to be waving goodbye or imploring help. The water has already reached the foot of the first large trees. I do not know what trees they are. They are tall and leafy, as compact as a wall and dark in the dark night. Some willows dip the top of their withered foliage into the yellowish water.

«It is not possible to wade here» says Peter.

«Not here. But it is possible over there. See? They are still wading» says Andrew.

In fact two quadrupeds are cautiously crossing the river. The water reaches up to the stomachs of the animals.

«If they can pass, so can boats.»

«However it is better to cross over at once, even if it is dark. The clouds have thinned out and it is moonlight. Do not let us miss this opportunity. Let us look for a boat...» And Peter utters three times a long moaning cry: «Hey!»

There is no reply.

«Let us go down, right down to the ford. Melkiah and his sons must be there. This is his best season. He will take us across.»

They walk as fast as they can on the little path along the river, which almost laps on it.

[8] «But is that not a woman?» says Jesus looking at the two peo- 361.8
ple who have already crossed the river on horseback and are now standing on the path.

«A woman?» Peter and the others cannot see or tell whether the person in dark clothes, who has dismounted and is now waiting, is a man or a woman.

«Yes. It is a woman. It's... Mary. Look now that she is in the moonbeam.»

«You are lucky that you can see. Blessed be your eyes!»

«It is Mary. What will she be wanting?» and Jesus shouts: «Mary!»

«Rabboni! Is it You? Praised be God that I have found You!» and Mary runs as fast as a gazelle towards Jesus. I do not know how she does not stumble on the uneven road. She drops her heavy mantle and is now coming forward with her veil and light mantle held tight against her dark dress.

When she reaches Jesus she drops at His feet without worrying about the mud. She is panting, but happy. She repeats: «Glory be to God Who made me find You!»

«Why, Mary? What is happening? Were you not at Bethany?»

«I was at Bethany with Your Mother and the women, as You told us... But I came to meet You... Lazarus was not able to come, because he is suffering too much... So I came with a servant...»

«You are about, all alone, with a boy and in this weather?»

«Oh! Rabboni! You are not going to tell me that You think that I was afraid. I was not afraid to do so much evil... I am not afraid now to do something good.»

«So? Why did you come?»

«To tell You not to cross over... They are waiting for You on the other side to injure You... I found out... I was told by one of the Herodians who once... who once loved me... Whether he told me out of love, still, or out of hatred, I do not know... I know that the other day he saw me through the gate and he said to me: "You silly Mary, are you waiting for *your* Master? You are doing the right thing, because it will be the last time, in fact as soon as He crosses the river and comes into Judaea, He will be captured. Look at Him carefully and then run away because it is not wise to be near Him, *now*...". Then... You can imagine how anxiously... I inquired... You know... I know many people... and even if they say that I am mad or possessed... they still speak to me... And I found out that it is true. Then I took two horses and I came, without say-
361.9 ing anything to Your Mother, not to worry Her... [9]Go back at once, Master. If they find out that You are here, beyond the Jordan, they will come here. Herod too is looking for You... and You are too close to Machaerus now. Go away, for pity's sake, Master!...»

«Do not weep, Mary...»

«I am afraid, Master!»

«What! You afraid? No, you have been so brave as to cross the river in flood by night!...»

«But that is a river, whereas *those* are men and they are Your enemies and they hate You... I am afraid of their hatred for You... Because I love You, Master.»

«Do not be afraid. They will not get Me as yet. It is not My hour. Even if they placed many formations of soldiers along all the roads, they would not capture Me. It is not My hour. But I will do as you wish. I will go back...»

Judas grumbles something between his teeth and Jesus replies: «Yes, Judas. Exactly as you say. But *just* in the first part of your sentence. I am listening to her, of course I am. But not because she is a woman, as you are insinuating, but because she is the one who has made most progress in love. Mary, go home, while you can. I will go back and cross over... wherever I can, and I will go to Galilee. Come with My Mother and the other women to Cana, to Susanna's house. I will tell you there what there is to be done. Go in peace and may you be blessed. God is with you.»

Jesus lays His hand on her head, blessing her. Mary takes Jesus' hands, kisses them, stands up and then goes back. Jesus watches her go away. He sees her pick her heavy mantle and put it on; she then reaches her horse, mounts it and goes to the ford and crosses over.

«And now let us go» He says. «I wanted to let you rest, but I cannot. I have your safety at heart, although Judas thinks otherwise. And believe Me, if you should fall into the hands of My enemies, that would do your health more harm than water and mud...»

They all lower their heads as they understand the implied reproach given in reply to their previous conversation.

[10]They walk all night in changeable weather, in fitful showers. 361.10
At a lurid dawn they find themselves near a very poor village, the muddy houses of which are lying close to the river. The river is a little narrower than at the ford. Some boats have been beached as far as the houses to protect them from the flood.

Peter utters his cry: «Hey!»

A vigorous elderly man comes out of a hovel. «What do you want?»

«Boats to cross over.»

«Impossible! The flood is too dangerous... The current...»

«Hey you! Are you telling me? I am a fisherman from Galilee.»

«The sea is one thing... but this is a river... I do not want to lose my boat. In any case... I have but one and you are many.»

«You liar! Are you telling me that you have one boat only?»

«May I go blind, if I am lying, I...»

«Watch that you may really go blind. This is the Rabbi from Galilee Who gives sight to blind people and Who can satisfy you by making you go blind...»

«Oh! Mercy! The Rabbi! Forgive me, Rabboni!»

«Yes, I do. But you should never tell lies. God loves sincere people. Why say that you have but one boat when the whole village can give you the lie? To lie and to be found out is too severe a humiliation for man! Will you give Me your boats?»

«All of them, Master.»

«How many do we need, Peter?»

«In normal conditions two would be enough. But with the river in flood it is more difficult to manoeuvre them and we need three.»

«Take them, fisherman. But how will I get them back?»

«Come in one of them. Have you no sons?»

«I have one son, two son-in-laws and some grandchildren.»

«Two in each boat are enough to bring them back.»

«Let us go.»

361.11 [11] The man calls the others and with the help of Peter, Andrew, James and John they push the boats into the water. The current is strong and threatens to drag them away. The ropes holding them to the closest tree-trunks are as taut as bows and creak under the stress. Peter looks. He looks at the boats, at the river and shakes his head, he ruffles his grey hair with one hand and casts an inquisitive glance at Jesus.

«Are you afraid, Peter?»

«Well!... almost...»

«Be not afraid. Have faith. And you, too, man. He who carries God and His messengers must not be afraid. Let us get into the boats. I will go into the first one.»

The owner of the boats makes a gesture of resignation. He must be thinking that his relatives' last hour or his has come. He must at least be afraid of losing his boats or ending no one knows where.

Jesus is already in the boat. He is standing in the bow. All the others embark, some in the same boat, some in the other two. Only an old man remains on the embankment, a servant perhaps, watching the ropes.

«Are we all on board?»

«Yes, we are.»

«Are the oars ready?»

«They are.»

«Let go, you, on the bank.»

The old man untwists the ropes off the wooden pin which held them in a knot on a tree-trunk. As soon as the boats are free, they list for a moment southwards towards the centre of the current.

But the power of miracle shines on Jesus' face. What He says to the river I do not know. I know that the current almost stops. The Jordan flows slowly as when it is not in spate. The boats cut across the water without any difficulty, in fact, they are so fast that their owner is amazed.

[12] They are now on the other side. They disembark with ease and 361.12
the current does not threaten to drag the boats away even when the oars are still.

«Master, I see that You are really powerful» says the owner of the boats. «Bless Your servant and remember me, a sinner.»

«Why powerful?»

«Ehi! That was no trifle! You stopped the current of the Jordan in flood!...»

* «Joshua had already worked that miracle, and it was even greater, because the water of the river disappeared to let the Ark pass...»

«And you, man, have carried across the true Ark of God» says Judas with self-sufficiency.

«Most High God! Yes, I do believe it! You are the true Messiah! The Son of the Most High God. Oh! I will tell the towns and villages along the river what You did and what I saw! Come back, Master! There are many sick people in my poor village. Come and cure them!»

«I will come. In the meantime preach in My Name faith and holiness to be acceptable to God. Goodbye, man. Go in peace. And be not afraid about your return.»

«I am not afraid. If I were afraid I would ask You to have mercy on my life. But I believe in You and in your goodness and I am going away without asking for anything. Goodbye.»

---

* **miracle**, in: *Joshua 3:14-17.*

He gets into his boat, he stands off and departs. He is sure of himself and soon reaches the other bank.

Jesus, Who has remained still until He sees him on the other bank, makes a gesture of blessing. He then withdraws towards the road.

The river resumes its vorticose flowing... And it all ends thus.

362. On the Other Bank. A Prophesy on the Mission and the Destiny of the Future "Voices of God". Jesus Meets His Mother and the Women Disciples.

16th December 1945.

362.1 [1] They are now on the other side of the Jordan and they are walking fast southwestwards, towards a second chain of hills, higher than the first one beyond which is the Jordan plain. I gather from their conversation that they came away from the plain to avoid the mud that they left on the other side and they are thinking of going to their destination along internal routes, which are better kept and more practicable, for walking, particularly in wet weather.

«Whereabouts are we?» asks Matthew who finds his bearings with difficulty.

«We are certainly between Shiloh and Bethel. I recognize the mountains» says Thomas. «We passed here not long ago with Judas, who was the guest of a Pharisee at Bethel.»

«You could have been his guest, too, but you would not come. Neither he nor I said to you: "Do not come".»

«I am not saying that you did say so. I am only saying that I preferred to stay with the disciples who were evangelizing here.»

And the argument is over. Andrew in fact is glad and says: «If there are friendly Pharisees in Bethel, we shall not be attacked.»

«But we are going in the other direction, not to Jerusalem» they point out to him.

«We shall have to go there for Passover in any case! I don't know how we shall manage...»

«Of course! Why did He say that He is going back to Cana? The women could have come back and we could have made our pilgrimage...»

«It is my wife's destiny that she should not spend Passover in Jerusalem!» exclaims Peter.

[2]John asks Jesus Who is talking animatedly to the Zealot: 362.2
«Master, how shall we manage to go and come back in time?»

«I do not know. I trust in God. If we are late, it will not be My fault.»

«You were right in being prudent» says the Zealot.

«Oh! As far as I am concerned, I would have gone on. Because it is not yet My hour. I can feel that. But how would *you all* have put up with the adventure, considering that for some time you have been so... tired?»

«Master... You are right. A demon seems to have been blowing poison among us. We have changed so much!»

«Man does get tired. He wants things quickly. And he dreams of silly things. When he realizes that his dreams are different from reality, he becomes upset and, if he is not of goodwill, he surrenders. He does not remember that the Almighty, Who could have made the Universe out of Chaos in a moment, made it in orderly separate stages in periods of time called days. From the spiritual Chaos of the whole world I have to make the Kingdom of God. And I will do so. I will build its foundations, I am now building them, and I have to split a very hard rock to lay the foundations that will not collapse. You will slowly build the walls. Your successors will continue the work, both in height and in width. As I shall die in the work, so will you and there will be many more who will die with or without bloodshed, consumed by this work for which spirit of sacrifice and generosity, tears, blood and endless patience are required...»

[3]Peter thrusts his grey-haired head between Jesus and John: 362.3
«Do you mind telling me what you are saying?»

«Oh! Simon! Come here. We were talking of the future Church. I was explaining that, contrary to your hurry, your tiredness, your discouragement and so forth, it exacts calm, perseverance, exertion and trust. I was saying that the sacrifice of *each* of its members is required. Starting with Me, the Founder. I am, in fact, its mystical Head, for you, for all the disciples, for all those who will be called Christians and will belong to the universal Church. And really in the great classification of the hierarchy the most humble people, who seem to be simple "numbers", will be the ones who will make the Church truly vital. In actual fact I will often have to seek refuge in them, to continue to keep alive the faith and the strength of the continuously renewed apostolic colleges, and I will have to allow those apostles to be tortured by Satan and by envious, proud, incredulous men. And their moral martyrdom will not be less painful than a material one, as they will find themselves between the active will of God and the wicked will of man, who will act as an instrument of Satan and by every means and effort will endeavour to make them appear as mendacious, mad, possessed persons, in order to paralyze My work in them and the fruits of My work, which are as many victorious blows against the Beast.»

«And will they resist?»

«They will resist, even if I am not physically with them. They will have to believe not only what is their duty to believe, but also in their secret mission, and they will have to believe that it is holy and useful, and that it originated from Me, While Satan will hiss around them to terrorise them and the world will shout to deride them and the not always perfectly bright ministers of God to condemn them. That is the destiny of My future voices. And yet I will have no other means to rouse men and bring them back to the Gospel and to the Christ! But for everything I have asked of them and imposed on them and received from them, Oh!
362.4 I will grant them eternal joy, a special glory. [4]In Heaven there is a closed book. God only can read it. All the truth is contained in it. But God at times removes the seals and revives the truth already revealed to men, selecting a man, chosen for that destiny, to know past, present and future, as contained in that mysterious book. Have you ever seen a son, the best in the family, or a schoolboy, the most clever at school, being called by his father or teacher to read a book for adults and have it explained to him? He stands beside his father or teacher, embraced by one of their arms, while the other hand of the father or teacher points at the lines which he wants to be read and understood by his dearest child. God behaves likewise with those consecrated to such destiny. He draws them to Himself and holds them with His arm and forces them to read what He wants and to understand the meaning and to repeat it later and suffer derision and grief because of it. I, the Man, am the Founder of the family of those

who speak the Truth of the heavenly book, and I therefore suffer mockery, grief and death. But the father is already preparing My Glory. And once I have risen to it, I will prepare the glory of those whom I compelled to read in the closed book the passages which I wanted, and in the presence of the whole risen Mankind and of the angelical choruses I will point them out for what they were, calling them beside Me while I open the seals of the Book, which it will no longer be necessary to keep closed, and they will smile seeing and reading once again the words that were clarified to them when they suffered on the earth.»

5 «And what about the others?» asks John who has paid great 362.5
attention to the lesson.

«Which others?»

«The others, who like me have not read that book on the earth, will they never know what it says?»

«Everything will be known to the blessed souls in Heaven. Being engrossed in the Infinite Wisdom, they will know.»

«Immediately? As soon as they die?»

«As soon as they enter Life.»

«Why then on the Last Day You will let everybody see that You call them to know the Book?»

«Because not only the blessed souls will be there to see that. All Mankind will be there. And on the side of the damned souls there will be many who laughed at the voices of God, as if they were the voices of mad or possessed people and tormented them because of their gift. It will be a long expected but fair revenge granted to those martyrs of the dull wickedness of the world.»

«How beautiful it will be to see all that!» exclaims John enraptured.

«Yes. And to see all the Pharisees grind their teeth, seized with anger» says Peter rubbing his hands.

«Oh! I think I will look only at Jesus and the blessed souls reading the Book with Him...» replies John, dreaming of that hour while his light-blue eyes, lost in I wonder what vision of light, are made brighter by emotional tears, which have welled in them, and an innocent smile appears on his red lips.

The Zealot looks at him; Jesus also looks at him. But Jesus does not say anything. The Zealot instead says: «You will look at yourself, then! Because if among us there is one who will be the "voice of God" on the earth and will be elected to read the passages of the sealed Book, you are that one, John, the favourite disciple of Jesus and the friend of God.»

«Oh! Do not say that! I am the most ignorant among you. And if Jesus did not say that the Kingdom of God belongs to children, I would think that I could never enter it, as I am good for nothing. Is that right, Master, that my only merit is that I am like a child?»

«Yes, you belong to blessed childhood. And may you be blessed because of that!»

362.6 [6]They continue to walk for some time, then Peter, who looks back along the track on which they are, exclaims: «Merciful Providence! That is the women's wagon!»

They all turn round. It is in fact Johanna's heavy wagon that is coming forward drawn by two strong horses. They stop waiting for it. As the leather tilt is completely lowered, it is not possible to see who is in the wagon. Jesus beckons to the driver to stop and the man utters an exclamation of joy when he sees Jesus standing on the edge of the road with His arm raised.

While the man stops the two panting horses, the lean face of Isaac appears through an opening in the tilt: «The Master!» he shouts. «Mother, rejoice! He is here!»

One can hear voices of women and shuffling of feet in the wagon, but before one of them gets off, Manaen, Marjiam and Isaac have jumped down and are worshipping the Master.

«Are you still here, Manaen?»

«I have remained faithful to orders, particularly now, as the women are afraid... But... We obeyed, because it is our duty to obey, but I can assure You that there was nothing to worry about. I know for certain that Pilate has called riotous fellows to order, stating that anyone giving rise to rebellions during the feast days would be severely punished. I think that Pilate's wife and above all her lady friends are connected with such protection. At the Court we know everything and nothing. But we know enough...»

362.7 [7]and Manaen moves to one side to make room for Mary, Who has got off the wagon and has walked a few steps towards them, and is clearly very anxious and deeply moved.

They kiss each other while all the women disciples worship the Master. Neither Mary nor Martha of Lazarus are there.

Mary whispers: «How much anguish since that evening! How everybody hates You, Son!» and tears stream down the red lines left on Her face by the many tears shed during the previous days.

«But You can see that the Father sees to everything. So do not weep! I defy all the hatred of the world bravely. But one tear of Yours depresses Me. Cheer up, Holy Mother!» and embracing Her with one arm, He turns around to greet the women disciples, and particularly Johanna, who wanted to come back to accompany Mary.

«Oh! Master! There is no difficulty in staying with Your Mother. Mary was held up in Bethany because her brother is suffering so much. So I came. I left the children with the wife of the guardian of the mansion as she is kind and motherly. But there is also Chuza to look after them, so You can imagine whether Matthias, who is my husband's pet, will lack anything! But Chuza also told me that it was not necessary to leave. The Proconsul's warning has also caused Herodias to draw her claws in. The Tetrarch, too, is trembling with fear and he is worried about one thing only: that Herodias may ruin him in the eyes of Rome. The death of John has destroyed many situations that were favourable to Herodias. And Herod is fully aware that the people are against him because of John's murder. The old fox realizes that the worst punishment for him would be to lose the hateful illusory protection of Rome. The people would attack him at once. So do not worry! He will do nothing on his own initiative!»

8 «In that case, let us go back to Jerusalem! You can proceed 362.8
without any fear about your safety. Let us go. Let the women get into the wagon again, and Matthew and whoever is tired will go with them. We will rest at Bethel. Let us go.»

The women obey. Matthew and Bartholomew go with them. The others prefer to follow the wagon on foot together with Manaen, Isaac and Marjiam. And Manaen tells them how he inquired to find out how much truth there was in the boasting of the Herodian who had caused so much anxiety in the peaceful gathering at Bethany, near Lazarus «who was suffering *so much*» says Manaen.

«Did a woman come to Bethany?»

«No, Lord. But we have been away three days. Who is she?»

«A disciple. I will give her to Eliza because she is young, alone and without means.»

«Eliza is in Johanna's mansion. She wanted to come. But she has a bad cold. She was dying to see You. She used to say: "But do you not understand that the sight of Him gives me peace?"»

362.9 «I will also give her joy through this young woman. [9]And what about you, Marjiam? Are you not saying anything?»

«I am listening, Master.»

«The boy listens and writes. He makes this one and that one repeat Your words and he writes them. But have we repeated them correctly?» says Isaac.

«I will examine the work of My disciple and add anything which should be missing» says Jesus caressing the bronzed cheek of Marjiam. And He asks: «And what about your old father? Have you seen him?»

«Oh! yes! He did not recognize me. He wept for joy. But we shall see him at the Temple, because Ishmael is sending them. He has even given them more days this year. He is afraid of You.»

«I should think so! After what happened to Hananiah in the month of Shebat!» says Peter laughing.

«But the fear of God does not build, it demolishes. It is not friendship. It is only expectation that often changes into hatred. But everybody gives what one can...»

They go on their way and I lose sight of them.

363. In Rama, in the House of Thomas' Sister. The Number of the Elect and the 'Narrow Door'. Invective Against Jerusalem.

17th December 1945.

363.1 [1]Thomas, who was at the back of the group speaking to Manaen and Bartholomew, leaves his companions and catches up with the Master, Who is in front with Marjiam and Isaac. «Master, we shall soon be near Ramah. Would You come and bless my sister's baby? She is so anxious to see You! We could stop there. There is room for everybody. Make me happy, Lord!»

«I will, and with great joy! We shall enter Jerusalem tomorrow and we shall be well rested.»

«Oh! I will go ahead and warn them! May I go?»

«Yes, go. But remember that I am not a worldly friend. Do not compel your relatives to spend a lot of money. Treat Me as a "Master". Is that clear?»

«Yes, my Lord, it is. I will tell my relatives. Are you coming with me, Marjiam?»

«If Jesus will allow me...»

«You may go, son.»

The others who have seen Thomas and Marjiam go towards Ramah, situated on the left hand side of the road, which, I think, takes one from Samaria to Jerusalem, quicken their paces to find out what is happening.

«We are going to the house of Tom's sister. I have stayed in all the houses of your relatives. It is fair that I should go to his as well. And that is why I sent him ahead.»

«Well if You do not mind, I will go away, too. I want to see whether there is anything new. If there is bad news I will be at the Damascus Gate when You arrive there. Otherwise I will meet You... Where, Lord?» says Manaen.

«At Bethany, Manaen. I am going to Lazarus' house at once. But I am leaving the women in Jerusalem. I will be going alone. Instead, I would ask you to escort the women to their houses after today's rest.»

«As You wish, Lord.»

«Tell the driver to follow us to Ramah.»

In fact the wagon is coming up slowly behind the apostolic group. Isaac and the Zealot stop waiting for it, while all the others take the side road, which with a good gradient leads to the very low little hill on which Ramah is built.

[2] Thomas, who is beside himself with joy and looks even more 363.2
rubicond as his face is so bright, is waiting at the entrance of the village. He runs to meet Jesus: «How happy we are, Master! All the family is here! My father who was so anxious to see You, my mother, my brothers!... How happy I am!» And he walks beside Jesus strutting through the village like a conqueror in triumph.

The house of Thomas' sister is at a cross-roads on the eastern side of the town. It is the typical house of a well to do Israelite, with very few windows, with an iron door with judas-hole, a terraced-roof and high dark walls enclosing the garden also at the rear of the house, with tall fruit trees standing above them.

Today the maidservant does not have to look through the peep-hole. The door is wide open and all the inhabitants of the house are lined up in the hall where the adults are busy holding back boys and girls, who, excited at the news, are restless and are continuously rushing to the front, thus infringing the hierarchical order, as the first row, the place of honour, is for Thomas parents, his sister and her husband.

But when Jesus appears at the door, no one can hold the children back. They are like a brood of chickens coming out of their nest after a night's rest. And Jesus receives the impact of the kind garrulous group who clash against His knees and press Him, raising their little faces to be kissed, and will not move away notwithstanding the fact that their fathers and mothers call them and Thomas gives a few slaps to restore order.

«Leave them! Leave them alone! I wish the whole world were like that!» exclaims Jesus Who has stooped to please all the children.

363.3 [3] At last He can go in and is welcomed by the more respectful greetings of the adults. What I particularly like is the greeting of Thomas' father, a typical elderly Jew, who is raised from his knees by Jesus, Who wants to kiss him «out of gratitude for his generosity in giving Him an apostle».

«Oh! God has loved me more than He loved anybody else in Israel, because while every Jew has one son, the first-born, consecrated to the Lord, I have two: the first and the last one; and the last one is even more sacred, because, although he is neither a Levite nor a Priest, he does what not even the High Priest does: he constantly sees God and receives His commands!» he says in the trembling voice of elderly people, made even more trembling by emotion. And he concludes: «Tell me one thing only to make my soul happy. Since You do not lie, tell me: this son of mine, by the way he follows You, is he worthy of serving You and deserving eternal Life?»

«You may rest in peace, father. Your Tom has a great position in the heart of God because of his behaviour, and he will have a great place in Heaven because of the way he will serve God till he breathes his last breath.»

Thomas gasps for air like a fish out of water, deeply moved

by what he has heard. The old man raises his trembling hands, while tears stream down the deep wrinkles of his face and disappear in his patriarchal beard, and he says: «May the blessing
* of Jacob descend upon you; the blessing of the patriarch upon the just one among his sons: may the Almighty bless you with the blessings of Heaven above, blessings of the deep lying below, blessings of breasts and womb. May the blessings of your father exceed those of his ancestors and until the desire of the eternal hills comes, may they rest upon the head of Thomas, upon the head of him who is nazirite among his brothers!»

And they all reply: «Amen.»

«And now, my Lord, will You please bless this house and above all these little ones who are blood of my blood» says the old man pointing at the children.

And Jesus, stretching His arms out, says the Mosaic blessing in a loud voice and He adds: «May God, in Whose presence your ancestors walked, God Who has nourished Me since My childhood to the present day, may the angel who has delivered Me from all evil, bless these children; may they be named after Me and after My ancestors and may they multiply copiously upon the earth» and He ends by taking the last born from his mother's arms to kiss his forehead saying: «And may the chosen virtues, that dwelt in the Just Man, after whom you have been named, descend upon you like butter and honey, making your name worthy of Heaven and adorned like a palm-tree laden with golden dates and a cedar covered with royal leaves.»

Everybody is moved and enraptured. Then they all utter a cry of joy while Jesus enters the house and they stop only when He is in the yard, where He introduces His Mother, the women disciples, the apostles and the disciples.

[4] It is no longer morning, neither is it noon. The weak ray of 363.4
sunlight which pierces the ruffled clouds with difficulty while the weather is still so unsettled, makes me understand that the sun is about to set and that twilight is approaching.

The women are no longer here. Neither are Isaac and Manaen. Marjiam instead is with Jesus, and is so happy to be with Him,

* **blessing of Jacob**, in: *Genesis 49:25-26.*

while He goes out with the apostles and all the male relatives of Thomas to see some vineyards, which appear to be of a special quality. Both the old man and Thomas' brother-in-law enlarge upon the position of the vineyard and the rarity of the vines, which at present have but a few tender leaves.

Jesus listens kindly to the explanations showing an interest in pruning and hoeing, as if they were the most useful things on the earth. At the end He says to Thomas smiling: «Shall I bless this dowry of your twin sister?»

«Oh! My Lord! I am neither Doras nor Ishmael. I know that Your very breath, Your presence in a place is already a blessing. But if You wish to raise Your hand on these plants, please do so, and their fruit will certainly be holy.»

«And will it not be plentiful? What do you say, father?»

«Holy... is enough. And I will press the grapes and will send You the wine for next Passover, so that You may use it in the ritual chalice.»

«Very well. I will look forward to that. At next Passover I want to use the wine of a true Israelite.»

They leave the vineyard to go back to the village.

363.5 [5] The news of the presence of Jesus of Nazareth in the village has spread and the people of Ramah are all in the streets and are anxious to approach Him.

Jesus notices it and says to Thomas: «Why do they not come? Are they perhaps afraid of Me? Tell them that I love them.»

Oh! Thomas does not wait to be told twice! He goes from one group to another so quickly that he looks like a large butterfly fluttering from flower to flower. And those who hear the invitation do not wait to be told twice either. They all run, passing the word round, and gather round Jesus, so that when they arrive at the cross-roads, where Thomas' house is, there is quite a large crowd speaking respectfully to the apostles and Thomas' relatives, asking various questions.

I realize that Thomas has worked hard during the winter months and much of the Gospel is already known in the village. But they wish to have detailed elucidations and one who has been deeply affected by the blessing given by Jesus to the little ones of the hospitable house and by what the Master said of Thomas, asks: «Will they thus be all just, because of Your blessing?»

«Not because of it, but because of their actions. I gave them the strength of My blessing to strengthen them in their actions. But it is for them to perform deeds and only good deeds to attain Heaven. I bless everybody... but not everybody in Israel will be saved.»

«On the contrary, only very few will be saved, if they continue to behave as they are behaving now» grumbles Thomas.

«What are you saying?»

«The truth. Those who persecute the Christ and calumniate Him, those who do not practise what He teaches will have no part in His Kingdom» says Thomas in his deep voice.

[6] One pulls him by the sleeve asking: «Is He very severe?» 363.6
pointing at Jesus.

«No, He is not. On the contrary, He is too good.»

«What do you think, shall I be saved? I am not one of the disciples. But you know what I am like and that I always believed what you said. But I do not know what I should do, in addition to that. What should I do exactly to be saved, besides what I already do?»

«Ask Him. His judgement will be more truthful and kind than mine.»

The man comes forward. He says: «Master, I comply with the Law and since Thomas repeated Your words to me, I try to comply more and more. But I am not very generous. I do what I must do. I refrain from doing what it is not right to do, because I am afraid of Hell. But I am very fond of a comfortable life and, I admit it, I endeavour to do things in such a way that while I do not commit sin, I do not trouble myself too much either. Shall I be saved by behaving so?»

«You will. But why be avaricious with a good God Who is so generous with you? Why do you only expect to be saved, and with some difficulty, and you do not wish to attain great holiness, which gives eternal peace at once? Come on, man! Be generous with your soul!»

The man says humbly: «I will think about it, my Lord. I feel that You are right and that I am wronging my soul by compelling it to go through a long purification period before having peace.»

«Very well. Your thought is already the beginning of perfectioning.»

363.7 [7]Another man from Ramah asks: «Lord, are only few people saved?»

«If man knew how to behave with respect towards himself and with reverential love towards God, all men would be saved, as God desires. But man does not behave thus. And like a fool, he plays with tinsel, instead of taking pure gold. Be generous in wishing Good. Does it hurt you? That is where is the merit. Strive to go through the narrow door. The other one, which is wide and ornate is an allurement of Satan to lead you astray. The gate of Heaven is narrow, low, barren and rough. In order to enter it one must be agile, light, without pomp and without materialism. One must be spiritual to be able to do so. Otherwise when the hour of your death comes, you will not be able to pass through it. And many will be really seen trying to pass through it without being successful, as they are so laden with materialism, so decked out with worldly pomp, so stiffened by the crust of sin, unable to stoop because of their pride, which acts as a skeleton. And the Landlord of the Kingdom will then come to close the gate, and those who are outside, those who have not been able to go in at the right time, will knock at the door shouting: "Lord, open the gate to us. We are here as well". But He will reply: "I really do not know you, neither do I know where you come from". And they will say: "What? Do You not remember us? We ate and drank with You and we listened to You when You preached in our squares". But He will reply: "I really do not know you. The more I look at you the more you seem to be sated with what I declared was impure food. The more I examine you, the more I see that you do not belong to My family. Now, I really see whose sons and subjects you are: the Other one's. Satan is your father, Flesh your mother, Pride your nurse, Hatred your servant, sin is your treasure, vices your gems. On your hearts there is written: 'Selfishness'. Your hands are dirty with the robberies committed against your brothers. Away from here! Away from Me, all of you, operators of iniquity". Then, while Abraham, Isaac, Jacob and all the prophets and the just of the Kingdom of God will come from the heights of Heaven shining with glory, those who did not love but were selfish, who did not sacrifice themselves but lived in the lap of luxury, will be driven away and confined to the place where there is eternal weeping and nothing but terror. And those who have risen gloriously and have come from east and west, from north and south, will gather around the nuptial table of the Lamb, the King of the Kingdom of God. And then one will see that many who appeared to be "the least" in the army of the earth, will be the first in the city of the Kingdom. And one will also see that not all the mighty ones in Israel are mighty in Heaven, and not all those chosen by the Christ to be His servants have deserved to be elected to the nuptial table. Instead one will see that many, who were considered to be "the first" will be not only the last, but not even the last. Because many are called, but few are those who can turn their election into true glory.»

[8] While Jesus is speaking, some Pharisees arrive with a pil- 363.8
grimage on its way to Jerusalem, or coming from Jerusalem looking for lodgings, the Holy City being overcrowded. They see the concourse of people and approach them to see. They soon see Jesus' fair-haired head shining against the dark wall of Thomas' house.

«Let us pass, because we want to speak to the Nazarene» they shout overbearingly.

The crowds open out with no enthusiasm and the apostles see the group of Pharisees come towards them.

«Peace to You, Master!»

«Peace to you. What do you want?»

«Are You going to Jerusalem?»

«Like every faithful Israelite.»

«Don't go! A serious danger threatens You there. We know because we have come from Jerusalem to meet our families. And we came to warn You because we heard that You were at Ramah.»

«Who told you, if you do not mind Me asking you?» asks Peter who has become suspicious and is ready to begin a discussion.

«It does not concern you, man. All you need know, since you call us snakes, is that there are many snakes near the Master and that you ought to mistrust the too many and *too powerful* disciples.»

«Hey! You are not insinuating that Manaen or...»

«Be silent, Peter. And you, Pharisee, you ought to know that no danger can dissuade a faithful believer from fulfilling his duty. If one loses his life, it is nothing. What is serious, is to lose one's soul by infringing the Law. But you know. And you know that I know. So why are you tempting Me? Do you perhaps not know that I am aware why you are doing it?»

«I am not tempting You. It is the truth. Many among us are
363.9 hostile to You. But not everybody. We do not hate You. [9]We know that Herod is looking for You and we say to You: go away. Go away from here, because if Herod captures You, he will certainly kill You. That is what he wants.»

«It is what he wants, but he will not do it. I know that for certain. In any case you may go and tell the old fox that He, Whom he is seeking, is in Jerusalem. In fact I come expelling demons and curing people, without hiding Myself. And I do and will do it today, tomorrow and the day after tomorrow, until My time is over. But I must proceed until I reach the end. And I must enter Jerusalem today and then once more, and once more and once more again, because it is not possible for Me to stop before. And it must be fulfilled with justice, that is, in Jerusalem.»

«The Baptist died elsewhere.»

«He died in holiness, and holiness means: "Jerusalem". If Jerusalem now means "Sin", that is only because of what is only earthly and will soon no longer be. But I am talking of what is eternal and spiritual, that is, of the Heavenly Jerusalem. All the just and the prophets die in it, in its holiness. And I will die in it and in vain you are trying to lead Me into sin. And I will die also among the hills of Jerusalem but not by Herod's hand, but by the will of him who hates Me more subtly than Herod does, because he sees in Me the usurper of the longed for Priesthood and the Purifier of Israel from all the infectious diseases polluting it. So do not throw on Herod all the eagerness to kill, but each of you should take his share, because truly, the Lamb is on a mountain which wolves and jackals are climbing on every side to slaughter it and...»

The hailstorm of burning truth makes the Pharisees flee.

that kill your prophets and stone those who are sent to you, how often have I longed to gather your children, as a hen gather s her brood under her wings, and you refused! So be it! Your House will be left to you devoid of its true Master. He will come, He will act, as prescribed by the rite, as the first and last son of Israel must act, and then He will go away. He will no longe r stay within your walls to purify you by means of His presence. A ndIassureyouthatyouandyourinhabitantswillnolongerseeMe, in My true figure, till the time comes when you say: “Blessings o nHimWhocomesinthenameoftheLord”...AndyoupeopleofRam ah, remember these words and all the others so that *you may not be inv*olved in the punishment of God. Be faithful... Go. Peace be with you.» And Jesus withdraws to the house of Thomas with- all his relatives and the apostles. <?> asYoudidwithSaul of kerioth, in 78.8. * runs northwards. M.V.s draft reproduc ed on the fo

llowing page, does not contain any additional indication beyond the explanations in t